GLORY TO GOD IN THE HIGHEST!

Four High School Years

Of A Life—Changing, Eternity—Focused Bible Curriculum

Year **1**

Life is not about us.
It is about living for
God's glory!

Year **2**

We want to
take His glory
to the nations!

Year **3** Ready 2016

How we live our lives
on earth prepares us
for eternal glory!

Year **4** Ready 2017

Heaven is about God
putting His glory on
display—forever!

Our Elementary Curriculum

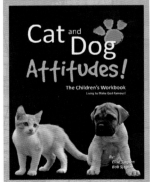

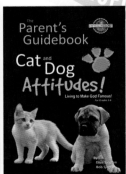

PLEASE CHECK OUR WEBSITE FOR MORE NEW PRODUCTS!

Cat and Dog Theology

By Bob and Debby Sjogren

(2nd Edition)

Debby Sjogren
MM Publishers
4663 Crown Hill Rd.
Mechanicsville, VA 23111.
www.MissionMindedPublishers.com

ISBN 978-0-9885187-0-4

Unless indicated otherwise, Scripture quotations are from: The Holy Bible, New International Version 1984, © 1973, 1978, 1984 by Biblica.

To obtain additional copies, contact UnveilinGLORY at 804.781.0386 or 888.661.9920.

To order 1,000 or more copies, e-mail Mission Minded Publishers at: Debby@MMPublishers.com

Dear students, teachers, or parents,

Only God is perfect.

Though we have tried and tried (and tried!) our best to make this workbook error free, there are certainly some mistakes somewhere. Please forgive us. Like this workbook, we too are not perfect.

The good news is that we are constantly upgrading it. We also have a page on our website (www.CatandDogTheology.org) that allows you to find up-to-the-minute updates. Go there and click on this icon:

If you find errors, please contact me and let me know what page they are on and where they are found. I would greatly appreciate it so we can make the next edition that much better. I'll also put major changes in the updates section.

Please check out our website for new materials. We are constantly creating new curriculum!

Seeking to glorify God in our products,

Debby Sjogren

Debby Sjogren
    President, Mission Minded Publishers
    debby@MMPublishers.com

P.S. A special thanks goes out to Stephani Jenkins who wrote the "Chris & Sarah" stories for us!

The Sjogrens

Bob and Debby have four children:
Luke (the oldest and married to Hannah with their daughter Layla),
Elise, Abby and Hunter.
Debby homeschooled all four children (grades K-12) over a 19-year period.
All have successfully graduated from college.

All love the Lord.

Bob and Debby live in Mechanicsville, Virginia (a suburb of Richmond).
Bob is the president of UnveilinGLORY.
Debby is the president of Mission Minded Publishers.

From the Authors To The Homeschool Students:

Welcome to UnveilinGLORY's first year's curriculum titled, *Cat and Dog Theology!* This material is

designed for 7th-12th graders. It has a proven track record of changing students' lives. ***Get ready for an eye-opening, life-changing experience!***

This curriculum covers 30 weeks. Each week has three lessons that are designed to take you approximately 30-45 minutes per day to do the work. There may be some days that are longer, but other days will be shorter.

Along with this workbook, you will need the following:

• the *Cat and Dog Theology* book,

• the *Cat and Dog Prayer* book,

• a *YouTeach CD* on Cat and Dog Theology, and

• the *Answer Key*.

If you bought a kit, it has it all. If you bought items separately, make sure you get them all.

The set up for the material is fairly simple. You are supposed to work through three lessons a week. They break down like this:

Days 1 and 2

> • Read assigned pages.
>
> • Answer questions about the reading.
>
> • Do a short Bible study.

Day 3

> • Review a cartoon and answer some questions.
>
> • Read a "teenage story" and answer four questions.
>
> • Take a quiz.
>
> • Talk about how this applies to your life. (Please take some time to think through this, and then write down your answer. Your answers will be in the back, so you and your parents can review them at a glance and see how you are accomplishing your goals.)

Each week there is a Bonus Lesson. We encourage you to do what it tells you. You will certainly learn more if you go through this additional material.

At both the middle and the end of this course, you will be asked to teach this material to someone else using "YouTeach." Our philosophy is simple: if you can't teach it, you don't know it. So get to know it well!

The first three weeks are different from all the other weeks and set a "baseline" for the curriculum as well as for your entire life. You will be reviewing the concept each week so the goal is for it to become a part of your life.

At the end of the year there is a final exam. It will be taken from the quizzes you will have already completed.

To get the most out of this study (and have the most lasting change in your life), there are two things you can do:

1. Go through this material together with your parent(s). This way you can both be learning at the same time. (This may have to replace their normal Bible study for the year because they may not be able to handle both.)

2. Become a part of a "Kennel Community." (This is where three or more families in your city come together and talk about what they are learning each week. You will find that you learn more by sharing your thoughts and listening to others. You can go to UnveilinGLORY's website and see if one is in your area or list your city for the first time!)

Thanks for taking this adventure in learning to live for God's glory. If you have any questions, please let either of us know.

For His kindgom and glory,

Mr. & Mrs. Sjogren

Mr. and Mrs. Sjogren
   bob@unveilinGLORY.com
   debby@MMPublishers.com

P.S. **CAUTION!** The more your life is changed, the easier it is to spot Cat behavior in those around you. Please don't ever use this material to judge others. ("Oh, they are just a bunch of Cats.") Once we start judging others, we too are acting like Cats. Use this material to encourage yourself and others to live for God's glory.

From the Authors To The Homeschool Parents:

Welcome moms and dads! *We believe you are going to find this to be one of the most pivotal teachings your child learns, not only this year, but for the rest of their lives.* God has already been pleased to use it greatly in the lives of many people. We hope the impact will be as great in your child's life as it has been in our own children!

There are lots of things you will want to know about this material, so we've listed them out for you:

1. Each lesson should take about 30-45 minutes each day.

    a. There are three scheduled each week with a bonus lesson to go deeper.

    b. The bonus material is teaching found on the internet from UnveilinGLORY.

2. We highly encourage you to take this material with your child. In our beta-test group, the parents discovered that they talked about the material as an entire family and found it extremely helpful in their walks with God.

    a. If you do this, we encourage you to have a separate workbook.

    b. Please share the other materials to minimize your costs.

3. We also highly encourage you to be a part of a "Kennel Community." A "Kennel Community" is where a group of families also going through the curriculum come together to discuss what they are learning. There is no "leader," just a group of parents and students who talk about what God is doing in their lives and about what they are reading.

4. Each week, your child is asked, "How is this changing your life?"

    a. They are to write these answers down in the back of the workbook so they (and you) can review them periodically to see how they are doing.

    b. We encourage you to talk to them about what they are writing down and help them implement the changes they want to see in their lives.

    c. If your child is *not* doing this, ***stop doing the curriculum***. Head-knowledge for the sake of head-knowledge won't do them any good. It will instead make them judgmental and hypocritical, which none of us want.

5. Each week there are also stories about a brother and sister who are in a youth group who are wrestling with what it means to live for God's glory. Be sure to ask your students about the story each week. There are only four questions per story, but there are many more topics in the stories that you could talk to them about. This could greatly help your child grow in the area of responsibility in using social media as well as handling interpersonal relationship problems.

6. In Appendix A, you will find additional questions you can ask your student from the scenarios they are learning. Feel free to use them to start conversations around the dinner table (or wherever you are most comfortable).

7. At the halfway point and end of the time together, **we ask your students to teach this material.** They will do this through UnveilinGLORY's "YouTeach" program. It is found on a CD (not DVD) and has four lectures on it. Your child will be using lessons 1 and 2. Here is what they need to do to utilize it the best:

  a. Copy the slides to a hard drive. (Do not try to play it from the CD/DVD slot.)

  b. Double click the slides. It will open up in Adobe Acrobat.

  c. There are notes to read to learn what to say if they do not know what the slide is trying to communicate. These should be opened up earlier and printed out before they try to teach.

  d. They can listen to me (Bob) giving the message so they can hear what it will be like.

  e. Once they are familiar with it, they can then give it on their own to two or three of their close friends or family members. You may want to co-teach with them.

  f. UnveilinGLORY has a simply philosophy:

  "When you hear this material, it will change your mind.

  When you study this material, it will change your heart.

  When you teach this material, it will change your life forever!"

8. This workbook has over 1500 fill-in-the-blank questions and approximately 300 quiz questions. There is a separate **Answer Key** that should be purchased with this workbook. You should have this in your possession. All of the blanks and quizzes have a footnote that will take you right to a corresponding number in the answer key.

  a. Please note that all multiple choice questions may have more than one answer.

  b. At times, all four can be circled as correct answers.

  c. Each multiple choice question will have at least one answer.

9. You will also find a **final exam** at the end of the workbook for your child.

10. In the following lessons, you will need to check up on your child regarding a specific action you need to confirm that has been done.

  a. Lesson 1 (footnote 6)

  This is to be sure that they are reading the material first, then rereading it to find the answers. This is the best way they will learn. (We don't want them looking for the answers the first time they read it.)

      b. Lesson 2 (footnote 28)

        This is very key! They need to draw for you the three lives they will be asked about in each lesson. Make sure they understand these circles!

11. Some days will require your student to use a computer. On those days in the Table of Contents you will find a mother pointing next to it. This is to let you know what week they will be using a computer.

12. Your student will need:

      a. A dictionary (or use the internet)

      b. A Bible (we use the NIV with this material)

13. Please note that no material is perfect, only God is! If you find mistakes, PLEASE let us know by e-mailing us at **bob@UnveilinGLORY.com** (please note there is one "g" not two in the word: UnveilinGLORY) or **Debby@MMPublishers.com**.

14. Please keep checking our website for new homeschooling materials being developed. **We are planning on this being the first of at least four years of material!**

15. You are free to give you student a final grade after adding up all of their scores on page 484. Please do put each of their quiz scores in there as well as thier final score and any bonus points you want to give them for their presentation.

We would love your feedback. Please let us know how this material is impacting your life and your child's life!

Thankful for you,

Bob and Debby Sjogren

From the Authors To The Christian School Students:

Hello and welcome to UnveilinGLORY's first year's curriculum titled, *Cat and Dog Theology.* This material is designed for 7th-12th graders. It has a proven track record of changing students' lives. ***Get ready for an eye-opening, life-changing experience!***

Along with this workbook, your teacher will have you work with the following:

• the *Cat and Dog Theology* book,

• the *Cat and Dog Prayer* book,

• a *YouTeach CD* on Cat and Dog Theology, and

• the *Answer Key.* (Your teacher may want to keep that themselves.)

Follow the instructions of your teacher.

The first week is different from all the other weeks and sets a "baseline" for the curriculum, as well as your entire life. You will be reviewing the concept each week and the goal is for it to become a part of your life.

In both the middle and the end of this course, you will be asked to teach this material to someone else using "YouTeach." Our philosophy is simple: if you can't teach it, you don't know it. So get to know it well!

At the end of the year there is a final exam taken from the quizzes you will have already completed.

Thanks for taking this adventure in learning to live for God's glory. If you have any questions, ask your teacher. If s/he can't help you, have s/he contact us.

For His kingdom and glory,

Mr. & Mrs. Sjogren

Mr. and Mrs. Sjogren

bob@unveilinGLORY.com
debby@MMPublishers.com

P.S. **CAUTION!** The more your life is changed, the easier it is to spot Cat behavior in those around you. Please don't ever use this material to judge others. ("Oh, they are just a bunch of Cats.") Once we start judging others, we too are acting like Cats. Use this material to encourage yourself and others to live for God's glory.

From the Authors To The Christian School Teachers:

Welcome to UnveilinGLORY's first year's curriculum titled, *Cat and Dog Theology*. If you are using this in a classroom situation, here's what you need to know.

1. This material is designed to take 30-45 minutes a day-three days a week. Obviously for some it will be a bit shorter, for others a bit longer. It should fit comfortably into one class period. (The materials used are listed in the letter to the students.) You can assign the reading assignments to the students as homework (with each child having a book), or you can buy just the two books for the entire class and read it aloud. (If the latter is done, it will make filling in the workbook blanks much harder than if they have their own book to read.) Each student must have their own workbook.

2. There are 90 lessons designed to be done over a 30-week period of time.

3. Each week there is a bonus lecture to go deeper into the material. If you want to do that as a class, simply visit our web site, log on to each lecture, and listen to it.

4. Each week your student is asked, "How is this changing your life?" *This is the most critical part of the entire study.* Please spend a lot of time on this and get the students talking to one another about practical things God is doing in their lives.

    a.   Review what the students are writing.

    b.   If students are not doing this, then the study will be useless to them. They will be filled with a lot of head knowledge and become hypocrites. This is not what we want nor what you want.

5. Each week there are stories about a brother and sister who are learning and struggling to live for the glory of God.

    a.   Students will respond to four questions at the end of each story, which will be used for discussion in class.

    b.   **In Appendix A, there are additional questions.** We encourage you to use those for changing lives.

6. In both the middle and the end of this course, we ask your students to train other students in the material. Our philosophy is simple; if they can't teach it, they don't know it. You can do this in any number of ways.

    a.   Have your students get another student (either not in the class or in a grade lower) and have them teach it.

    b.   They can teach it at their homes to siblings or parents.

    c.   They can teach it to their youth group.

    d.   They can teach it to each other in class (one student teaches the first third, another the second third, and another the final third). Repeat this process until all students have taught a portion of it.

7. This workbook has over 1500 fill-in-the-blank questions and approximately 300 quiz questions. **There is also a separate *Answer Key*.** All of the blanks and quizzes have a footnote that will take you to a corresponding number in the *Answer Key*.

    a.   Note that all multiple choice questions may have more than one answer. Your students can do these individually (if they have their own books--the best option), in small groups, or as a class.

    b.   At times, all options can be circled as correct answers.

    c.   Each multiple choice question will have at least one answer.

8. **You will also find a final exam at the end for your students.** All of the answers are in the *Answer Key*. (The *Answer Key* must be purchased separately.)

9. **In the following lessons, you will need to check up on your student regarding a specific action that must be completed.**

    a.   Lesson 1 (footnote 6): This is to be sure that they are reading the material first, then rereading it to find the answers. This is the best way they will learn. (Don't let them look for the answers the first time they read it unless they don't have their own copy and the book is being read loud.)

    b.   Lesson 2 (footnote 28): This is key! They need to draw the three lives they will be asked about in each lesson. Make sure they understand these circles! You can have them do it in front of the class to other students, or have them do it student to student.

10. Your students will need access to a computer. The Table of Contents clearly shows which lessons require this with an icon of a teacher pointing next to it.

    a.   You can have them do the assignment as a class in your class period.

    b.   You can assign it as homework for them to do the night before at home.

11. All Scripture used comes from the New International Version (NIV, 1984).

We would love your feedback to improve this workbook for the next printing. Please send us anything that can help make it better!

For His kingdom and glory,

Bob and Debby Sjogren

    bob@unveilinGLORY.com

    debby@MMPublishers.com

How To Use The Answer Key!

Some people have found the answer key to be somewhat difficult. But once you understand it, it is so easy! Here's how you use it.

1. Note that after each blank or question, there is a footnote. One footnote contains all the answers for that single question. Here is a sample from Lesson 41, page 226. Note, it is footnote #782. It has four answers corresponding to that footnote.

> 2. Humanism has so permeated our culture, that it has _____ _____ into our Christianity creating two types of _____ _____. (782)

2. Now go to the Answer Key and look for that number. They are in numerical order.

    *   As you flip through the Answer Key, you'll notice numbers on the left side of the left page. This will help you find out where you are chronologically.

    *   As an example, if you flip to page 16, you'll see you're in the 500's. "Hmm, I'm somewhat close to 782," you'll be thinking.

    *   Then look down at the bottom of page 17 and you'll see it ends at #558. So turn the page and look at the bottom of page 19. You'll find #617. You're still not there.

    *   Do this two more times and you'll see #810 on page 25. Then you'll know it is somewhere on page 24 or 25.

DO NOT look to find the lesson number. They are not listed by lessons or by page numbers in the actual workbook. *They are only listed numerically.*

There are page numbers in the top right and left of the pages so if you are following along with your child each day, you'll remember, "I think our answers were on page 17 yesterday...."

People have asked that we put the lesson numbers in for an even easier time of finding the answers. We will be doing this, but we have 1,000 of the originals to sell out of first. So, it's not going to happen very soon!

If you can think of any other way to make it easier, please let me know. I'd love to update the *Answer Key* in an even better way.

Hope this helps!

Bob

Bob

TABLE OF CONTENTS

LESSON 1

"Thawing The Chicken"

READING ASSIGNMENT

Scientists at NASA built a gun designed specifically to launch dead chickens at the windshield of airlines, military jets and the space shuttle all traveling at maximum velocity.

The idea was to simulate the frequent incidents of collisions with airborne fowl to test the strength of the windshields.

British engineers heard about the gun and were eager to test it on the windshields of their high-speed train. Arrangements were made. But when the gun was fired, the engineers stood shocked, as the chicken hurled out of the barrel, crashed into the shatterproof shield, smashed it to smithereens, crashed through the control console, snapped the engineers headrest in two, and embedded itself in the back of the wall of the cabin.

Horrified Britons sent NASA the disastrous results of the experiment along with the designs of the windshield and begged the U.S. scientists for suggestions.

NASA's response was just one sentence:
Thaw the chicken!

Sometimes when we open up our Bibles, we haven't "thawed the chicken." We read our Bibles without first trying to consider how the Bible is to be read. And as a result, we misunderstand the Scriptures. We miss what God is doing. We miss where God wants to go. Sometimes, we can even miss God Himself. Reading our Bibles like this can bring about disastrous results.

The Current State of the Church

Let's be honest. The church today in America is hurting. No one likes to talk about it. No one likes to admit it. But it's because most Christians haven't read the instructions. The church is not being the salt of the earth or the light of the world. It is "limping along." Some have described it as being 3,000 miles wide but only a one-half inch deep. How do you know this? The answer is easy: simple statistics.

We'd love to list them for you, but we're going to allow you to guess at them first. Your mom/dad/teacher can tell you if you are right or wrong. And quite honestly, we hope you are wrong. Why? Because if your guess is wrong, you're more likely to remember the right answer! So, here it goes.

Guess at the following statistics:

What percent of the churches in America have either plateaued or are in decline?

Your Guess: _____%   Correct Answer: _____% [1]

What percent of Christian high school seniors ditch God when they go off to college?

Your Guess: _____%   Correct Answer: _____% [2]

What percent of their personal income does the average Christian tithe?

Your Guess: _____%   Correct Answer: _____% [3]

What percent of all abortions are done by women claiming to be Christians?

Your Guess: _____%   Correct Answer: _____% [4]

In terms of percentages, what is the difference between the divorce rate among believers and the divorce rate among non-believers?

Your Guess: _____%   Correct Answer: _____% [5]

*(Before you go further, talk to your parent/teacher or check your **Answer Key** to find out what the right answers are and write them in.)*

Those statistics are pretty startling aren't they?

They prove that most believers haven't "read the instructions." The fact is, if you walk down the average street in America, you can't really tell the difference between who is Christian and who isn't. They live the same lifestyle, they pursue the same goals. They have the same dreams. One may say "Praise the Lord" and go to church while the other swears and wouldn't even think of stepping into a church. That's the only difference. They both are living for the "Great American Dream." They want to get a good education to get a good job, and then get married, have kids and then own a nice home, a couple of cars and a boat. (Well, maybe not a boat, but you get the idea!)

Because you can't tell the difference between Christians and non-Christians, it is obvious that Christians are failing to live like Jesus and be the salt of the earth and the light of the world. That is why this curriculum has been written. It is designed to get believers back to living like Jesus and being the salt of the earth and the light of the world. It is designed to get us to live a life that glorifies God. This will be accomplished by helping you see the difference between a people-centered versus God-centered theology.

We've got to face reality. Business as usual isn't working. Something's got to change in our Christianity to get us living more like Jesus.

How This Curriculum Is Designed

This curriculum is designed to help you understand what it means to "thaw the chicken." It is designed to help you understand "how" you are to read your Bible. Once you understand "how" to read it, you'll be able to live more like Jesus and everything else begins to make a lot more sense.

This curriculum is designed to be done over a three-day period with an optional fourth day. Each day is designed to take approximately 30-45 minutes of your time.

Days one and two have two parts.

Starting on week two, the first thing you are to do is to read the pages assigned to you from this curriculum in the books *Cat and Dog Theology* and *Cat and Dog Prayer*. **Do not read the book while looking for the answers. Read the book first, then look at the questions.** By doing this, you will probably have to go back through the pages a second time to find those answers. This will help you learn the material. The questions will be in various forms.

Please put a check mark in the following box signifying you will not read the pages while looking at questions at the same time. ☐ 6

The second thing you are to do is a Bible study, which will parallel what you have just learned in the book. You will be asked a series of questions. These questions will be in the same type of format.

Day three Is an application of what you have learned that week. It contains:

1. A story/scenario revolving around what you just learned.

2. A quiz. (Please note: all quizzes may have more than one correct answer. At times you will see that all four are the correct answer. When that is the case, circle all four of them!)

3. A cartoon to view and answer questions.

4. An application point where you determine what you are going to do to live out this material. This is very important. It is what is called "obedience discipleship." As you obey what you are learning, the Lord will give you more and more insight to what you are studying.

The optional fourth day has you watching a video clip on the UnveilinGLORY web site. It is for those who want to go even deeper in the material. You may do this or you are free to simply catch up.

How You Really Learn The Material

At UnveilinGLORY we have a saying:
- If you listen to this material, it will change your mind.
- If you study this material it will change your heart.
- If you teach this material, it will change your life forever!

This curriculum has been designed to change your life forever! We don't want this to be another "Bible Study" that has no long-term lasting impact on you.

To help accomplish this, you are going to be teaching two Bible studies to a few people in your life. It may be fellow students, siblings, friends, parents, aunts, or uncles and can be done at your kitchen table or in your living room, in the classroom setting, or wherever you are the most comfortable. One will be in the middle of your school year, the other will be at the end of the year. You'll be teaching material you've already learned and hopefully know by heart.

You are going to be doing this by getting two or more people that you can teach. (Feel free to seek out people younger than you!) It will only last about 20-30 minutes. Don't be afraid. It has already been prepared for you and what you need to say has already been written out. In a "worst case scenario" all you will have to do is to show the slides (already prepared) and read the text written down for each slide.

By teaching this material, your life will be changed in a greater way. We also hope that will change those you will be teaching as well.

Repeat, Repeat, Repeat

This curriculum is designed to repeat lessons you've learned. Why is this? The more you repeat it, the more likely you will learn it. Don't be surprised if a passage comes up a second time or if you are asked a question you've already answered before. This theory is simple: The more you review, the better.

This curriculum is designed to repeat lessons you've learned. Why is this? The more you repeat it, the more likely you will learn it. Don't be surprised if a passage comes up a second time or if you are asked a question you've already answered before. This theory is simple: The more you review, the better. ☺

BIBLE STUDY!

1. Read Romans 11:36.

2. When the text says that everything is "from him," what do you think it means?

_____

_____

_____ 7

3. When the text says "through him," what do you think it means?

_____

_____

_____ 8

4. How does Colossians 1:17 agree or disagree with this?

_____

_____ 9

5. When the text says everything is "to him," what do you think it means?

_____

_____

_____ 10

6. Explain what the difference would be if the text read, "For from Him and through him and to him are most things."

_____

_____

_____ 11

7. In a nutshell, try to summarize what life is all about by filling in the blank below.

Life is all about _____. 12

8. Summarize what the text would be communicating if it said, "For from us, through us and to us are all things."

_____

_____

_____ 13

9. What if it said, "For from the lost, and through the lost and to the lost, are all things." What would it be communicating?

_____

_____

_____ 14

10. The text clearly communicates that everything revolves around God. If that is the case, circle which lessons can we learn from the text.

 A. I should be constantly asking the question, "What does God get out of this?"

 B. When I start to think that everything is here for me, then I'm drawing close to the very heart of God.

 C. The paper I am reading this from is designed to point me to God.

 D. I was created to glorify God.

 E. I should focus my prayer life on the thought of, "What can God do for me?"

 F. The music that I listen to should point me to me. [15]

11. The main point of the "thaw the chicken" story is to help me to see that this life is primarily about God and I should constantly be asking, "What does God get out of this?" not "What do I get out of this?"

 Circle One: True False [16]

LESSON 2

"Three Lives"

READING ASSIGNMENT

In order to learn from this study, you need to be walking in the power of the Holy Spirit. That's a phrase you may or may not have heard before. If you haven't heard of it, it simply means that God needs to be in control of your life and that you are yielding to Him. To help you better understand this, and learn to walk in the power of God's Holy Spirit, we are going to be going over three lives in this lesson, the next lesson, and then in every lesson you do!

Below is a diagram of three lives. Each life represents a different type of person. Each day you start your Bible study, you are going to be asked "Which circle represents your life?" This is a part of the "repetition" talked about in Lesson 1, but it is also a challenge to you as a person to think through your life. If God is *not* in control of your life, odds are you aren't going to be learning the material.

This is not something we are asking you to do that we do not do ourselves. The simple concept shown in the circle diagram below has transformed our lives forever. We are so thankful for having been taught it while we were in college through the ministry of CRU, formerly Campus Crusade for Christ. Because it has been so foundational, we are teaching it to you as well.

THREE LIVES
Which One Are You?

#1 NON-CHRISTIAN
1 John 5:12

#3 SAVIOR
1 Corinthians 3:15

#2 SAVIOR AND LORD
Galatians 5:22,23

Understanding the elements in the diagram for each life: [17]

- Each circle represents a person's life.
- Each chair represents a "throne" which indicates who is in charge of the life.
- The colored icons represent what is going on in a person's life. Some people have "bombs" that are ready to explode in their lives. Some people have circumstances causing them to be unhappy. Life is full of events in each person's life.
- The cross represents Christ.

These three circles represent three types of lives in the world today.

Circle #1 represents the non-Christian life.

- "Self" is on the throne and thinks he/she is strong and can live life in his/her own power and strength.
- Christ is outside the life and has never been invited in.
- His/her life is out of balance.

Circle #2 represents a Christian life where Christ is both Savior and Lord.

- Christ is on the throne and in control of a person's life. Because of this, things are "pretty much in order."
- "Self" is off the throne and has not only yielded to Christ, but worships Christ.
- His/her life is pretty much in balance as he/she trusts God each and every day to guide them.

Circle #3 represents a "Carnal Christian" life where Christ is his/her Savior, but not their Lord. This is where *90%* of most Christians live.

- They have invited Christ into their lives.
- Christ is not on the throne of their lives, they are.
- Christ is taking a "back seat." They know Him as their Savior, but not their Lord.
- Their lives are out of balance as well.

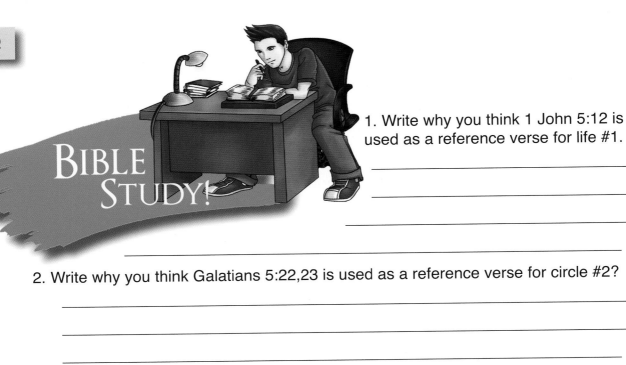

BIBLE STUDY!

1. Write why you think 1 John 5:12 is used as a reference verse for life #1.

_____

_____

_____

_____ [18]

2. Write why you think Galatians 5:22,23 is used as a reference verse for circle #2?

_____

_____

_____ [19]

3. Read 1 Corinthians 3:10-15. The foundation Paul is talking about is Christ. As we live for Christ, there are two types of ways we can live for Him. One is with gold, precious stones and silver, or the other is with wood, hay or straw. Which circle represents gold, precious stones and silver, and which circle represents wood, hay or straw?

    Wood, hay and straw represented by Circle # _____. [20]

    Gold, silver and precious stones represented by Circle # _____ . [21]

4. What do you think "the Day" (NIV verse 13) is referring to?

_____

_____ [22]

5. How does 2 Corinthians 5:10 agree or disagree with "the Day" Paul is referencing in 1 Corinthians 3:13?

_____

_____ [23]

6. Circle which activities you think represent "wood, hay and straw."

    A. Watching TV

    B. Playing video games

    C. Studying God's Word

    D. Feeding the poor

    E. Doing chores [24]

7. Do you think Christians will get rewards based on "wood, hay or straw?"

_____ 25

8. Do you think Christians will get rewards based on "gold, precious stones and silver?"

_____ 26

9. Write why you think 1 Corinthians 3:15 is used as a reference verse for life #3?

_____

_____

_____ 27

The following question will be asked to you each time you open up this study (so get used to it! :) Which circle best represents your life **right now?** Check One:

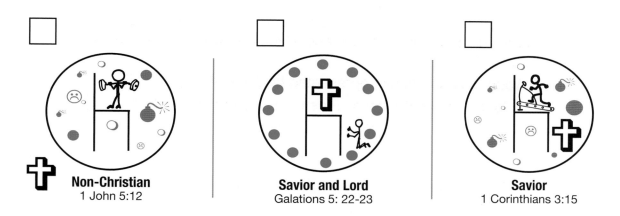

Non-Christian
1 John 5:12

Savior and Lord
Galations 5: 22-23

Savior
1 Corinthians 3:15

Go to the parent who is homeschooling you (or follow your teacher's directions) and without this curriculum, draw the three circles and explain to them what they mean. Place a check mark when this has been done. (Your parent/teacher will check up on you with this assignment.)

Yes, I did this! ☐ 28

LESSON 3

CHECK WHICH CIRCLE BEST REPRESENTS YOUR LIFE TODAY:

☐

☐

☐

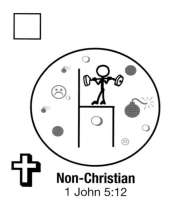

Non-Christian
1 John 5:12

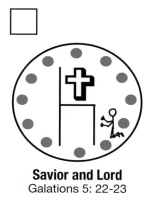

Savior and Lord
Galations 5: 22-23

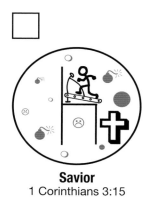

Savior
1 Corinthians 3:15

READING ASSIGNMENT

Living in life #2 becomes easier and easier the more you live in it. But for many, starting off in it is very difficult. This is because living a perfect life is impossible. Only Jesus has done it. And because of our old nature, we sin. We are going to define "sinning" as taking back control of the throne of our lives. When we do this, we move from life #2 to life #3.

What does this "sinning" look like? Well, it is **doing something we know we should not do.** Circle the following items that you know would be sinning (as described above.)

A. Having a quiet time.

B. Talking back to your parents.

C. Hitting a sibling.

D. Lying to a friend.

E. Being jealous of someone else's success.

F. Reading the Bible.

G. Speaking poorly about one friend to another friend.

H. Getting angry at your parents because they want you to do your chores.

I. Purposefully missing your chores. [29]

There is a key point we'd like to highlight. **Moving from life #2 (the Spirit Filled life) to life #3 (the Carnal Life)** involves doing something you know you should not do. You know it is wrong to hit a sibling. You know it is wrong to talk back to your parents. You know it is wrong to lie. And if you do what you know is wrong and yet still do it, you are taking back control of the throne of your life and moving to life #3.

In the options above we talked about "purposefully" missing your chores. Why did we put the word "purposefully" in there? Because sometimes you forget to do them, but you were not purposefully forgetting them. It just happened because you forgot! This is not sin. (It should be worked on, but it is not sin.)

The best way I had all of this sin described to me was in what was called the "iceberg" theory. Look at the iceberg below.

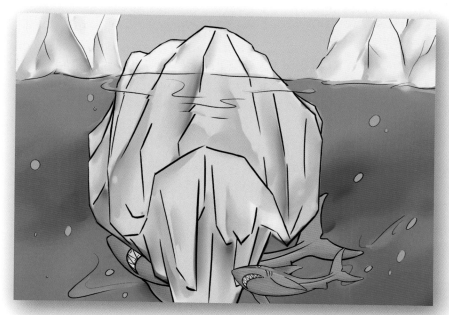

10% of the iceberg is above the water. This 10% is what the Holy Spirit has allowed us to understand and know what is "right and wrong." (You know hitting your sibling is wrong. That is in the 10% area. You know lying is wrong. That is in the 10% area. You know stealing is wrong. That is the 10% area.)

But there is another 90%. This represents things we do that are sinful, but we are unaware of it. For someone, it could be watching too much T.V. For another it could be playing video games for too long. For another, it could be having an addiction to Social Media. But because the Spirit of God hasn't convicted them of this yet, it is a part of the 90%. To them, it is not sin. God is basically saying, "You're not ready to know this yet. As a result, I'm not going to make you aware of it so you don't freak out each time you do it! For you right now, it is not sin." (Though for someone else, it might be.) It moves from the 90% to the 10% once you are convicted of it. Then the Holy Spirit lets you know that it is wrong.

Explain how James 4:16,17 agrees or disagrees with this.

_____

_____

_____ 30

Explain how Luke 12:47,48 agrees or disagrees with this.

_____

_____

_____ 31

We move from life #2 (the Spirit Filled Life) to life #3 (the Carnal Life) by doing something you know is wrong (something in the 10% area.) So, the next time you lie, the next time you steal something, the next time you hit your sibling and you know it is wrong, you have "successfully" moved back on the throne of your life. You are now in control of your life.

The question is, how do we move from life #3 (the Carnal Life) back to life #2 (the Spirit Filled Life?)

Moving from life #3 to life #2 is actually quite easy and can be done in a matter of seconds. You practice something called "*Spiritual Breathing!*" Spiritual Breathing is based on exhaling and inhaling.

Exhale: In the exhale part of *Spiritual Breathing*, you are physically exhaling and in that moment, you are confessing your sin. While letting air out, you say, "Lord, I know that what I did was wrong. Please forgive me."

When we ask for forgiveness, God does forgive us. How do we know? Because of 1 John 1:9. Look it up and answer the questions below:

1. What is the first step of 1 John 1:9?

_____

_____
32

2. Why do you think the word "faithful" is in there?

_____

_____
33

3. Why is He also just?

_____

_____
34

4. After confessing our sins, the text says that God will do two things. What are these?

    A. _____

    B. _____
35

5. Though "forgiveness" and "cleansing" may sound similar in 1 John 1:9, they are very different. When God speaks about forgiving us our sins, which part of the

iceberg do you think he is talking about? (Hint, if you are confessing it, you already know about it.)

Circle One: 10%   90% [36]

God is saying, "If you confess your sins—that which you know you did wrong (in the 10%)—I am going to forgive you of that. But there is a lot more sin in the 90% that you are not aware of that you are doing and I want you to know that I forgive that as well." This is where God takes it one step further by saying, "and cleanse you from all unrighteousness." This is a cleansing of all of the things we didn't know we had done in the 90% that were wrong. (Look up Psalm 19:12 and see how David agrees.)

6. Write in your own words what John is referencing regarding the 90%.

_____

_____ [37]

Inhale: Now that you have "Exhaled" and confessed your sin and been forgiven, "Inhaling" is then saying to God, "Now that I have confessed and been forgiven, I want to yield to you and give you back control of my life."

7. In Ephesians 5:17,18 it says to "not be unwise, but know what the will of the Lord is." It then says to not get drunk. If it ended there, the command would be simple. "Don't get drunk." But it goes on from there, so it is not merely saying, "Don't get drunk" but it is also communicating that there is a parallel here. What happens to the personality of an individual when they are drunk?

_____

_____ [38]

8. After saying, "Don't get drunk," it then tells you to be "filled with the Spirit." Just as an individual's personality changes when they are drunk, what happens to an individual's personality when they are filled with the Spirit?

_____

_____ [39]

Being "filled with the Spirit" is what we are calling "putting Christ back on the throne of our lives." As one student put in during our beta-test review, "Get high on God, not alcohol!" (It isn't actually Christ Himself, but rather His Holy Spirit that will guide us and control us. It is His Spirit that lives inside of us. Jesus is seated right next to God the Father who is on His throne.)

The entire *Spiritual Breathing* process can be done in a matter of seconds. Right when you know you've done something wrong, you can spiritually breathe. And then in moments, the Holy Spirit can be in control of your life. You only have to live in life #3 (the Carnal Life) for a matter of seconds. The majority of your life can be lived in the power of the Holy Spirit.

The Train Diagram

The above train diagram (originally taught to Debby and me by Campus Crusade for Christ when we were college students) illustrates how you *know* you can be walking in the power of the Holy Spirit. This is the question I get asked the most, "How do I really know I am Spirit-filled?"

For the purpose of answering the previous question, let's learn how this "diagram train runs." The coal car puts coal into the engine to burn. The fire heats up the water to make steam, which powers the engine. The engine then pulls both the coal car and the caboose. The train can run with or without the caboose, but it cannot run without the coal car.

The "engine" is labeled "Fact." This represents the Word of God. The "coal car" is labeled "Faith," and the "caboose" is labeled "Feelings."

This helps us understand that we are to put our "faith" (coal) in God's Word (the engine). When we put our faith in God's Word, the train runs and our lives will run much more smoothly. As we do this, our feelings may come with us (great joy), but they may not come (we may still feel "without God" or "guilty.")

Either way it doesn't matter, the train (our lives) are running the way they should. God will be in control of our lives because we asked Him for something we know He wants for us: to be "filled with the Spirit."

Many Christians worry about how they "feel." "Do I feel like God is answering my prayers? Do I feel close to God? Do I feel like God is in charge." If they don't feel God's closeness, they assume God is not in control. This is not necessarily the case. If they have confessed their sins and asked God to forgive them and yielded back control of their lives to Christ, then God is on the throne of their lives (sitting on the throne), whether they feel it or not.

In **1 John 5:14,15**, we read these words, "This is the confidence we have in

approaching God: that if we ask anything according to his will, he hears us. And if we know that he hears us—whatever we ask—we know that we have what we asked of him." In applying this passage to *Spiritual Breathing* (specifically the "Inhaling Part"), answer the following questions.

1. What does the text say we can have in approaching God?

   _____ 40

2. Is asking Him to fill us (take control of our lives) something He desires?
   Circle One: Yes   No [41]

3. If we know it is His will, the text clearly says "God hears us." And if we know that He hears us, what else do we know?

   _____ 42

4. Would God ever give a promise like 1 John 5:14,15, then hear us ask Him to fill us, and then say, "Well, I really don't feel like it today, sorry."
   Circle One: Yes   No [43]

5. Write out what guarantee you have regarding the "Inhaling" part of *Spiritual Breathing*.

   _____

   _____

   _____ 44

I have taught this principle to many people. And after they pray to ask God to take back control of their lives, I ask them, *"How you do know you are filled with the Holy Spirit?"*

They usually respond, "I don't know, I don't feel any different." They are looking for a feeling, but it isn't there. They aren't suppose to "feel" God, they are to be assured by faith. So I walk them back referencing their faith and the train analogy and **1 John 5:14,15.** Then I ask them again. If they still aren't sure, I go through it all again. I know when they have finally gotten it when they say, "I know by faith and faith alone that He is in control of my life." That's when they are walking by faith in the power of the Holy Spirit and are pleasing to God.   This is why **2 Corinthians 5:7** says, "We live by faith and not by sight" (feelings).

There is the story of a couple in church that were given an altar call to be filled with the Spirit. As the wife saw her husband walk up front, she yelled, "Don't do it Lord, he leaks!"

We all "leak." We all have an old nature that wants to take back control of our lives.

But the beauty is that when it does, we can confess it and give back control immediately to God. Some people breathe spiritually multiple times a day. Others, multiple times in a week. Others, a few times a month. The more you learn to walk in the power of the Holy Spirit, the less you'll find yourself having to spiritually breathe because you are learning more and more of how to give God control of your life.

When I (Debby) was 13 years old, I use to save up all my sins and confess them at the end of the night. I had no idea that I didn't need to carry those sins the entire day and that I could confess them immediately.

You only need to be in circle #3 for a matter of seconds. Once you are convicted, you can confess your sins and ask God to take back control of your life immediately!

Please note one clarification! In our beta-test one student asked, "Is life #3 the Cat?" Great question! No. Circle 3 is not necessarily a Cat Christian. A Cat Christian can be life 2 or 3. You can have Christ as Lord of your life, and be pursuing God, and what you are pursuing is not incorrect, but incomplete. This can be a Cat in circle #2.

BIBLE STUDY!

1. Read Revelation 3:14-22.

2. Write down what you think the words "hot" and "cold" mean.

Hot:

_____

_____

45

Cold:

_____

_____

46

3. What would a Christian's life look like if they were "lukewarm?"

_____

_____

_____ 47

4. What does God say He wants to do with lukewarm Christians?

_____

_____ 48

5. These people not only had all of their needs met, but were rich in the world's eyes. Though they were rich, God calls them _____,

_____, _____, _____ and

_____. 49

6. In light of the statistics that you looked at earlier in Lesson One (pg. 3), how do you think this could apply to the American church?

_____

_____ 50

7. Circle the following lessons we can learn from this passage:

   A. God isn't impressed at all with those who are "playing the game of Christianity" but don't really love God with all their heart, soul, mind and strength.

   B. God wants us passionate about Him, not just "kinda excited" about Him.

   C. God can get sick.

   D. Having our physical needs met generously can really blind us to our spiritual needs. 51

Oh Lord, I need to pass this quiz.

QUIZ!

(Remember, all quizzes may have more than one correct answer. At times, all four may be correct. If that is the case, circle all of them! These are "tricky" to prepare you for the SAT's.)

1. Romans 11:36 says:

    A. All things are from us, through us and to us.

    B. Most things are from Him, through Him and to Him.

    C. Everything is about saving the lost.

    D. All things are from Him, through Him and to Him. [52]

2. The reason we point to Romans 11:36 is to tell us that:

    A. Life is about God and not us.

    B. Life is about us and not God.

    C. God lives for us.

    D. We are to live for God. [53]

3. This curriculum has been designed to:

    A. Entertain you.

    B. Change the way you think.

    C. Get you to live more like Jesus and change your life forever. [54]

4. What percent of churches in North America have either plateaued or are in decline:

    A. 80%

    B. 70%

    C. 50%

    D. 30% [55]

5. 2 Corinthians 5:10 tells us that all Christians will be:

    A. forgiven

    B. judged

    C. both

    D. neither [56]

6. The statistics were given to help you realize that:

    A. We're doing a great job!

    B. We, the church, are desperately hurting.

    C. Business as usual isn't working. [57]

7. God wants you to repent for hours before you give Him back control of your life to be sure you are really sincere about it.

    A. True

    B. False [58]

8. You are to read each day's material while looking at the questions.

    A. True

    B. False [59]

9. You can feel quite guilty about something yet be walking in the power of the Holy Spirit (Life #2) directly after "spiritual breathing."

    A. True

    B. False [60]

10. What does God do with Lukewarm Christians?

    A. He wants to nurture them until they walk with Him.

    B. He wants to spit them out.

    C. He's putting them on "hold" until they get hot toward Him. [61]

PUT ALL QUIZ SCORES ON PAGE 484

What are you going to do differently as a result of what you've learned? **Go to the end of this workbook and write it in for Lesson 3.**

PERSONAL APPLICATION

OPTIONAL LESSON

No work today. Just be sure you understand the material given in the last two days. It is vital to your future walk with the Lord. If it is not clear, please review it.

LESSON 4

CHECK WHICH CIRCLE BEST REPRESENTS YOUR LIFE TODAY:

☐   ☐   ☐

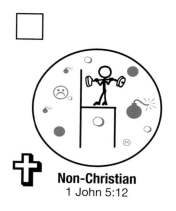

Non-Christian
1 John 5:12

Savior and Lord
Galations 5: 22-23

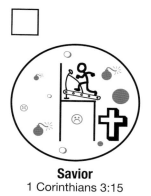

Savior
1 Corinthians 3:15

Since my last lesson,
I have practiced
Spiritual Breathing:

☐ 20⁺ Times
☐ 11 - 19 Times
☐ 6 - 10 Times
☐ 0 - 5 Times

READING ASSIGNMENT

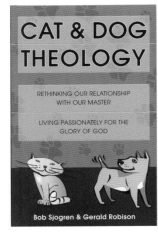

CAT & DOG THEOLOGY

RETHINKING OUR RELATIONSHIP WITH OUR MASTER

LIVING PASSIONATELY FOR THE GLORY OF GOD

Bob Sjogren & Gerald Robison

(From the book *Cat and Dog Theology*)

Page 1: Start with the introduction and read all the way through the top paragraph on page 6 (Stop at "Obedience, Glory and Blessings")

Questions to answer from the reading assignment:

1. According to page 1, the goal of this study is to draw us _____ to God. [62]

2. Some theologies can actually pull us _____ from God. [63]

3. Write down how the Sjogrens' cat and dog greet them differently?

_____

_____

_____ [64]

4. Write down how the Sjogrens' cat and dog get outside differently?

_____

_____

_____ [65]

5. It is a common joke that says, "Dogs have _____ , cats have _____." [66]

6. List three characteristics commonly attributed to a dog: _____, _____ and _____. [67]

7. List two characteristics commonly attributed to a cat: _____ and _____. [68]

8. The joke that conveys their differences perfectly is, "A dog says, you pet me, you feed me, you shelter me, you love me, _____ must be God. A cat says, you pet me, you feed me, you shelter me, you love me, _____ must be God." [69]

9. Do Cat Christians actually think they're God?

Circle one: Yes   No   [70]

10. Is pure cat theology ever taught from the pulpit or sung in songs?

     Circle One: Yes   No   [71]

11. Though Cats will never say, "I must be God" what they do say is, "It's _____ about _____." [72]

12. Deep down inside, Cat Christians think that God not only _____ for them, but He _____ for them as well. [73]

13. How could a cat lover take offense at this book?

    _____

    _____ [74]

14. Should a cat lover take offense at this book and why?

    _____

    _____ [75]

BIBLE STUDY!

1. Read Genesis 1 and then answer the following questions:

   A. Were you bored with this chapter from the Bible?

      Circle one: Yes   No   [76]

   B. Why do you think most Christians are bored with the chapter?

      _____

      _____ [77]

   C. What does this tell you?

      _____

      _____ [78]

   D. What is this non-verbally communicating to God?

      _____

      _____ [79]

2. When reading the Bible, Cat Christians are constantly asking one question, "What do _____ get out of this?" And if they're not in it, they are not really interested in the text. [80]

3. Dogs ask a different question when reading the Bible. They ask, "What does _____ get out of this?" [81]

LESSON 5

CHECK WHICH CIRCLE BEST REPRESENTS YOUR LIFE TODAY:

☐

☐

☐

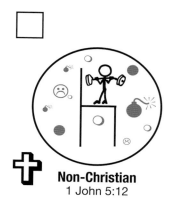

Non-Christian
1 John 5:12

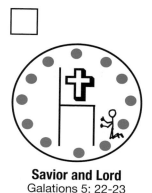

Savior and Lord
Galations 5: 22-23

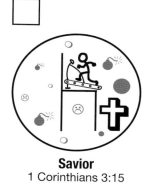

Savior
1 Corinthians 3:15

Since my last lesson,
I have practiced
Spiritual Breathing:

☐ 20+ Times

☐ 11 - 19 Times

☐ 6 - 10 Times

☐ 0 - 5 Times

READING ASSIGNMENT

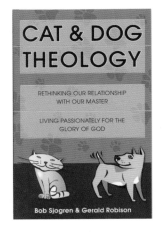

CAT & DOG THEOLOGY

RETHINKING OUR RELATIONSHIP WITH OUR MASTER

LIVING PASSIONATELY FOR THE GLORY OF GOD

Bob Sjogren & Gerald Robison

Start at the top of page 6 ("Obedience, Glory and Blessings") and read to the end of the chapter (page 10).

Questions to answer from the reading assignment:

1. Do Cat Christians and Dog Christians both want obedience in their Christian life?

　　Circle one:　Yes　　No　　[82]

2. Look at the following picture and answer the questions below:

A. Write a sentence as to why the picture is so funny!

_____

_____ [83]

B. In dog obedience school, dogs learn to obey their _____. [84]

C. Cats want their _____ to learn to obey _____. [85]

3. Theologically, Dogs think they should obey God whereas Cats think _____ should obey _____. [86]

4. Devern Fromke's book states, "Today we are reaping a harvest of man-centered conversions because we are more concerned for _____ than for _____. We are more interested in God _____ man than we are in _____ _____ God. [87]

5. This is usually reflected in a Cat's _____ life. Cat prayers have a lot of _____, _____ and __'s in them. [88]

6. James Mulholland writes, "In December, I addressed my request to _____ _____, the rest of the year I petitioned _____. My _____ _____ is how to get God to give me what I want. My desire is to _____ God rather than to _____ Him." [89]

7. Martin Luther said, "The essence of sin is that man _____ _____ _____ in everything, even in _____." [90]

8. Cats are into Christianity for what they _____ _____ _____ of _____. [91]

9. What does Romans 15:8,9 not say was the primary purpose as to why Christ came?

_____

_____ [92]

10. What does Romans 15:8,9 say is the primary reason why Christ came?

_____

_____ [93]

11. What is the reason as to why you have been saved according to this passage?

_____

_____ [94]

12. Why do you think the living creatures in Revelation 4:6-8, while praising God day and night, never mention us?

_____

_____ [95]

13. Fill in what the authors say about how Revelation 4:9-11 can be translated: "for your _____ they were created and have their being." [96]

14. If you were to summarize what the authors are saying thus far, how would you fill in the following blanks?

Life, it's _____ _____ _____, it's _____ _____. [97]

BIBLE STUDY!

1. Look up Matthew 10:38,39. How does this text coincide with what Cat and Dog Theology is teaching?

_____

_____

_____

_____

98

2. Do a search on the internet for "High Places Old Testament" and list a brief definition of it below:

_____

_____

_____ 99

3. Read 2 Kings 15:1-5. What part of the passage shows that this king (Azariah of Judah) was part Dog?

_____

_____ 100

4. What part of the passage shows that this king was part Cat?

_____

_____ 101

LESSON 6

CHECK WHICH CIRCLE BEST REPRESENTS YOUR LIFE TODAY:

☐

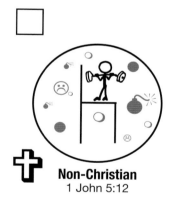

Non-Christian
1 John 5:12

☐

Savior and Lord
Galations 5: 22-23

☐

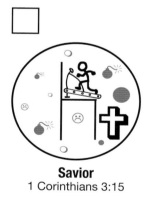

Savior
1 Corinthians 3:15

Since my last lesson,
I have practiced
Spiritual Breathing:

☐ 20⁺ Times
☐ 11 - 19 Times
☐ 6 - 10 Times
☐ 0 - 5 Times

CARTOON

How Cats And Dogs View God

1. Look up the word "staff" and write its definition:

_____

_____

_____

_____

_____

_____ 106

2. In your own words, how does this reflect what is happening among some Christians in their attitudes toward God.

_____

_____

_____ 107

CHRIS and SARAH

Sarah surveyed the crowd of old friends in the room and grinned. She was so excited for her first year in the "older kids' youth group" as her mother called it. Her older brother, Chris, loved this youth group and she had only heard good things about it from him.

Because her mother was from Taiwan and her dad from America, Sarah and her brother were the only Asian Americans in the room, yet they felt totally accepted. They had grown up in this church, and they knew almost everyone at youth group. Bobby was the clown and never seemed to be able to wear clothes that matched. Jessica was a few years older than Sarah, but the two girls became fast friends when Sarah finally convinced her mom to stop homeschooling her and Jessica befriended her at the Christian private school. Jim was one of Chris' fellow homeschooled friends and basketball buddies. The twins, Luke and James, teased Sarah relentlessly. Her mom said it was probably because they liked her.

Then there was Bryan. He was a junior who also attended Sarah's school, and she secretly had a crush on him for almost a year. There were twenty others she and Chris could talk about. Not only did they know them all well, they also knew their parents and most of their siblings. Now that Sarah was a freshman, she could hardly wait to dive in to the church's busy, popular youth group.

One reason their youth group was so popular was their pastor. Jake was a passionate, dynamic youth pastor, riding on the cutting edge of technology and fashion, filled with fire for God and young people. He and his wife had been youth pastors at this church for five years, which Chris and Sarah heard was a church record. Chris was even going through their leadership program and felt really good about how he was growing in his walk with the Lord.

The music was pretty fantastic as well. Recently, Sarah had heard a song speak of how God was jealous for her. It was now one of her favorite songs—she even downloaded it from iTunes and put it on her phone. The following week she heard another song, which told her how Jesus died thinking about her above all. Sarah thought both songs were awesome! *What an amazing God*, she thought to herself. *Who would ever think that God would send His Son, just for me?* She was just beginning her freshman year and she was firm in her mind, *God thinks the world of me and simply wants to bless me!*

Every week, Jake's youth group received a heavy dose of God's love and a fresh realization that God sacrificed everything just for them. Tonight's message was on how much God loved them and wanted to bless them.

To bring it all home, Jake ended the message by chanting with the youth group, "God is good!" All the youth replied, "All the time!" Jake picked it up, "All the time…"

Sarah and Chris screamed as loud as they could, trying to outdo the students around them, "God is good!"

I can't get enough of this, Sarah thought to herself, I want to keep coming to youth group every week. This is going to be great!

After the final prayer, Sarah gathered with all of the other freshmen and caught up on the latest gossip about those who didn't go to her school—homeschoolers and the public-schoolers alike.

After 45 minutes of this steady diet, Chris came over to her and caught her attention. "Time to go, Sis." She said goodbye to her friends and walked with Chris to the car.

Pulling out of the parking lot, Chris asked her, "Well, how was it?"

"Oh, you wouldn't believe what I heard about Elizabeth...."

Chris cut her short, "Not the latest gossip, silly. What did you think about youth group. Did you like it?"

"Oh yeah, I loved it. I can't wait to go next week!"

Lesson 6 Questions: (The suggested answers are on page 49 in the *Answer Key.*)

1. What was good about the story that could help Chris and Sarah become better Dogs?

_____

_____

2. What could be bad about the story that might make them become more like a Cat?

_____

_____

3. In what ways was Sarah a Cat at the youth group?

_____

_____

4. In one sentence, what wrong idea could Sarah and all of the other youth be learning?

_____

_____

Oh Lord, I need to pass this quiz.

QUIZ!

1. Deep down inside, Cat Christians really think that:

   A. They are guilty.

   B. They should live for God.

   C. God lives for them. [108]

2. Why is it that most Christians are bored with Genesis chapter 1?

   A. They're always worried about what they get out of it.

   B. People aren't there until the last few sentences.

   C. They've heard it all before and so they think there's nothing new to it.

   D. All of the above. [109]

3. Cat Christians want

   A. God to obey people.

   B. People to obey God. [110]

4. People following Cat Theology are more interested in

   A. People serving God.

   B. God serving people. [111]

5. Romans 15:8,9 says that you were saved for a purpose. That purpose is so that

   A. You can get to heaven.

   B. You can glorify God.

   C. You can be blessed here on this earth. [112]

6. Revelation 4:9-11 can be very accurately translated as "for your pleasure they were created and have their being."

   A. True

   B. False [113]

7. Which of the following statements are true:

   A. Life, it's all about God, it's not about us.

   B. Life, it's all about us, it's not about God. [114]

8. Which of the following statements are true about Cat Theology:

   A. Cats are more concerned for man than for God.

   B. Cats are more interested in God serving man than in man serving God.

(There are three more possible answers on the next page.)

C. Cats want to serve God, but only comfortably.

D. Cats want obedience in their lives.

E. All of the above. [115]

9. Martin Luther says, "The essence of sin is that man seeks his own in everything, even in God."

A. True

B. False [116]

10. Most Cats are into Christianity for

A. Glorifying God

B. What God gets out of it.

C. What they get out of it.

D. They're not really into Christianity. [117]

PERSONAL APPLICATION

What are you going to do differently as a result of what you've learned? **Go to the end of your workbook and write it in for Lesson 6.** [118]

OPTIONAL LESSON

Go to **www.UnveilinGLORY.com** and click on the left side: Free Online Teaching. Once there, click on "Guest." In the top right where it says "Choose a Series" choose "Cat and Dog Theology."

• Listen to Cat and Dog Lesson 1.

There is no quiz, no notes to be taken. Just enjoy and learn!

LESSON 7

CHECK WHICH CIRCLE BEST REPRESENTS YOUR LIFE TODAY:

☐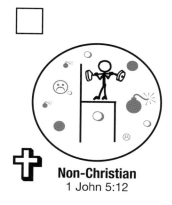

Non-Christian
1 John 5:12

☐

Savior and Lord
Galations 5: 22-23

☐

Savior
1 Corinthians 3:15

Since my last lesson,
I have practiced
Spiritual Breathing:

☐ 20+ Times
☐ 11 - 19 Times
☐ 6 - 10 Times
☐ 0 - 5 Times

READING ASSIGNMENT

Start on page 11 and read through to the bottom of page 16 where it says "Worship."

Questions to answer from the reading assignment:

CAT & DOG THEOLOGY

RETHINKING OUR RELATIONSHIP WITH OUR MASTER

LIVING PASSIONATELY FOR THE GLORY OF GOD

Bob Sjogren & Gerald Robison

1. What makes Christian Cats and Dogs look alike?

_____

_____ 119

2. What do the authors say makes them different?

_____

_____ 120

3. What is a Cat's motivation for getting to heaven?

_____

_____ 121

4. Who are Cats primarily focused on getting into heaven?

_____ 122

5. What is a Dog's motivation for getting to heaven?

_____

_____ 123

6. What do the authors say is a Cat's assurance of salvation?

_____

_____ 124

7. What would a Cat say Christianity is all about?

_____

_____ 125

8. What do the authors say is a Dog's assurance of salvation?

_____

_____

_____ 126

9. When a Cat prays, "Lord please bless our church," what is a Cat possibly thinking?

_____

_____ 127

10. When a Dog prays, "Lord please bless our church," what is a Dog possibly thinking?

_____

_____ 128

11. Cats basically pray, "Lord, we really need you to build _____ 129 kingdom."

12. Dogs basically pray, "Lord, we really need you to build _____ 130 kingdom."

13. It's OK for Dogs to pray for blessings, but when Dogs do pray for blessings, it is not usually their _____ focus. 131

14. How would you describe your conversion? When you first came to the Lord, would you say you were more "walking away from hell" or "walking toward heaven" and why?

_____

_____

_____

_____ 132

BIBLE STUDY!

1. Read Matthew 13:44. There are two possible ways of looking at the "treasure." One way is that we are the treasure and that God gave up everything for us. This is very biblical and accurate—not only as seen in the life of Christ, but also in the context. But another way (which also is very biblical) is that He is the treasure and we are finding Him.

2. Write down why this second way allows you to become more like a Dog in getting to heaven than a Cat.

_____

_____ 133

3. According to Matthew 13:44, what is supposed to characterize a Christian's life?

_____ 134

4. What is the first step Matthew 13:44 talks about before a person becomes a believer?

_____ 135

5. Circle which of the following are hard to give up in any person's life for the treasure:

   •My goals in life.

   •My plans for life.

   •My dreams.

   •My cell phone.

   •The things I own. [136]

6. How does this treasure compare in value to everything else in a person's life?

_____

_____ 137

LESSON 8

CHECK WHICH CIRCLE BEST REPRESENTS YOUR LIFE TODAY:

☐   ☐   ☐

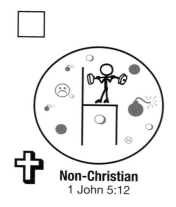

Non-Christian
1 John 5:12

Savior and Lord
Galations 5: 22-23

Savior
1 Corinthians 3:15

Since my last lesson,
I have practiced
Spiritual Breathing:

☐ 20⁺ Times
☐ 11 - 19 Times
☐ 6 - 10 Times
☐ 0 - 5 Times

READING ASSIGNMENT

CAT & DOG THEOLOGY

RETHINKING OUR RELATIONSHIP
WITH OUR MASTER

LIVING PASSIONATELY FOR THE
GLORY OF GOD

Bob Sjogren & Gerald Robison

Begin at "Worship" (page 16) and finish out the chapter (page 21).

Questions to answer from the reading assignment:

1. Cats worship God primarily for what He has _____ _____ _____. [138]

2. Dogs worship God primarily for _____ _____ _____. [139]

3. The three favorite words in a Cat's worship song are "_____, _____, and _____." [140]

4. What do the authors say about Cat songs? Are they wrong?

_____

_____

_____ [141]

5. Write down what happened to the pastor after having gone through a Cat and Dog Theology seminar.

_____

_____

_____ [142]

6. Explain the essence of Lordship to a Cat.

_____

_____

_____ [143]

7. According to the authors, when Cats no longer allow God to be Lord in their lives, do they keep going to church? Why?

_____

_____

_____

_____ 144

8. In Dog Theology, Christ has complete Lordship. A Dog says,
"_____, _____, _____" even if it
means going _____. 145

9. What do the authors mean when they say Cats only focus on half of God?

_____

_____

_____ 146

10. Dogs cry out, "Why do we always keep saying 'God bless America?' We need to be saying '_____ _____ _____.'"147

11. List three of the differences you liked on pages 20 and 21:

_____

_____

_____ 148

12. No one is a perfect Dog or Cat. The authors say that we are either _____ with moments of _____ or we are more _____ who slip back into their _____ ways. 149

13. All Christians are somewhere _____ _____ being a Dog and a Cat. 150

14. What is the warning that goes with this book?

_____

_____

_____ 151

BIBLE STUDY!

1. Read Luke 18:9-14.

2. What words would the common Jew have used to describe the Pharisee?

_____

_____

_____ 152

3. What are the attitudes stated by the Pharisee?

_____ 153

4. Who and what did the Pharisee trust in for his righteousness?

_____ 154

5. Would the words "disciplined in the Jewish faith" have applied to the Pharisee?

    Circle One: Yes   No 155

6. Did the Pharisee seek to honor God with his body and wealth?

    Circle One: Yes   No 156

7. How did the Pharisee see others who were not as righteous as he was?

_____ 157

8. What words would the common Jew have used to describe the tax-collector?

_____ 158

9. What words might we use to describe the tax-collector in this parable?

_____ 159

10. Why do you think the tax-collector would not look up to heaven?

_____ 160

11. The parable says the Pharisee "stood up" and tax-collector "stood at a distance?" What do you think was the motivation of each?

_____

_____ 161

12. Which one represents a Dog and which one represents a Cat?

_____ 162

LESSON 9

CHECK WHICH CIRCLE BEST REPRESENTS YOUR LIFE TODAY:

☐

☐

☐

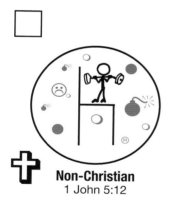

Non-Christian
1 John 5:12

Savior and Lord
Galations 5: 22-23

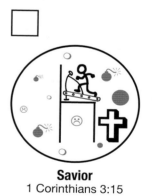

Savior
1 Corinthians 3:15

Since my last lesson,
I have practiced
Spiritual Breathing:

☐ 20⁺ Times
☐ 11 - 19 Times
☐ 6 - 10 Times
☐ 0 - 5 Times

CARTOON

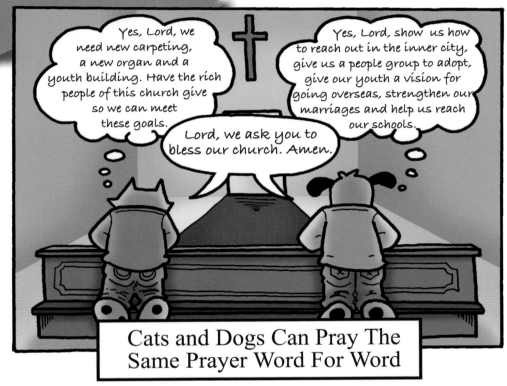

1. Suppose the prayer the Cat and Dog prayed was not "Bless our church" but rather, "Lord, bless my family" (as in mom, dad, my siblings, etc.). Write below what an in-depth Cat prayer would look like and what an in-depth Dog prayer would look like.

Cat:

_____

_____

_____ 163

Dog:

_____

_____

_____ 164

CHRIS and SARAH

It was going to be a weekend to remember. Sarah knew the minute Pastor Jake had announced their youth fall retreat that she wanted to go. But really, who wouldn't? She had already heard about the rock climbing, white-water rafting, cute cabins to stay in, and a giant water slide – it was a no brainer.   But there was one minor problem.

Their parents were all for Chris going, but they hesitated about Sarah going.

"Sarah, can I see you in the master bedroom please," her dad said. *Oh no, not the bedroom talk. I hate these.* Sarah thought to herself, *What have I done wrong now?*

"I know you want to go on the retreat, but your attitude hasn't been the best lately," her dad told her in a loving way, but it was hard to receive anyhow.

Sighing, Sarah's eyes started to tear up. "You got this from mom, didn't you?" Her mother hated confronting her directly and almost always had her father do it. It was a typical Asian way of communicating an uncomfortable message.

"Yes, I did," her dad answered, "but that doesn't mean I haven't noticed too."

"Dad, you know this is why I'm in private school and Chris is still homeschooled. Mom and I just don't get along."

"I agree, but that doesn't give you permission to be mean to her. You are still her daughter and you need to respect her—even if you are spending eight hours a day away from her."

"Dad, I so want to go on this retreat. It's got the coolest things and all my friends are going too. Please don't keep me from doing this," her dark eyes pleaded with him.

Her father looked away and took a deep breath. "Okay, I'll make you a deal. If you can change your attitude around your mother and give her the respect that is due her, we'll let you go. But remember, you've got to earn it."

Sarah sat upright and grinned, wiping the few tears that had fallen. She then threw her arms around him and said, "Don't worry, Dad, I'll be on my best behavior. You can bet on that!"

Her dad knew he could. Sarah could act any way she wanted. However, he worried about how it would be after the retreat. Sarah kept her promise. Several weeks later she joined Chris and dozens of fellow students on the church buses.

It was everything Pastor Jake had promised and more. Chris enjoyed the white-water rafting and the paintball games most of all. He and his team came in second place, nearly making it to the top. Despite gashing his leg on a tree stump, he still had a blast. Then came the old "shaving-cream-on-the-face-in-the-middle-of-the-night" trick. He and his friends targeted some of the freshmen that hadn't been initiated into youth group yet. He hadn't laughed that hard in a long time.

Meanwhile, Sarah and her friends screamed down the water slide no less than ten times. She talked late into the night with her roommates, and to her surprise, she only slipped once on the rock climbing wall.

However, the highlight for Sarah was a few special moments with Bryan. Nothing epic, just a few laughs, a few jokes, and during small group discussion, she had caught him looking at her from across the circle. He didn't look away either when he realized she caught him. Just flashed that impish grin of his, which made her blush. She hoped Chris didn't see it.

Then came Saturday night. The band had been destroying it with fantastic worship all weekend, but Saturday night they gave it everything they had. So did Pastor Jake when he gave the message.

Sarah had heard this kind of message a million times before. People had sinned against the God who loved them, and now they were separate from Him forever. But that wasn't good enough for God. God loved the people He created, and His plan for them was bigger than this. He didn't want them to live and die without Him. He wanted to give them a future and a hope. He wanted to give them joy and peace and a life filled with passion and hope.

Pastor Jake said those who were separated from God would be flung into darkness, lost, alone, and hopeless. That wasn't what God wanted.

And something clicked for Sarah. She had heard all her life that God loved her and wanted the best for her. But something about that moment helped her realize it in a newer, deeper way. God was passionate about her. God had a plan for her. God wanted to bless her. All she had to do was respond to His love.

Though she had given her life to the Lord as a little child, something inside of her wanted to do more. So, cheeks streaked with tears, she rededicated—or was it dedicated?—her life to the Lord. She wasn't really sure. She just knew something was changing.

Seeing Sarah, Pastor Jake was surprised. He thought he had communicated clearly that this was for first-time conversions. But none-the-less, he walked over to her and put his hand on her shoulder, thanking God for what was happening in her life.

As Sarah rode home in the church van on Sunday, she could hardly help but smile thinking of Bryan and remembering Jake's words after the service, "This is only the beginning, Sarah. God is going to bless you so much more."

Part of her hoped that Bryan was God's way of blessing her.

Lesson 9 Questions: (The suggested answers are on page 49 in the *Answer Key.*)

1. What was Sarah's motivation for being a good/obedient/respectful child and how does it differ from a Dog?

   _____

   _____

2. How was Sarah's perspective of the weekend mostly Cat? List the ways.

   _____

   _____

3. If Sarah went from circle 1 to circle 2, what happened when she was a four-year-old child and invited Christ into her life?

   _____

   _____

4. Was her focus Catish or Dogish driving home from the retreat?

   _____

   _____

Oh Lord, I need to pass this quiz.

QUIZ!

1. Cats and Dogs can pray the exact same prayer word for word and have two totally different meanings.

    A. True

    B. False [165]

2. Cats want to get to heaven because:

    A. They are focused on God's glory.

    B. They have fallen in love with God.

    C. They want fire insurance.

    D. They are worried about going to hell. [166]

3. If someone "prayed the prayer" as a young child growing up, they are definitely saved and guaranteed to go to heaven.

    A. True

    B. False [167]

4. Dogs know they are guaranteed eternal salvation because:

    A. They prayed a prayer asking Jesus into their lives.

    B. They see a hunger for God in them they didn't have before.

    C. They see their life changing in a more godly way. [168]

5. When we find Jesus, He should be like a treasure and we should be willing to give up anything and everything to get to know Him.

    A. True

    B. False [169]

6. Cats worship God primarily for who He is, secondarily for what He's done for them.

    A. True

    B. False [170]

7. All Cat songs are

    A. Wrong.

    B. Incomplete.

    C. Stupid.

    D. Unworthy. [171]

8. Lordship to a Cat means

    A. Christ is Lord as long as it is comfortable.

    B. When God says, "Jump" a Cat only asks, "How high?"

    C. Christ is Lord as long as he/she doesn't have to move.

    D. Going anywhere, anytime, for any reason. [172]

9. Everyone is part Dog and part Cat. No one (except Jesus) is a perfect Dog. At best, we can be "more Dog" and "less Cat."

    A. True

    B. False [173]

10. Because you now understand the differences between Dog and Cat Theology, you should always point out the Catness in others, so they can become more like you, a Dog.

    A. True

    B. False [174]

PERSONAL APPLICATION

What are you going to do differently as a result of what you've learned? **Go to the end of your workbook and write it in for Lesson 9.**[175]

OPTIONAL LESSON

Go to **www.UnveilinGLORY.com** and click on the left side: Free Online Teaching.

• Once there, click on "Guest."

• In the top right where it says "Choose a Series" choose "Cat and Dog Theology."

• Listen to Cat and Dog Lesson 2.

There is no quiz, no notes to be taken. Just enjoy and learn!

CAUTION! The more your life is changed, the easier it is to spot Cat behavior in those around you. **Please don't ever use this material to judge others.** ("Oh, they are just a bunch of Cats.") Once we start judging others, we too are acting like Cats. **Use this material to encourage yourself and others to live for God's glory.**

LESSON 10

CHECK WHICH CIRCLE BEST REPRESENTS YOUR LIFE TODAY:

☐   ☐   ☐

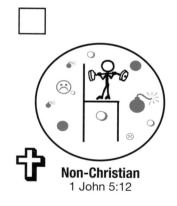

Non-Christian
1 John 5:12

Savior and Lord
Galations 5: 22-23

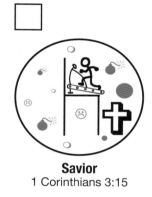

Savior
1 Corinthians 3:15

Since my last lesson,
I have practiced
Spiritual Breathing:

☐ 20+ Times
☐ 11 - 19 Times
☐ 6 - 10 Times
☐ 0 - 5 Times

READING ASSIGNMENT

CAT & DOG THEOLOGY

RETHINKING OUR RELATIONSHIP WITH OUR MASTER

LIVING PASSIONATELY FOR THE GLORY OF GOD

Bob Sjogren & Gerald Robison

Begin chapter 3 (page 23) and read through until you complete the first paragraph on page 28.

Questions to answer from the reading assignment:

1. The authors say that Cat Theology is not _____ but it is _____. [176]

2. Because Cat Theology is incomplete, it _____ Christianity. [177]

3. To a Dog, salvation is a _____ _____ to something far greater: _____ _____. [178]

4. To a Cat, salvation is an _____ in _____. *(This answer is not actually in the book but take a good guess at it!)* [179]

5. There is a huge difference between being saved _____ something and being saved _____ something. [180]

6. When you are saved from something, the focus is on _____. When you are saved for something, the focus is on _____. [181]

7. Would you say that up until this point in your life, you were primarily focused on what you were saved from or for and why?

_____

_____

[182]
_____

8. Why is the prayer "Lord, thank you for dying on the cross for our sins" Catish?

_____

_____

[183]
_____

9. Because Cats are so focused on not going to hell, once they hear that their sins are forgiven, they forget about the _____ as to why they are saved. [184]

10. According to Genesis 12:2,3 what is the reason why God blesses us?

[185]
_____

11. Cats want to keep the blessings _____ _____. [186]

12. Dogs want to enjoy the blessings themselves as well as _____ them on to others! [187]

13. What lesson does a Cat focus on in the story of Daniel in the lion's den?

_____ [188]

14. Is what a Cat learns incorrect?

   Circle One: Yes   No   [189]

15. What other lesson does a Dog see from the story of Daniel and the lion's den?

_____

_____

_____ [190]

1. Read Daniel chapter 6.

2. According to verse three, what got Daniel into trouble with the administrators and satraps?

   _____

   _____

_____ [191]

BIBLE STUDY!

3. What attitudes of the king and the government officials led to Daniel being put into the lion's den?

_____ [192]

4. When Daniel found out about the decree, he certainly thought about it for a long time. Assuming he was single *(since his wife was not thrown into the lion's den with him like the others in verse 24)*, what did this mean *(as a single man)* he was forced to give up in order to follow God?

_____ [193]

5. This tells you that his zeal for the _____ of God was _____ than his desire to be married. [194]

6. How did verses 20-23 make God look?

_____ 195

7. Verse 24 tells us that when we sin, it can affect not only us, but _____ as well. 196

8. Would Daniel be described as more of a Dog or a Cat?

    Circle One: Dog   Cat   197

9. What does this tell you about Dogs when faced with adversity?

_____

_____ 198

10. Do you think Daniel, in his wildest dreams, would have ever thought of God using his predicament for reaching the nations and why or why not?

_____ 199

11. What does this tell you about your life and how God can use it?

_____

_____

_____ 200

12. Does this passage tell you that God can use the sinful attitudes and actions of others for His glory among the nations?

    Circle One: Yes   No   201

LESSON 11

CHECK WHICH CIRCLE BEST REPRESENTS YOUR LIFE TODAY:

☐

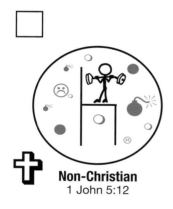

Non-Christian
1 John 5:12

☐

Savior and Lord
Galations 5: 22-23

☐

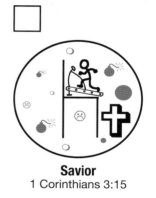

Savior
1 Corinthians 3:15

Since my last lesson,
I have practiced
Spiritual Breathing:

☐ 20⁺ Times
☐ 11 - 19 Times
☐ 6 - 10 Times
☐ 0 - 5 Times

READING ASSIGNMENT

CAT & DOG THEOLOGY

RETHINKING OUR RELATIONSHIP WITH OUR MASTER

LIVING PASSIONATELY FOR THE GLORY OF GOD

Bob Sjogren & Gerald Robison

Start at the first full paragraph on page 28 ("Do you need another example") and read through until the end of the chapter (page 32).

Questions to answer from the reading assignment:

1. What do Cats learn from the story of Solomon asking God for wisdom?

   _____

   _____ 202

2. What a Cat learns from Solomon's request for wisdom is not _____ but it is _____ [203]

3. What do Dogs also learn from this story?

   _____

   _____

   _____ 204

4. How does a Dog see this lesson being applied in America?

   _____

   _____

   _____ 205

5. International Students Incorporated tells us that _____ to _____ percent of all international students _____ make it into an American home. [206]

6. Why are Christians so rarely focused on reaching international students in their own cities?

   _____

   _____ 207

7. Why is it that most people only know the first 1/3rd of Psalm 46:10?

   _____

   _____ 208

8. According to the authors, Cats are only reading (focused on) _____ of their Bibles. [209]

9. Explain what lesson a Cat learns from "the bird in the birdcage" and what lesson a Dog learns.

Cat: _____

_____

_____

_____ [210]

Dog: _____

_____

_____

_____ [211]

10. Why does a Cat pray for God to bless America?

_____

_____ [212]

11. Why does a Dog pray for God to bless America?

_____

_____ [213]

12. Romans 11:36 says, "For from Him, and through Him and to Him are most things. To Him be the glory forever."

Circle One: True   False?   [214]

13. Does a "Dog church" ever reference the idea that God wants to bless them, and why?

_____

_____

_____

_____ [215]

14. Dog Theology is not the _____ of Cat Theology, rather it is the _____ of it. [216]

BIBLE STUDY!

1. Read 1 Kings 10:1-13.

2. What was Queen of Sheba's motivation in coming to see Solomon?

_____

_____

_____ 217

3. How did Solomon treat the one who was seeking to put him to a test?

_____ 218

4. What does verse 6 tell you about one of the reasons as to why God wants to bless you?

_____

_____ 219

5. To whom did Queen of Sheba give credit for Solomon's life (vs. 9)?

_____

_____ 220

6. As the queen blessed Solomon, did Solomon use what she gave him completely for himself and/or for God (vs. 10-12)?

_____

_____ 221

7. Do an internet search ("Where was Queen of Sheba from") and find out where scholars think Sheba was located?

_____

_____

_____ 222

8. How can you link Acts 8:27 with 1 Kings 10:1-13?

_____

_____ 223

LESSON 12

CHECK WHICH CIRCLE BEST REPRESENTS YOUR LIFE TODAY:

☐

☐

☐

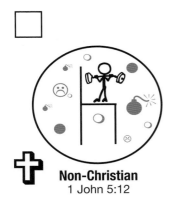

Non-Christian
1 John 5:12

Savior and Lord
Galations 5: 22-23

Savior
1 Corinthians 3:15

Since my last lesson,
I have practiced
Spiritual Breathing:

☐ 20⁺ Times
☐ 11 - 19 Times
☐ 6 - 10 Times
☐ 0 - 5 Times

CARTOON

Praying After 9/11

If you are not familiar with what happened on 9/11, ask your parents.

1. What is the Cat primarily focused in light of this major event?

    _____

    _____

    _____ 224

2. What is the Dog primarily focused on when it comes to a major event?

    _____

    _____

    _____ 225

 Lesson 12

CHRIS and SARAH

"Sarah, have a seat."

Sarah's heart sank a little bit. So much for the high she was on from the fall retreat.

Mrs. Brewer frowned slightly as Sarah flopped into the chair by the algebra teacher's desk. Sometimes she missed being homeschooled like Chris, but Sarah and her mother just didn't get along. One of them would have ended up murdering the other, and Sarah wasn't sure who would have drawn first blood!

"Your grades have been good," Mrs. Brewer remarked, still frowning over a few sheets of homework. They must have been another student's homework, because Sarah could hardly miss the big "F" scribbled across the front in thick red ink.

"Um, thank you," Sarah chirped. Mrs. Brewer had a reputation for being severe and exacting. Although it was a Christian school, a few teachers had notorious tempers— Mrs. Brewer being one of them. Sarah had hoped her good grades would keep her out of Mrs. Brewer's radar.

Apparently they hadn't.

"Yes, I've been very impressed with you," the teacher continued, "You seem to catch on very quickly to all the new material we cover, and that's why I'm going to ask for your help."

"Help?" Sarah wasn't sure what she meant, but it couldn't be a reprimand. She was thinking that maybe this would be good, but she held her breath.

"You know Isabel?"

"Yes, ma'am," Sarah answered, then she let her breath out, feeling her heart sink even lower.

"I'm sure you can imagine the trouble she's been having in Algebra. It's hard enough to learn a new language, and I think Isabel could use some one-on-one tutoring. Math just isn't her thing. I hear from Mr. Chase you do really well in Spanish."

"Well, maybe, but – "

"You've heard her speak enough in class to know she won't be too hard to under-stand. She just needs a little extra help, and the school counselor recommended I find a fellow student to tutor her once a week. What do you think?"

Sarah was dumbfounded. Isabel was an exchange student from Peru that Sarah and her friends avoided like the plague. Not only did she dress in what Sarah was pretty sure were old drapes, but the Spanish girl's heavy accent was made more difficult to understand by her thick metal braces and gawky over bite. Not exactly someone with whom Sarah wanted to spend the few precious hours after school.

Besides, there was Bible club after school. It used to be a club populated solely by people like Seymour Richards, the guy who dressed like he was Amish and brought a smelly ham sandwich in a paper sack for lunch. But then Bryan and some of his popular friends started going, and the group was really taking the school by storm. That's when Sarah and her friends started attending. Bryan was the bomb!

Sarah's mom had a policy about too many after-school activities. Between Bible Club and cross-country practice, Sarah would be at her limit of afternoons she could come home late.

"I'm sorry, Mrs. Brewer, I'm starting Bible club, and my mom says I can't be gone any more days. "

Mrs. Brewer raised her eyebrows.

"Bible Club? Well, I guess I can't ask you to give up that. But are you sure? Isabel could really use your help, and I'm going to be honest, too, because I can see that you're a smart, mature girl. She could really use a friend, too."

Sarah looked down at her lap. Her mind raced—*Are you crazy, Mrs. Brewer? Me, friends with Isabel? What will Bryan think if I start hanging out with a nerd? What will my friends think?*

Her teacher sighed and picked up a few more papers with various grades scribbled over them in red ink. "Alright, I'll keep looking. I'll see you tomorrow, Sarah."

Sarah said goodbye and left the room, breathing a sigh of relief. Then she pictured Isabel's wide, confused eyes behind her thick-rimmed glasses during that day's algebra class, and she felt a twinge of guilt.

What would be so hard about tutoring Isabel?

But what about Bible Club?

Sarah shook her head. Surely Bible Club was the right choice. God wanted her to study the Bible, right? God wanted her to be a good steward of her time and obey her mom's rules about too many after-school activities, right?

Besides, the idea of tutoring awkward, stuttering Isabel made Sarah nervous. She had never tried teaching someone before – especially not someone from another culture. Especially not someone dressed in drapes. How would they understand each other? What would they talk about?

Sarah's pastor had talked about the peace of God that comes when you're walking in His will. He blesses those who love Him. Sarah definitely couldn't see anything peaceful or blessed about stumbling through hours of tutoring an exchange student.

There were plenty of other students who were good at math. Mrs. Brewer would find someone else to help Isabel.

Lesson 12 Questions: (The suggested answers are on page 49 in the *Answer Key*.)

1. Do you think Sarah's intentions and reasons for joining Bible Club were glorifying to God?

_____

_____

2. What was Catish about Sarah's reasons for not wanting to tutor Isabel?

_____

_____

3. How do you think God was feeling regarding Isabel's lack of friends?

_____

_____

4. What would have to change in Sarah's mind in order to give her peace and blessings even though tutoring Isabel would be difficult?

_____

_____

Oh Lord, I need to pass this quiz.

QUIZ!

1. Cat Theology is not incorrect.

    A. True

    B. False [226]

2. To a Dog, salvation is

    A. An end in itself.

    B. A means to an end.

    C. Just a stepping stone to something greater.

    D. A necessary first step to try and find Jesus. [227]

3. Praying, "Lord, thank you for dying on the cross for my sins" is not incorrect, but it is incomplete.

    A. True

    B. False [228]

4. With regards to salvation

    A. Cats are more focused on what they are saved for.

    B. Dogs are more focused on what they are saved for.

    C. Cats are more focused on what they are saved from.

    D. Dogs are more focused on what they are saved from. [229]

5. The reason God blesses us is for us to enjoy the blessings and pass them on to others as well.

    A. True

    B. False [230]

6. 70% to 80% of all international students studying here in America never make it into an American home.

    A. True

    B. False [231]

7. Most Cats only read

    A. Half of their Bible.

    B. The part that talks about them being blessed.

    C. Scriptures that will point them to a safe, soft comfortable life.

    D. All of the above. [232]

8. Cats pray "America bless God" whereas Dogs pray, "God bless America."

    A. True

    B. False [233]

9. Dog Theology is not the absence of Cat Theology, rather it is the completion of it.

    A. True

    B. False [234]

10. Romans 11:36 says, "For from Him, and through Him and to Him are most things. To Him be the glory forever."

    A. True

    B. False [235]

What are you going to do differently as a result of what you've learned? **Go to the end of your workbook and write it in for Lesson 12.** *(This may be the same as last week. That's OK! Write it down again.)* [236]

PERSONAL APPLICATION

OPTIONAL LESSON

Go to **www.UnveilinGLORY.com** and click on the left side: Free Online Teaching.

• Once there, click on "Guest."

• In the top right where it says "Choose a Series" choose "Cat and Dog Theology."

• Listen to Cat and Dog Lesson 3.

There is no quiz, no notes to be taken. Just enjoy and learn!

LESSON 13

CHECK WHICH CIRCLE BEST REPRESENTS YOUR LIFE TODAY:

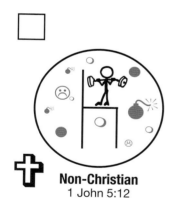

Non-Christian
1 John 5:12

Savior and Lord
Galations 5: 22-23

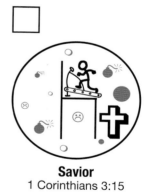

Savior
1 Corinthians 3:15

Since my last lesson,
I have practiced
Spiritual Breathing:

☐ 20+ Times

☐ 11 - 19 Times

☐ 6 - 10 Times

☐ 0 - 5 Times

READING ASSIGNMENT

CAT & DOG THEOLOGY

RETHINKING OUR RELATIONSHIP WITH OUR MASTER

LIVING PASSIONATELY FOR THE GLORY OF GOD

Bob Sjogren & Gerald Robison

Start chapter 4 (page 33) and read through until page 39 where you see the words "Jealous God Ministries."

Questions to answer from the reading assignment:

1. As Christ was talking to His Father about his upcoming death, what does He not say?

_____

_____ 237

2. How does it make you feel that when thinking about the cross, you weren't the highest priority on His mind?

_____

_____ 238

3. The authors suggest that Christ's death _____ for our sins, but that it is _____ to living for His Father's glory. 239

4. John 14:13 says, "I will do whatever you ask in my name so that you might have a safe, soft, easy and comfortable life."

   Circle One: True   False   240

5. What is Christ's motivation for answering our prayers?

_____

_____ 241

6. Tell why seeking to get a definition for the glory of God is a tricky thing.

_____

_____ 242

7. Luke 2:9 (along with other passages) tells us that the glory of God can be very _____ and _____. 243

8. The authors tell us that not only is God's glory revealed in His presence, but also in His _____. 244

9. What does Psalm 19:1 tell us that the heavens are doing?

_____

_____ 245

10. God's creativity also tells us that every flower, every blade of grass, every rock, every leaf is here to show off God's _____. 246

11. According to Exodus 33, when Moses asked the Lord, "Show me Your glory," God talked about His _____. 247

12. Write the author's definition of Glory below:

_____

_____ 248

13. Explain how, even though we have no glory to give, we are told to "glorify God" using the moon analogy.

_____

_____

_____

_____ 249

14. A simple way of defining what it means to live for the glory of God is:

_____

_____ 250

15. Name three people in your life to whom you could make God famous.

_____

_____ 251

BIBLE STUDY!

1. There are no perfect Dogs here on earth. The only one that was perfect was Jesus. We all fluctuate between being "mostly Dog and part Cat" or "mostly Cat and part Dog." This is also true of the great men of the Bible. How did David make God famous in the story of David and Goliath?

_____

_____ 252

2. Read 2 Samuel 11.

3. What was David supposed to be doing at this time?

_____

_____ 253

4. Why do you think David didn't go out and fight?

_____

_____ 254

5. David had 30 trusted fighting men who would give their lives for King David. Who is the last one listed in the list of 30? (See 2 Samuel 23:24-39)

_____ 255

6. David ends up sleeping with the wife of one of his most trusted and loyal soldiers. He was willing to lay down his life for David by fighting his wars. How do you think David's actions affected God's reputation?

_____

_____ 256

7. Because Uriah was so righteous and would not sleep with his wife while his men were out fighting a war (he was more righteous than King David) David sent an order to have him killed. Who took that order to Joab, the commander of David's army?

_____ 257

8. Do you think Joab was wondering why he was supposed to kill off Uriah?

Circle One: Yes   No 258

9. Do you think Joab "put two and two together" and realized why Uriah was killed?

      Circle One: Yes   No   [259]

10. What do you think was Joab's understanding of David's character after this event?

    _____

    _____ [260]

11. Do you think Uriah's parents or Bathsheba's parents (not mentioned in the story) wanted to worship the God of David?

    _____ [261]

12. How did all of this affect God's reputation, since David worshipped and lived for God?

    _____

    _____ [262]

13. One of the greatest lessons we learn from King David's wrong choices is that not only do our actions affect us and the lives of others, but they also affect God's

    _____. [263]

LESSON 14

CHECK WHICH CIRCLE BEST REPRESENTS YOUR LIFE TODAY:

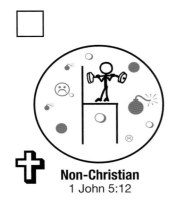

Non-Christian
1 John 5:12

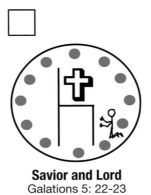

Savior and Lord
Galations 5: 22-23

Savior
1 Corinthians 3:15

Since my last lesson,
I have practiced
Spiritual Breathing:

- ☐ 20⁺ Times
- ☐ 11 - 19 Times
- ☐ 6 - 10 Times
- ☐ 0 - 5 Times

READING ASSIGNMENT

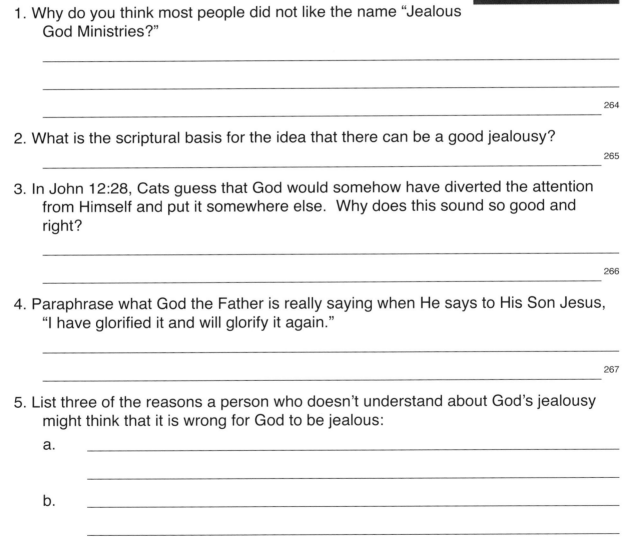

CAT & DOG THEOLOGY

RETHINKING OUR RELATIONSHIP
WITH OUR MASTER

LIVING PASSIONATELY FOR THE
GLORY OF GOD

Bob Sjogren & Gerald Robison

Start on page 39 where you see the words "Jealous God Ministries" and read through to the end of the chapter (pg. 46).

Questions to answer from the reading assignment:

1. Why do you think most people did not like the name "Jealous God Ministries?"

_____

_____

_____ 264

2. What is the scriptural basis for the idea that there can be a good jealousy?

_____ 265

3. In John 12:28, Cats guess that God would somehow have diverted the attention from Himself and put it somewhere else. Why does this sound so good and right?

_____

_____ 266

4. Paraphrase what God the Father is really saying when He says to His Son Jesus, "I have glorified it and will glorify it again."

_____

_____ 267

5. List three of the reasons a person who doesn't understand about God's jealousy might think that it is wrong for God to be jealous:

a. _____

_____

b. _____

_____

c. _____

_____ 268

6. List the four options of what God could live for:

a. _____

b. _____

c. _____

d. _____ 269

7. Why would it be ridiculous for God to live for creation and what is the Biblical basis for it?

_____ 270

8. Why would it be foolish to live for Satan, the greatest and most glorious of all angels?

_____ 271

9. List the 13 things that Mark 7:20-23 says comes out of a man's heart:

a. _____

b. _____

c. _____

d. _____

e. _____

f. _____

g. _____

h. _____

i. _____

j. _____

k. _____

l. _____

m. _____ 272

10. Would lifting us up as an example and living for us be a wise thing for God to do?

     Circle One: Yes   No [273]

11. If we had to choose between the four options, it would be a _____ -

    _____. Why would God be any _____? [274]

12. List the four reasons that, even though God doesn't live for us, He still died for us:

    a. _____

    b. _____

    c. _____

    d. _____ [275]

13. If we were to live for ourselves, we would be sinning.

    But when God lives for Himself, He _____ sin. [276]

1. Read Jeremiah 2:1-13.

2. Summarize verses 1-11 in your own words:

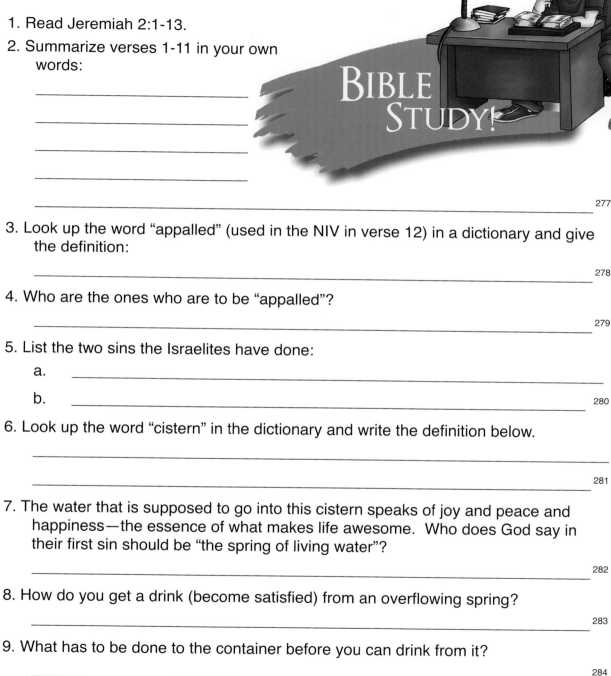

BIBLE STUDY!

_____

_____

_____

_____

_____ 277

3. Look up the word "appalled" (used in the NIV in verse 12) in a dictionary and give the definition:

_____ 278

4. Who are the ones who are to be "appalled"?

_____ 279

5. List the two sins the Israelites have done:

    a. _____

    b. _____ 280

6. Look up the word "cistern" in the dictionary and write the definition below.

_____

_____ 281

7. The water that is supposed to go into this cistern speaks of joy and peace and happiness—the essence of what makes life awesome. Who does God say in their first sin should be "the spring of living water"?

_____ 282

8. How do you get a drink (become satisfied) from an overflowing spring?

_____ 283

9. What has to be done to the container before you can drink from it?

_____ 284

10. Where do most Christians get their joy and satisfaction out of life? (With what do they fill their cistern?)

_____

_____ 285

11. What is the one characteristic spoken about this well/container?

_____ 286

12. After the cistern leaks, what do you have to do to fill it back up?

_____ 287

13. What do the words "leaking cistern" imply about how long you'll enjoy the "water" from a cistern?

_____

_____ 288

14. How long do you think God's infinite glory will satisfy us?

_____ 289

15. After learning that God Himself, manifested in His glory, is something that will satisfy us forever and ever, and the temporary things of this earth will only satisfy us momentarily, why do you think the heavens would be appalled?

_____

_____

_____ 290

16. Do you agree or disagree with the words of C.S. Lewis, "_...if we consider the unblushing promises of reward and the staggering nature of the rewards promised in the Gospels, it would seem that our Lord finds our desires, not too strong, but too weak. We are half-hearted creatures, fooling about with drink and sex and ambition when infinite joy is offered us, like an ignorant child who wants to go on making mud pies in a slum because he cannot imagine what is meant by the offer of a holiday at the sea. We are far too easily pleased._" And why?

_____

_____

_____

_____ 291

_____

LESSON 15

CHECK WHICH CIRCLE BEST REPRESENTS YOUR LIFE TODAY:

☐   ☐   ☐

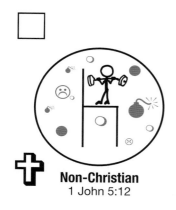

Non-Christian
1 John 5:12

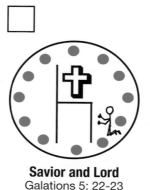

Savior and Lord
Galations 5: 22-23

Savior
1 Corinthians 3:15

Since my last lesson,
I have practiced
Spiritual Breathing:

☐ 20⁺ Times
☐ 11 - 19 Times
☐ 6 - 10 Times
☐ 0 - 5 Times

CARTOON

Worship As A Part Of Life

1. What is the Cat focused on?

_____
292

2. Is what the Cat is focused on bad or wrong?

_____
293

3. What did the Cat miss that the Dog saw?

_____
294

4. What can you learn from this?

_____

_____
295

CHRIS and SARAH

Chris loved it when his grandparents came during the fall. They were a spunky, active couple in their early 70's who drove their camper all across the country, visited national parks, went water skiing, and brought him and Sarah fun and interesting souvenirs.

The one thing Chris didn't like about their visits was when their grandpa started talking about religion. Granddad was a staunch atheist who believed nothing mattered outside this life, and organized religion was the root of all evil. Chris' dad said Granddad didn't speak to him for months after he became a Christian in college. Then Granddad gave him an even harder time when he married their mom, a Taiwanese studying at the same college.

It took a long time before his granddad warmed up to Chris' mother. Eventually, her unconditional respect for him and love had won him over. However, his acceptance never made it to their spiritual beliefs. He still was adamantly against the "judgmental, homophobic hypocrites," as he called Christians.

So visits were fun as long as no one brought up the word "church", or "God", or "Jesus". This visit had been fantastic until the night Chris and Sarah went to youth group.

"Hey big shot! Where've you been?" Granddad asked when Chris and Sarah came in the kitchen door. "You missed the story about mine and Grandma's brush with a bear up in Montana."

"I was at youth group. Bear, huh?"

"What is that, a church thing? They trying to rope the young people into spreading out tracts and hellfire now?" Granddad's eyes were disapproving as he took a sip of coffee.

Chris felt the tension in the room spike. His mother and father were nowhere to be found so Chris and Sarah were on their own! Sarah didn't know how to handle this one and said a little white lie, skipping out and leaving it up to Chris. "I've got to finish up some homework, so I'm going to my room. Love you, Grandpa."

"Love you, sweetie!" Grandpa called after her.

Chris sighed, "Yeah, it's a church thing. But we don't hand out tracts or anything."

Granddad wasn't going to miss a chance to tell Chris what he thought about religion. "Your parents make you go to these meetings?"

"No, I like them."

"What do they teach you?"

Chris said a quick, silent prayer and did his best to humbly explain it. He told Granddad about the homeless ministry the youth group did once a month. He also told him about playing basketball and doing Bible study and about the mentoring program he was a part of – meeting with two middle-schoolers and helping them follow Jesus. Chris had a mentor too – one of the adult youth leaders, who was encouraging Chris to not just memorize scripture, but to put it into action – loving others, inviting exchange students to his family's house, making smart decisions about money and dating.

"One of the greatest things I've learned Granddad is that 'No one's going to care how much you know until they know how much you care.'"

"Say that again," his granddad interrupted with a quizzical look on his face.

"No one is going to care how much you know, until they know how much you care." Our youth pastor didn't make it up; he got it from somebody else but it really makes sense. That's why I'm trying to get to know the middle school guys and why we go to the homeless and just try to meet their needs. Until they see how much we care, they won't listen to what we have to say."

Chris didn't expect Granddad to agree with everything. In fact, he expected him to laugh and tell Chris he was wasting his time.

Instead, his grandpa looked thoughtful.

"How old are you, Chris?"

"Seventeen."

Granddad scratched the back of his hand and took another sip of coffee.

"Well, it sounds like there's a lot worse things you could be doing."

That was the end of the conversation, and Chris almost forgot about it until the day his grandparents left.

After waving goodbye, his parents came back inside where Chris was on the computer.

"Chris," asked his dad, "what did you say to Granddad the other day?"

Chris looked up, "What do you mean?"

"He said you told him about your young church group. I guess he meant youth group." Then Dad smiled, "'Said he was proud of you, and it looked like church wasn't completely brainwashing you kids. I think that's the most positive thing I've ever heard him say about Christianity."

Lesson 15 Questions: (The suggested answers are on page 50 in the *Answer Key*.)

1. What did Chris' quick silent prayer communicate to God?

_____

_____

2. Even though Chris didn't preach the whole gospel to his grandfather, how did his answers glorify God?

_____

3. Was there anything Cat about Chris' answer?

_____

_____

4. How were Sarah's actions Catish?

_____

_____

5. How do you think God used this in his grandfather's life?

_____

_____

Oh Lord, I need to pass this quiz.

QUIZ!

1. Christ, knowing He was going to the cross to die for our sins, focused solely on us when talking to His heavenly Father about his upcoming death.

    A. True

    B. False [296]

2. Christ's death for our sins

    A. Was secondary to glorifying the Father.

    B. Was a part of God's plan to reveal His glory.

    C. Was solely for us.

    D. None of the above. [297]

3. Jesus says that He will do whatever we ask in His name so that

    A. We might have a safe, soft, comfortable life.

    B. That our kingdom might expand.

    C. He may bring glory to the Father. [298]

4. Every blade of grass is really here to show off God's glory.

    A. True

    B. False [299]

5. A simple way to define "living for the glory of God" is

    A. Living in such a way as to make God famous.

    B. Living to point to how you look.

    C. Living to point to how you act.

    D. All of the above. [300]

6. God is a jealous God.

    A. True

    B. False [301]

7. God lives for the sake of His name means

    A. God lives to glorify God

    B. God's glory is so awesome it is the only thing worth living for, even for God.

    C. God lives to protect His glory at all times.

    D. All of the above. [302]

8. If God lived primarily for the sake of lifting up, exalting and saving people, that would be a very bad move

    A. True

    B. False [303]

9. Though we can't live for ourselves, God can live for Himself because

    A. He won't sin.

    B. He can handle it.

    C. The above statement isn't true, God can't live for Himself.

    D. None of the above. [304]

10. It's a no-brainer for us to live for God because He is so awesome and wonderful. And since it is a no-brainer for us, it's a no-brainer for God as well.

    A. True

    B. False [305]

What are you going to do differently as a result of what you've learned? **Go to the end of your workbook and write it in for Lesson 15.** [306]

PERSONAL APPLICATION

Go to **www.UnveilinGLORY.com** and click on the left side: Free Online Teaching.

- Once there, click on "Guest."

- In the top right where it says "*Choose a Series*" choose "*Cat and Dog Theology.*"

- Listen to Cat and Dog Lesson 4.

There is no quiz, no notes to be taken. Just enjoy and learn!

OPTIONAL LESSON

LESSON 16

CHECK WHICH CIRCLE BEST REPRESENTS YOUR LIFE TODAY:

☐

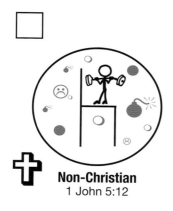

Non-Christian
1 John 5:12

☐

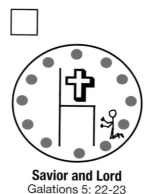

Savior and Lord
Galations 5: 22-23

☐

Savior
1 Corinthians 3:15

Since my last lesson,
I have practiced
Spiritual Breathing:

☐ 20⁺ Times
☐ 11 - 19 Times
☐ 6 - 10 Times
☐ 0 - 5 Times

READING ASSIGNMENT

CAT & DOG THEOLOGY

RETHINKING OUR RELATIONSHIP WITH OUR MASTER

LIVING PASSIONATELY FOR THE GLORY OF GOD

Bob Sjogren & Gerald Robison

The last reading was so foundational and significant, please re-read it. Start on page 39 where you see the words "Jealous God Ministries" and read through to the end of the chapter (pg. 46).

Questions to answer from the reading assignment:

1. Explain how the bowl of cereal and carpeting story helps us understand how God can live for God and it be right.

_____

_____

_____ 307

2. Look up 1 John 4:8. What does it tell us about God?

_____ 308

3. What does 1 Corinthians 13 tell us about God's character based on Who He is?

_____

_____ 309

4. If God is going to exalt anything that is good, He _____ exalt Himself. [310]

5. No matter how good something is, if God were to elevate it over Himself, He would _____ be pointing to the best. [311]

6. God living for God is His only option and it is not a

_____. [312]

7. Describe what the Greek word "holy" means.

_____

_____ 313

8. When the Scriptures say "Holy, holy, holy is the Lord God Almighty" write in your own words what this really means?

_____

_____

_____

_____ 314

9. Although it seems paradoxical, when you think of God living for Himself, what this really means is that He is constantly _____ ____ _____. 315

10. When God wakes up in the morning (a terrible analogy we know, but work with it please!), which of the following do you think he is thinking:

    A. I want to focus on myself.

    B. I want to live for others.

    C. I want to do what I want to do today. 316

11. If God were to live for any one or any thing else, He would be committing _____. 317

12. If God gave you second best, would He be very loving?

    Circle One: Yes   No   318

13. Therefore, in order for God to love you the most by giving you the very best, He must be a _____ God. 319

14. In order for God to be as loving as He can be, He must _____ us to Himself. 320

15. The fifth grader learned a valuable lesson when taught this:
It's OK for God to be _____-_____.
And she was right! 321

1. Another way of saying that "God lives for God" is seen in the words "for the sake of His great name." God does things to make His name look great, so that others will look to him and forever be satisfied with infinite joy! Read the following Scriptures and list the motivation as to why God did what He did.

BIBLE STUDY!

2. According to 2 Samuel 7:23, why did God choose Israel?

_____ 322

3. For whose sake did God save the Israelites from the Egyptians? (Psalm 106:7,8)

_____ 323

4. When Israel chose to have a king, God was very angry, but He did not destroy them. Why? (1 Samuel 12:22)

_____ 324

5. Why did God not destroy Israel when they strayed so far from Him? (Isaiah 48:9)

_____ 325

6. In Ezekiel 36:22, God tells why He is going to bring back Israel from captivity. You would think it is because He loves them, but it is not about them. It is for a different reason. What is it?

_____ 326

7. Though not explicitly in the text, if God had destroyed His own people because they were disobeying Him, what would people from all the other nations have been thinking about God?

_____
_____ 327

8. For whose "name's sake" does God forgive your sin? (Psalm 25:11)

_____ 328

9. What does Psalm 31:3 tell us should be our motivation for asking God to guide and lead us?

_____ 329

10. What does 1 Peter 2:9 tell us about why we were created?

_____ 330

11. Why does God want us to accept each other? (Romans 15:7)

_____ 331

12. 1 Corinthians 10:31 tells us that whether we eat or drink or what we do, we should do it all for…

_____ 332

13. Does this mean you should be doing your homework for God's glory?
    Circle One: Yes   No   333

14. What should be your main motivation for obeying your parents?

_____ 334

LESSON 17

CHECK WHICH CIRCLE BEST REPRESENTS YOUR LIFE TODAY:

☐   ☐   ☐

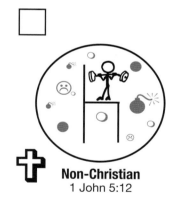

Non-Christian
1 John 5:12

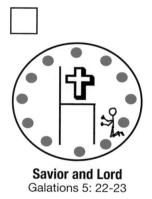

Savior and Lord
Galations 5: 22-23

Savior
1 Corinthians 3:15

Since my last lesson,
I have practiced
Spiritual Breathing:

☐ 20+ Times
☐ 11 - 19 Times
☐ 6 - 10 Times
☐ 0 - 5 Times

READING ASSIGNMENT

CAT & DOG THEOLOGY

RETHINKING OUR RELATIONSHIP WITH OUR MASTER

LIVING PASSIONATELY FOR THE GLORY OF GOD

Bob Sjogren & Gerald Robison

Begin chapter 5 (page 47) and read up to "Four Sick People" (page 53.)

Questions to answer from the reading assignment:

1. When reading the Bible, there are two possible main characters. They are _____ or _____. [335]

2. If God is the main character, we assume that _____ exist to serve _____. [336]

3. But if people are the main character, we assume that _____ exists to serve _____. [337]

4. Living to make God famous (living to glorify God) should be the _____ _____ in our lives. [338]

5. When Cats read their Bibles, they are trained to ask a few questions: "What am ____ suppose to get from this? How does this apply to _____ life? How does this affect _____?" [339]

6. Cats have a _____ - _____ theology. [340]

7. A Cat's goal for the Christian life is to have a _____, _____, _____ Christian life. [341]

8. Satan's primary goal is to rob God of the _____ of which only He is worthy. [342]

9. Satan's greatest way to get our focus off of the glory of God, is to get us to focus on something that is _____ and _____ to God's heart, but get our focus off of His glory. He makes us think its all about _____. [343]

10. Cats are so caught up with God's desire to _____ them, that it has become a higher priority over _____ God. [344]

11. How could someone's focus on glorifying God through saving the unborn become a higher priority than the glory of God itself?

_____

_____ [345]

12. How can wanting God to bless your church become unhealthy (a greater priority than glorifying God)?

_____
346

BIBLE STUDY!

1. Read Genesis 3. In verse 1, Satan misquotes what God said to Adam and Eve. Do you think he is still misquoting scripture for believers today?

   Circle One: Yes   No [347]

2. Write a sentence on how memorizing God's Word can help in times of temptation.

_____

_____
348

3. In verse 4, what does Satan get Eve to believe about God's Words?

_____
349

4. In verse 5, what was Satan's motivation to get Eve to eat the fruit?

_____
350

5. If she became like God, would she become "equal" to Him and share His glory?

_____
351

6. So instead of getting Adam and Eve to focus on God and His goodness, Satan wanted them to focus on _____ becoming like God. [352]

7. Where does verse 6 suggest Adam was when Eve was being tempted by the serpent?

_____
353

8. What should Adam have done?

_____
354

9. Why do you think Adam ate from the fruit?

_____

_____ 355

10. Before they ate from the fruit, they were naked, but not ashamed. Now that they have eaten from the fruit, they were ashamed. How does this help us understand the meaning of "their eyes were opened?"

_____

_____

_____ 356

LESSON 18

CHECK WHICH CIRCLE BEST REPRESENTS YOUR LIFE TODAY:

☐

☐

☐

Non-Christian
1 John 5:12

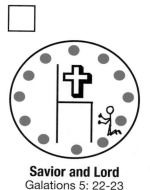

Savior and Lord
Galations 5: 22-23

Savior
1 Corinthians 3:15

Since my last lesson,
I have practiced
Spiritual Breathing:

☐ 20+ Times
☐ 11 - 19 Times
☐ 6 - 10 Times
☐ 0 - 5 Times

CARTOON

On Trying To Decide A Name For A New Church Plant

1. In trying to decide the name for a church, the Cats think up the name "You'll Feel Great Here" Church. Where is their focus and how do you think a jealous God feels about that?

_____

_____

_____

357

_____

2. How do you think a jealous God would respond to the Dog's suggestion of a name for the church?

_____

358

_____

CHRIS and SARAH

"Hey guys! Are you ready to worship the Lord tonight?" Matt's strong, confident voice rang out through the speakers, and the room of teenagers exploded with cheers and applause. This is wonderful, thought Sarah, the same enthusiasm captured at the fall retreat has now come to the youth group.

Matt had led the youth group's worship band for three months. He was a senior, had an obvious passion for music and worship, and confidently led the team of students who played with him at the weekly youth meetings.

Chris offered his applause along with the crowd, but he couldn't help feeling a twinge of jealousy as Matt started leading them in an old favorite. *That could've been me up there instead of Matt.*

At the beginning of the year, Pastor Jake and the other leaders held auditions for the next student worship leader. Matt and Chris had been the first choices, but Matt won out because he was a senior and this was his last chance to lead worship. There were already plenty of guitar players in the band, so Chris was told he could try again next year.

Chris knew it wasn't a personal jab, but he felt it. Matt was way cooler than Chris had ever felt. He had done an internship with Jake last summer, and Chris was positive their time together had played a much bigger part in the choosing of a new worship leader than any of the other leaders would admit. Everyone liked Matt.

Matt segued into the next song with a guitar solo, and Chris started mentally critiquing his style.

There was no doubt Chris was the better guitar player. Matt had picked up the guitar a year or two ago, but Chris had been taking lessons since he was 10. It wasn't fair. People said Matt had a gift. And they had a point. Worship at youth group had gone from so-so to amazing in the last few months. It was clear that Matt had a passion for the Lord and was helping draw other teenagers closer to God through music. But that didn't heal Chris' pride.

One year, Chris thought. In a little over half a year Matt would be in college. Then it could be Chris' turn.

But what if Chris' basketball schedule interfered with his chance next year? He might not ever get to lead. This was supposed to be his year.

Knock if off, Chris, he thought to himself, *you're not doing yourself any favors by being jealous. Besides, this worship time was supposed to be about God.* Chris was amazed at how easy it was to be in worship yet have his attention totally on something other than God.

"Oh, Father," Chris prayed quietly to himself. "I repent from being so selfish. Help me get over this…."

During the next song, Sarah—totally oblivious to Chris' struggle—lit up when her favorite song began. But then it happened. She felt her phone vibrate. Quietly, she took it out and read the text. *I can't believe it,* she thought to herself. *Abby and Paul are dating now?* Sarah texted back, "How do u know?"

Sarah stared at her phone, waiting for the reply. It came quickly, "i overheard them talking outside the gym. but they want 2 keep it quiet."

Abby was the "untouchable" good girl at school. The prettiest girl, the smartest in the class, and a strong Christian who vowed to never date. I guess turning 16 changed things, Sarah thought to herself. Her parents wouldn't let her date until she turned 16. She couldn't wait.

Sarah knew Abby, but not very well. The church she attended was pretty far away, and she never wanted to go anywhere else but her youth group, so the two never really became friends. Their "friendship" was mostly based on competition—who had the best grades, who got the best times in track, or who got the best parts in school plays. Unfortunately, Sarah almost always came in second. Now, she had ammunition to beat her.

So you want to keep it quiet, huh? Sarah grinned devilishly. During the next few songs, she texted, "Abby and Paul are dating!" to all of her friends from school. Before she knew it, the music had ended and Matt was praying for the upcoming message. *That was a quick worship,* Sarah thought to herself. *Where did the time go?*

Lesson 18 Questions: (The suggested answers are on page 50 in the *Answer Key.*)

1. How were Chris' attitudes robbing God of His glory?

_____

_____

2. How were Sarah's actions robbing God of His glory?

_____

_____

3. How did Chris act like a Dog?

_____

4. What could Sarah have done to her phone to keep her focused in worship?

_____

_____

1. We are to be like God in every way except in living for ourselves.

   A. True

   B. False [359]

2. Due to 1 Corinthians 13, since God is love (1 John 4:8)

   A. He does not boast.

   B. He is not rude.

   C. He is not self-seeking.

   D. All of the above. [360]

3. For God to exalt anything that is good, He must exalt Himself.

   A. True

   B. False [361]

4. Since God tells us to die to ourselves, He too must be dying to himself and doing that by putting us as a higher priority than His glory.

   A. This is why Christ left the Father's glory to die for us.

   B. This is why Christ died for us.

   C. This is true.

   D. This is a bunch of garbage.

   E. A through C only. [362]

5. If God were to live for anyone or anything other than Himself He would be

   A. Righteous

   B. Holy

   C. Committing idolatry

   D. All of the above. [363]

6. If God did not live for Himself and point to Himself He would not be very loving.

   A. True

   B. False [364]

7. The most loving thing God has ever done was to live for us over everything and everyone.

   A. True

   B. False [365]

8. It's OK for God to be self-centered.

    A. True

    B. False [366]

9. Satan's goal is to

    A. Rob God of His glory.

    B. Take God's place.

    C. Keep us from focusing on God's glory.

    D. All of the above. [367]

10. Which of the following good causes could actually take a higher priority than living for God's glory?

    A. Stopping abortion.

    B. Going "green"

    C. Saving the animals.

    D. Stopping the Sex Trade Industry

    E. All of the above. [368]

PERSONAL APPLICATION

What are you going to do differently as a result of what you've learned? **Go to the end of your workbook and write it in for Lesson 18.** [369]

Go to **www.UnveilinGLORY.com** and click on the left side: *Free Online Teaching.*

• Once there, click on "Guest."

• In the top right where it says "Choose a Series" choose "Cat and Dog Theology."

• Listen to Cat and Dog Lesson 5.

There is no quiz, no notes to be taken. Just enjoy and learn!

OPTIONAL LESSON

LESSON 19

CHECK WHICH CIRCLE BEST REPRESENTS YOUR LIFE TODAY:

☐

☐

☐

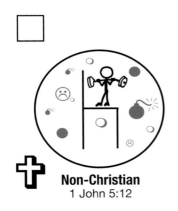

Non-Christian
1 John 5:12

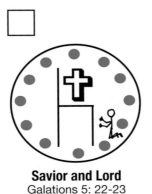

Savior and Lord
Galations 5: 22-23

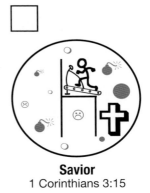

Savior
1 Corinthians 3:15

Since my last lesson,
I have practiced
Spiritual Breathing:

☐ 20⁺ Times
☐ 11 - 19 Times
☐ 6 - 10 Times
☐ 0 - 5 Times

READING ASSIGNMENT

CAT & DOG THEOLOGY

RETHINKING OUR RELATIONSHIP WITH OUR MASTER

LIVING PASSIONATELY FOR THE GLORY OF GOD

Bob Sjogren & Gerald Robison

Start on page 53 ("Four Sick People") and finish out the chapter (page 57).

Questions to answer from the reading assignment:

1. Was praying for the four sick people in the church (page 53) wrong?

    Circle One: Yes   No   ³⁷⁰

2. By not praying for the earthquake victims in Turkey, what did the pastor non-verbally communicate to His congregation?

    _____ ³⁷¹

3. On page 54, a pastor named Paul spoke to his congregation about not telling God they're with a particular denomination. What did you think God thought about that?

    _____ ³⁷²

4. Many Christians assume the glory of God is central in their lives, but they never actually are _____ it. ³⁷³

5. Many times what hurts us in the church is not what is said, but what is _____ said. ³⁷⁴

6. Do you think it is easy to have our primary focus on our own particular church/denomination and secondarily on God's glory?

    Circle One: Yes   No   ³⁷⁵

7. Imagine a church raising 8 million dollars to build a new sanctuary in the inner city of a state's capital.   They've got the best carpeting, the best lighting, the best sound system, the best seating. They've spared no expense. Yet right next door to the church are the homeless and the poor who don't have adequate heating in their homes or food on their tables to feed their families. What has the church non-verbally communicated to those who attend their church?

    _____ ³⁷⁶

8. Explain how the story of "Four Hands" shows how we can be "Americans first and Christians second."

    _____ ³⁷⁷

9. Why might a Cat resent a revival that is happening right down the road?

_____ 378

10. It's easy to become a Cat, because just about everything a Cat focuses in on is _____ and _____ and _____ to God's heart. 379

11. The authors wanted to be very clear about what they were communicating. Therefore they restated that Cat Theology is not _____ . _____ on it is wrong, and _____ of the applications that we learn from it may be wrong, but the theology in and of itself is not wrong. (Pages 56,57) 380

12. If at this point you've learned that the majority of your life has been "Catish" don't be discouraged. It hasn't been a waste. What you've learned is not _____, it is simply _____. 381

1. Read Acts 16:6-10.

2. How many "companions" do you think Paul had with him (the text gives no indication so it is a complete guess.)

_____

_____ 382

BIBLE STUDY!

3. What had God kept them from doing?

_____ 383

4. Do you think they prayed about going to Bithynia after having been kept out of Asia?

    Circle One: Yes   No   384

5. What does this tell you about Paul (and his companions) in "determining God's will through prayer?"

_____

_____ 385

6. Why do you think God kept them from going those places? (Again there is no right or wrong answer.)

_____

_____ 386

7. God stopped Paul and his companions right as they were in the midst of serving Him. Suppose you are wanting to go to the mission field, but you are not sure if it is God's will. If you were to pursue it (because you don't want to sit around and do nothing), does God have the right and ability to stop you?

    Circle One: Yes   No   387

8. Being rejected from Bithynia, they traveled to Troas. This is about a 200-mile trek on foot. Since the text gives no hint at the idea that God told them to go to Troas, our guess is that they may have been thinking, "Well, we're really not sure where to go now, but we can't stay here. Let's go down to Troas." Here is Paul, one of the greatest men of God, who (it seems) wasn't sure of what to do, and simply did something. How could that encourage a Dog?

    _____

    _____ 388

9. Why do you think God spoke to Paul (and not the others) about the where they were to go? (Again there is no right or wrong answer.)

    _____

    _____ 389

10. Note the words, "we," "us" and "concluding" in verse 10 (NIV). It sounds like there was discussion among the companions. What had they concluded?

    _____

    _____ 390

11. If there were a Cat in one of the "companions," do you think they may have been thinking while the discussion was taking place, "Why didn't God give me the dream? Why is it always Paul? Why doesn't God speak to me directly?"

    Circle One: Yes   No   391

12. Circle which lesson you think some Cats need to learn from this passage:

    A. God's will for my life can be revealed through someone else hearing from the Lord.

    B. I need to respect my leader's understanding of God's will for my life.

    C. I'm a part of a team and God may speak to the team through one person, not necessarily to the entire team.

    D. Since God didn't speak directly to me, I'm not sure if I should follow my leader's vision. 392

LESSON 20

CHECK WHICH CIRCLE BEST REPRESENTS YOUR LIFE TODAY:

☐   ☐   ☐

Non-Christian
1 John 5:12

Savior and Lord
Galations 5: 22-23

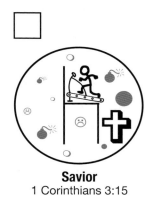

Savior
1 Corinthians 3:15

Since my last lesson,
I have practiced
Spiritual Breathing:

☐ 20+ Times
☐ 11 - 19 Times
☐ 6 - 10 Times
☐ 0 - 5 Times

READING ASSIGNMENT

Start at page 61 and read through until you see the words, "Selective Reading and Listening" (page 68).

Questions to answer from the reading assignment:

1. What did you think about the story on pages 61 and 62?

_____

_____ 393

2. What was the authors' purpose in putting it in the book?

_____ 394

3. The story of Bob's family biking teaches us that even though we start off saying "It's all about God," over time, we can end up "making wrong turns" without even realizing it and saying "It's all about _____!" Often, we're not even _____ of it. 395

4. Most Christians have a _____ _____ going on in their minds and as a result, they only focus on verses that make them _____ _____. 396

5. Many times when you're hungry, you go to the refrigerator and look for things that will satisfy you. How does that analogy fit how most Christians read their Bibles?

_____

_____ 397

6. Why do you think most Christians don't know about their call to suffer according to 1 Peter 2:18?

_____

_____ 398

7. Do you think most Christians can give an answer as to why God is a jealous God? (Explain your answer.)

_____

_____ 399

8. Why is Matthew 5:23,24 difficult to live out?

_____

_____ 400

9. What is the way most Cats get out of obeying Matthew 28:18-20?

_____

_____ 401

10. Have you ever prayed Paul's prayer of Philippians 3:10 and if not, why not?

_____

_____ 402

11. Most Christians don't know these tough passages because it doesn't make them

_____ _____. 403

12. Remember from past chapters, a Cat's goal is to get from birth to death in the

_____, _____ most _____ fashion possible. And if anything gets in that way, they don't want to deal with it, so they

_____ it. 404

13. Many Christians hide their "**Catness**" when reading some of these texts and say, "*I just don't get it,*" or "That verse must not apply to me." Not realizing that what they are subconsciously saying is, "***That verse didn't make me feel good, therefore I'm not going to focus on it, much less*** _____ 405 ***it.***" (This answer is not found in the book but take your best guess at it.)

14. Cats rarely read, much less memorize passages that don't make them feel good.

    Circle One: True   False   406

1. Read Matthew 28:16-20

2. Why do you think Jesus started off talking about "authority?

_____

_____ 407

BIBLE STUDY!

3. If you were to obey this passage, circle which of the following you would most likely need to do:

    A. Get a passport

    B. Get a college degree   (turn page for more possible answers...)

C. Go to Bible School

D. Go to seminary

E. Get a job overseas

F. Learn a new language

G. Leave your family and friends behind

H. Not be able to attend your local church

I. Trust God to plant a church through you [408]

4. The average Cat parents have a goal for their children. Circle which one you think would be the best "Cat goal."

A. To get a good grades in school, so they can go to a good college and get a good career, so they can get a good job, make lots of money and live a safe, soft comfortable life

B. Live to glorify God by making God look famous anywhere in the world. [409]

5. Now if a child did obey Matthew 28:18-20 and took their spouse and children overseas, what would that mean to the grandparents?

_____

_____ [410]

6. How could a Cat Parent rationalize away the idea that God would want their child to obey Matthew 28:18-20?

_____

_____ [411]

7. Which of the following verses apply to Matthew 28:18-20?

Matthew 10:37,38

Matthew 10:16-21

Matthew 9:37

Mark 11:25

Mark 14:6-9

Luke 24:45-47 [412]

8. Do you agree or disagree with the statement: "One of the greatest bottlenecks holding up world evangelization is parents!" and why?

_____

_____ [413]

LESSON 21

CHECK WHICH CIRCLE BEST REPRESENTS YOUR LIFE TODAY:

☐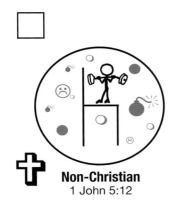

Non-Christian
1 John 5:12

☐

Savior and Lord
Galations 5: 22-23

☐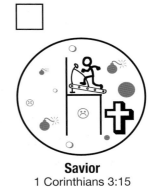

Savior
1 Corinthians 3:15

Since my last lesson,
I have practiced
Spiritual Breathing:

☐ 20+ Times
☐ 11 - 19 Times
☐ 6 - 10 Times
☐ 0 - 5 Times

CARTOON

Ending The Church Prayer Meeting

1. Where is the Dog's focus and is God pleased?

_____

_____

414

_____

2. Where is the Cat's focus and is God pleased?

_____

_____

415

_____

CHRIS and SARAH

The morning after youth group, Chris pulled out his Bible. He was finally going to do it. His mentor, Brett, had encouraged him to memorize scripture for weeks, and after wrestling with jealousy the night before, it was more than time. Chris realized if he didn't take advantage of his memorizing skills now while he was young, it would only grow more difficult as he got older.

So he flipped through his Bible, glancing over the highlighted parts, comparing them to the suggestions Brett had made, and created a master list of what to memorize.

Psalm 46: 10: Be still, and know that I am God;

Jeremiah 29:11-13: For I know the plans I have for you," declares the Lord, "plans to prosper you and not to harm you, plans to give you hope and a future. Then you will call on me and come and pray to me, and I will listen to you. You will seek me and find me when you seek me with all your heart.

Psalm 55:22: Cast your cares on the LORD and he will sustain you; he will never let the righteous be shaken.

1 Timothy 4:12: Don't let anyone look down on you because you are young, but set an example for the believers in speech, in conduct, in love, in faith and in purity.

There were a few suggestions from Brett that Chris wasn't sure what to do with. They just didn't jive with everything Chris had heard about God, and he wondered if maybe he misunderstood them.

Philippians 3:10: I want to know Christ—yes, to know the power of his resurrection and participation in his sufferings, becoming like him in his death.

Chris didn't want to suffer. Nor did he think the Christian life was about suffering. He scratched his head, reading the next verse.

1 Peter 1:6-7: In all this you greatly rejoice, though now for a little while you may have had to suffer grief in all kinds of trials. These have come so that the proven genuineness of your faith—of greater worth than gold, which perishes even though refined by fire — may result in praise, glory and honor when Jesus Christ is revealed.

Here was another one Chris didn't understand. *Rejoicing in trials? Why rejoice in the middle of a trial?* He passed on that one too.

2 Timothy 3:12: In fact, everyone who wants to live a godly life in Christ Jesus will be persecuted.

Persecution? Chris wanted to know God more and more— but persecution? Those were things that happened in Bible times, or in China, but not in America, not among his friends; they were all homeschooled. Sometimes the scriptures were just hard to understand. He checked that one off the list as well.

Nevertheless, in the end Chris was pretty pleased with this new step closer to God. He had typed out the verses he liked, added some graphics with sleek fonts, printed them out, laminated them and stuck them up around his room. A few were taped to his mirror. A few were stuck on the ceiling above his loft bed, and some were in the bathroom. He knew this effort pleased God and he asked God to help him memorize the verses quickly.

That evening, when Sarah walked into the bathroom to brush her teeth she yelled, "Hey Chris, what is this?"

He came over to see what she was talking about. "Oh, that? It's scripture, silly."

"Duh, I know that. But what's it doing here?"

"I'm trying to memorize these verses so I put them on the mirror where I'll see them every morning and every night."

"But you put them right in the middle. They're sticking over on my side. Move them and put them over on your side."

"Don't you want to memorize them too? We could keep each other accountable and make it into a type of competition or something."

She hesitated, "No… I'm not into that stuff. I go to youth group and church. That's enough."

"Okay, but I think this is something that will really draw me even closer to God," Chris sighed. *There. Try to argue with that.*

"Yeah, well once a week everyone in our school has to go to chapel. It's so boring, but we're all forced to go. Believe me, that's enough. I think God is pleased with me enough for doing that. Move your verses off my side."

"So you don't want to go to chapel and learn about God?"

"Quit judging," she snipped, "I'm saved, remember? I've got God in my life. That's enough. I've got too many other things to worry about besides memorizing your Bible verses."

Chris wanted to wring her neck, but didn't think that would be the Christian thing to do.

"Now if you please, Saint Christopher, take these down and put them on your side."

Chris couldn't believe what he was hearing. Really, we're arguing about Bible verses? Nevertheless, he moved the cards onto his side of the mirror while Sarah shot him a satisfied look over her toothbrush.

"Oh Lord, help my sister quit being so selfish before I kill her," he prayed half-jokingly.

Lesson 21 Questions: (The suggested answers are on page 50 in the *Answer Key*.)

1. Which verses are more likely to be found in a Cat's home and which in a Dog's home?

   _____

   _____

2. Should Chris not memorize the "Cat-friendly" verses? Why or why not?

   _____

   _____

3. Why should he memorize the verses about suffering even though he lives in a place with low risk of persecution like they talked about?

   _____

   _____

4. How was Sarah acting like a Cat?

   _____

   _____

Oh Lord, I need to pass this quiz.

QUIZ!

1. What forms of communication can we use to communicate that life is all about us, it's not about God.

    A. Verbal

    B. Non-verbal

    C. Both [416]

2. For a pastor to announce in his church, "We're trusting God for literal miracles in this church." This can be

    A. glorious.

    B. kind of embarrassing.

    C. self-centered.

    D. All of the above. [417]

3. Cat Theology is flat out wrong.

    A. True

    B. False [418]

4. Getting stuck on Cat Theology can be very, very dangerous.

    A. True

    B. False [419]

5. It's very easy to be stuck in Cat Theology because what a Cat focuses on is

    A. safe and close to God's heart.

    B. what our old nature naturally focuses on.

    C. Both

    D. None of the Above. [420]

6. Cats have a tendency to focus on

    A. verses that make them feel good.

    B. tough verses that are challenging.

    C. verse to make their lives safe, soft and comfortable.

    D. None of the above. [421]

7. Cat Christians read their Bible the way most Christians go to their refrigerator. They look inside, take out what they want, and leave the rest.

    A. True

    B. False [422]

8. According to 1 Peter 2:19-21, the Bible tells us only a few believers are called to suffer.

    A. True

    B. False [423]

9. Cats avoid tough passages because

    A. they can't read very well.

    B. the print is so small.

    C. it doesn't make them feel good. [424]

10. A Cat's life goal is to get from birth to death in the safest, softest, easiest most comfortable fashion possible.

    A. True

    B. False [425]

What are you going to do differently as a result of what you've learned? **Go to the end of your workbook and write it in for Lesson 21.** [426]

PERSONAL APPLICATION

Go to **www.UnveilinGLORY.com** and click on the left side: Free Online Teaching.

• Once there, click on "Guest."

• In the top right where it says "Choose a Series" choose "Cat and Dog Theology."

• Listen to Cat and Dog Lesson 6.

There is no quiz, no notes to be taken. Just enjoy and learn!

CAUTION! The more your life is changed, the easier it is to spot Cat behavior in those around you. **Please don't ever use this material to judge others.** ("Oh, they are just a bunch of Cats.") Once we start judging others, we too are acting like Cats. **Use this material to encourage yourself and others to live for God's glory.**

LESSON 22

CHECK WHICH CIRCLE BEST REPRESENTS YOUR LIFE TODAY:

☐   ☐   ☐

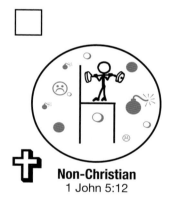

Non-Christian
1 John 5:12

Savior and Lord
Galations 5: 22-23

Savior
1 Corinthians 3:15

Since my last lesson,
I have practiced
Spiritual Breathing:

☐ 20⁺ Times
☐ 11 - 19 Times
☐ 6 - 10 Times
☐ 0 - 5 Times

READING ASSIGNMENT

Begin reading on page 68 where you see "Selective Reading and Listening" and end when you read the words "Selective Application" at the bottom of page 72.

Questions to answer from the reading assignment:

1. What's missing from the phrase, "God loves you and wants to bless you"?

   _____

   _____

   _____

   _____ 427

2. Compare the phrase "God loves you and wants to bless you" with the two paragraphs "completing" it found on page 69. How do those two paragraphs make you feel?

   _____

   _____ 428

3. Before you took this course, had you ever thought about "thunder" or "a child's laughter" as a revelation of God's glory?

   Circle One: Yes   No   429

4. Even though the pastors in Liberia had been taught about Cat and Dog Theology, many of them never really "got it" until their familiar chant "God is good, all the time" was changed. Why do the authors suggest that for many of them it was only then that the change took place?

   _____

   _____ 430

5. According to Ephesians 2:6,7, what is the reason why God saved us?

   _____

   _____ 431

Lesson 22

6. From page 72, summarize the reasons a Cat would say why we are saved?

_____

_____ 432

7. How do Cats and Dogs read John 3:16 differently?

    A Cat: _____

_____

_____

_____ 433

    A Dog: _____

_____

_____

_____ 434

8. When a Dog hears about God's love, they think not only of the love that God has for them, but the love that He has for everyone: _____, _____, _____ and others. [435]

9. Cats usually can't see _____ _____. [436]

10. What are the implications of the idea that two people (a Cat Christian and a Dog Christian) can read the exact same passage from the Bible, but have two totally different understandings?

_____

_____ 437

BIBLE STUDY!

1. Read Philippians chapter 1.

2. Read the following commentary found on the internet* regarding Philippians 1:6:

"I am persuaded of this. I am certain of this." Paul was certain that the God who launched a good work in the Philippians would continue it. When God begins the work of salvation in us, he will finish it. God never starts anything that he cannot finish. When God begins a work in us, he will see it through to completion.

God will either work in us or he will work on us, but he will finish the job. He will finish it whether we want it finished or not! Once we have come to know Christ we cannot say, "Stop the process–I want out." Paul says, "I am certain of this; this is not debatable; I am sure; I am confident."

It was this confidence that gave Paul joy. "Confidence" means to come to a conclusion based on a reasonable ground. God has taken care of billions of people over thousands of years and has not let one person down. Paul's confidence was in the capacity of God, not in men. The Greek tense indicates that this was a settled confidence in Paul's mind. Paul's faith in God's ability to finish what he starts did not waver.

*(www.versebyversecommentary.com)

H. Summarize in your own words what this commentator is saying:

_____

_____

438
_____

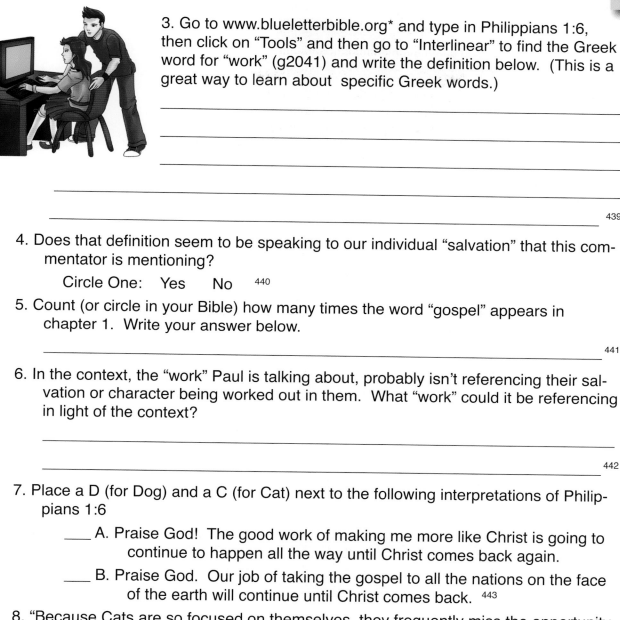

3. Go to www.blueletterbible.org* and type in Philippians 1:6, then click on "Tools" and then go to "Interlinear" to find the Greek word for "work" (g2041) and write the definition below. (This is a great way to learn about specific Greek words.)

_____

_____

_____

_____

_____ 439

4. Does that definition seem to be speaking to our individual "salvation" that this commentator is mentioning?

Circle One: Yes   No   440

5. Count (or circle in your Bible) how many times the word "gospel" appears in chapter 1. Write your answer below.

_____ 441

6. In the context, the "work" Paul is talking about, probably isn't referencing their salvation or character being worked out in them. What "work" could it be referencing in light of the context?

_____

_____ 442

7. Place a D (for Dog) and a C (for Cat) next to the following interpretations of Philippians 1:6

____ A. Praise God! The good work of making me more like Christ is going to continue to happen all the way until Christ comes back again.

____ B. Praise God. Our job of taking the gospel to all the nations on the face of the earth will continue until Christ comes back. 443

8. "Because Cats are so focused on themselves, they frequently miss the opportunity and responsibility for reaching the nations." Do you agree or disagree with this statement?

Circle One: Disagree   Agree   444

*(Over time, the BlueLetterBible.org changes its format. It may be different since this was printed.)

LESSON 23

CHECK WHICH CIRCLE BEST REPRESENTS YOUR LIFE TODAY:

☐   ☐   ☐

Non-Christian
1 John 5:12

Savior and Lord
Galations 5: 22-23

Savior
1 Corinthians 3:15

Since my last lesson,
I have practiced
Spiritual Breathing:

☐ 20⁺ Times
☐ 11 - 19 Times
☐ 6 - 10 Times
☐ 0 - 5 Times

READING ASSIGNMENT

CAT & DOG THEOLOGY

RETHINKING OUR RELATIONSHIP WITH OUR MASTER

LIVING PASSIONATELY FOR THE GLORY OF GOD

Bob Sjogren & Gerald Robison

Begin reading on page 72 where you see "Selective Application" and finish out the chapter (page 76).

Questions to answer from the reading assignment:

1. If Cats are only reading and listening to selective portions of Scripture, it _____ _____ that they can only apply select portions of Scripture to their lives. [445]

2. In Selective Application, Cats only apply the parts of Scripture that speak to their own _____, the parts of Scripture that speak only of _____. [446]

3. Ten generations lived under Egyptian captivity. Which one do most Christians tend to focus on and why?

_____

_____ [447]

4. Did God love those other nine generations in slavery?

Circle One: Yes   No   [448]

5. Did God have a plan for their lives?

Circle One: Yes   No   [449]

6. What was God's plan for their lives?

_____

_____ [450]

7. We're not doing the Christian family any _____ by only preparing them for the good, happy, and blessed events in life. [451]

8. Because some theologians are so steeped in Cat Theology (remember the railroad analogy from your reading!) they teach that Christians are _____ from the tough things of life; disaster, sorrow, frustration, etc. [452]

9. List three of the lessons found on pages 75 and 76 that really stood out to you.

_____

_____

_____ [453]

10. Why don't churches commonly teach these lessons?

_____

_____ 454

11. Many people who have deadly diseases don't even know it until it is too late. The authors say that Cat Theology is rampant in our churches, like a silent deadly _____. For many Christians, it will be "too late" and they'll stand before the Lord having lived a self-centered Christian life and will not hear the words "well done, good and faithful servant." 455

1. Read Daniel chapter 3.

2. Why do Cats want to latch on to the last verse?

_____

_____

_____

_____ 456

3. What words help you understand that the three men were not completely assured that they would be saved from the fire?

_____

_____ 457

4. In order to reveal God's glory by coming through the blazing fire unharmed, certain major events had to take place to set this up. List them according to the verses:

Verse 1: _____

_____ 458

Verse 5: _____

_____ 459

Verse 8: _____

_____ 460

Verse 19: _____

_____ 461

5. The king's attitude completely changed (due to pride) toward the three men of God. At first he appreciated them, then he was furious with them. Do you think this caught God by surprise?

   Circle One: Yes   No   462

6. Since we cannot interview God here on this earth to find out why He did things, we can only guess at a few things. But let's take a guess. Do you personally think God wanted them thrown into the fire to show off His glory and why?

   _____

   _____ 463

7. If God did want them (or merely allowed them) to be thrown into the fire, what does that teach you about how God "ranks" His glory and our safety? Circle One:

   A. God's glory is His highest priority and our safety is a secondary concern.

   B. Our safety is always God's first and primary concern. His glory is secondary. 464

8. Sometimes terrible scenarios have to be played out (with people furious at you and others wanting you killed) before you can radiate God's _____ in a greater way. Don't be discouraged. God will use it all for His _____. 465

LESSON 24

CHECK WHICH CIRCLE BEST REPRESENTS YOUR LIFE TODAY:

☐

☐

☐

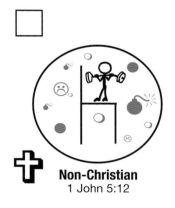

Non-Christian
1 John 5:12

Savior and Lord
Galations 5: 22-23

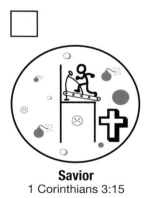

Savior
1 Corinthians 3:15

Since my last lesson,
I have practiced
Spiritual Breathing:

☐ 20⁺ Times

☐ 11 - 19 Times

☐ 6 - 10 Times

☐ 0 - 5 Times

CARTOON

How Cats and Dogs Pray For Their Kids

1. Was there anything wrong with the prayer the Cat parent prayed for his child?

_____
466

2. Do you think a Dog would pray those same prayers for his children? Why or why not?

_____

_____
467

3. Though a Dog would pray the same prayers, what is the cartoon communicating as the essence of a Dog's heart in praying for his child?

_____

_____
468

CHRIS and SARAH

"Guys, I want you to really think about these words," Pastor Jake was deep into his message at youth group. "This passage is from Romans 14, verse 8, and when I read it, I want you to consider its implications. How can it apply to you and to how you choose to face situations in your life?

"Romans 14:8 says, 'If we live, we live to the Lord; and if we die, we die to the Lord. So, whether we live or die, we belong to the Lord.'"

Jake pulled his Bible off of the pulpit and faced the students in front of him.

"Think about that! Most of us have heard about living for God. But have you thought about how to glorify God in your death?"

The room was silent, and he reminded himself that these were teenagers who never thought about death. Setting the Bible down and putting his hands in his jeans, he sighed, "I know, I know. No one likes to talk about dying. You guys are all young, you have your whole lives in front of you, and death is the last thing that even occurs to you. And that's okay, guys, I'm not here to scare you or kill your fun tonight.

"We talk a lot here about how God loves us and wants to bless us. But I gotta tell you, I've been really convicted lately to tell you how big God's plan is for that blessing. He doesn't just want to make your life happy and soft and comfortable. He wants to make you into the men and women you were made to be, who will be filled with His power and light and can bring His glory to the nations so that other people can know Him and be filled with Him as well. So tonight I want to challenge you."

Jake went on to share a series of stories and videos about people who had given their lives to share the love and glory of God. Some of the people were from history. Some were modern-day missionaries and business people. Some lived peacefully and happily. Most of them did not.

"We all want to relate to Job. None of us want to relate to Job's kids. Well it's time we start being Biblical and at least open our hearts to the idea of dying so someone else can come to know the Lord."

Right after that, Chris' friend Jim stood up. Chris watched as he slid past everyone in his row and walked to the back of the room. Presently, the door to the meeting room opened and shut.

A few minutes later, Jake wrapped up his message, and Chris decided to check on Jim. He had seen the troubled look on Jim's face when he left.

"Hey, man," Chris said when he found him lounging in an arm chair near the doors of the church. He was listening to music and texting.

"Oh, hey."

Pulling the headphones out of his ears, Jim looked up, "Couldn't take any more of it either, huh?"

"Umm," Chris was confused, "What?"

Jim closed his phone.

"The whole thing about God wanting us to die. Weird, right?"

"I guess I never thought about it. But the way Jake said it kind of makes sense."

"You're kidding, right? You really think God wants us to get speared by some savage tribe in Ecuador?"

Shrugging, Chris replied, "No, I mean, I don't think that's what Jake's trying to say. I think he just wants us to be willing to die for God's glory, not to go looking for it."

Jim shook his head. "That's insane. There's no way God would want me to die early for his glory. Jesus did that for us so we won't have to. I didn't give my life to God so I would die. Last I checked, God was love. Why would He want me to die? That's a pretty lame version of love."

"Yeah, but didn't you hear what Jake said? It's not about dying. It's about living for God no matter what. It's about becoming the people we're meant to be, not just being happy and blessed."

"And you think we're meant to die in a jungle?"

Chris was taken by surprise. Sure, it was a hard concept to swallow, but he didn't expect Jim to be so passionate against what the scriptures plainly taught.

Jim's phone buzzed with a new text. He checked it. "Look, my mom's here. I gotta go." And he walked out without another word.

When Chris slid back into his seat, the worship team was in full swing. Still bothered by his talk with Jim, he took his phone out and began texting him. "Look, I'm not trying to scare you. I just want to challenge you. If God is everything He says He is, He is worth living for, He is worth suffering for, and He is even worth dying for. He is everything we have and more. We might not all end up missionaries in Asia, but I think we should at

least try what Jake said – ask God to give us the attitude Paul had when he said, "If we live, we live to the Lord; and if we die, we die to the Lord. So, whether we live or die, we belong to the Lord'"

Lesson 24 Questions: (The suggested answers are on page 50 in the *Answer Key*.)

1. Why did Jim get up and leave?

_____

_____

2. How do you answer Jim's claim that since Jesus died early for us, we won't have to die early ourselves?

_____

_____

3. Read Philippians 1:20 and comment on the similarities between it and Romans 14:8.

_____

_____

4. Would you say you are at the point where you are willing to die for the Lord if called upon by God to do so?

_____

_____

Oh Lord, I need to pass this quiz.

QUIZ!

1. The phrase, "God is good all the time" as well as "God is jealous all the time" are both

    A. correct.

    B. incomplete without the other.

    C. "A" and "B"

    D. None of the above [469]

2. According to Ephesians 2:6,7, heaven is more about

    A. us getting there!

    B. what God gets to do.

    C. God revealing His grace forever.

    D. "B" and "C" [470]

3. You can actually read John 3:16 and totally miss out on God's heart for the world.

    A. True

    B. False [471]

4. Two people reading the same verse will always come out with the same understanding.

    A. True

    B. False [472]

5. According to the context, the "good work in you" that Paul talks about in Philippians 1:6 refers to

    A. taking the gospel to all nations.

    B. making us more like Christ.

    C. None of the above. [473]

6. When reading their Bible, Cats

    A. usually only focus on the parts that make them feel good.

    B. have selective reading and listening.

    C. learn only lessons that are not that difficult to implement.

    D. All of the above. [474]

7. There were ten generations that endured slavery in Egypt. Cats usually tend to focus on

    A. The nine that were enslaved.

    B. The one that got free. [475]

8. God loved the one generation that got free more than He loved the other nine generations that didn't get free.

    A. True

    B. False [476]

9. God's plan for the nine generations was

    A. to live and die in slavery.

    B. to get free.

    C. to show future generations to be kind to internationals.

    D. none of the above. [477]

10. We are not doing Christian families any favors if we are only talking to them about having a safe, soft comfortable life and not preparing them to possibly suffer.

    A. True

    B. False [478]

PERSONAL
APPLICATION

What are you going to do differently as a result of what you've learned? **Go to the end of your workbook and write it in for Lesson 24.** [479]

Go to **www.UnveilinGLORY.com** and click on the left side: Free Online Teaching.

• Once there, click on "Guest."

• In the top right where it says "Choose a Series" choose "Cat and Dog Theology."

• Listen to Cat and Dog Lesson 7.

There is no quiz, no notes to be taken. Just enjoy and learn!

LESSON 25

CHECK WHICH CIRCLE BEST REPRESENTS YOUR LIFE TODAY:

☐   ☐   ☐

Non-Christian
1 John 5:12

Savior and Lord
Galations 5: 22-23

Savior
1 Corinthians 3:15

Since my last lesson,
I have practiced
Spiritual Breathing:

☐ 20+ Times
☐ 11 - 19 Times
☐ 6 - 10 Times
☐ 0 - 5 Times

READING ASSIGNMENT

Start chapter 7 on page 77 to the bottom of page 83 (finishing the page).

Questions to answer from the reading assignment:

1. God's goals don't necessarily include our _____ and _____. They might, but they might not either. [480]

2. American Christians have "cultural blinders" on. Looking upon the past history of America, they believe that we can _____ up and make anything, our enemies will be _____, and we always expect to come out on _____. [481]

3. Because of this, Cats _____ relate to the winner, the victor, the champion in the Scriptures. [482]

4. Another way of saying this is that Cats always relate to the _____ character of the Bible, they never relate to the _____ character in the Bible. [483]

5. What do American Cats think God wants for every believer here on the earth?

_____

_____ [484]

6. Who do most Cat Christians relate to in the book of Job?

_____ [485]

7. Who are other people that we can relate to in the book of Job?

_____ [486]

8. Why does a Cat not want to relate to Job's kids?

_____ [487]

9. Did God love Job's kids as much as He loved Job?
   Circle One: Yes   No   [488]

10. Write down God's plan for Job's kids in your own words.

_____

_____

_____ 489

11. Although God loves all people equally, their _____ in revealing His glory can be quite _____. Some He blesses with things, some He allows to be persecuted, some He brings home early. 490

12. What lesson did David's 70,000 fighting men learn when David sinned and they were killed?

_____

_____ 491

13. Write down God's will for the widows of the fighting men.

_____

_____ 492

1. Read Numbers 16:1-35.

2. What lesson do most Christians learn from this passage?

_____

_____

_____

_____

_____ 493

BIBLE STUDY!

3. Go to www.blueletterbible.org and type in "Numbers 16:32." Click on tools and find other definitions for the phrase "and their house" (H1004). Write them in below.

_____

_____

_____

_____

_____

_____

_____

494

_____

4. Circle below what words could be represented by the word "household" (NIV).

      A. Wives

      B. Children

      C. Aunts

      D. Uncles

      E. Grandparents

      F. Servants/Slaves [495]

5. What lesson do you think Korah's wife learned?

_____

496

_____

6. How could this help a young Christian single woman who is looking for a spouse?

_____

497

_____

7. What do you think Korah's servants learn?

_____

498

_____

8. How can this help a Christian employee whose boss is doing unethical things?

_____

499

_____

9. How can this help an elder in a church whose pastor "just doesn't seem right?"

_____

500

_____

LESSON 26

CHECK WHICH CIRCLE BEST REPRESENTS YOUR LIFE TODAY:

☐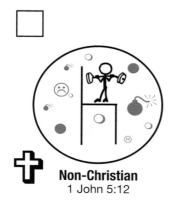

Non-Christian
1 John 5:12

☐

Savior and Lord
Galations 5: 22-23

☐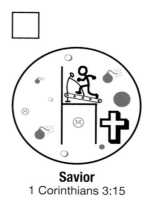

Savior
1 Corinthians 3:15

Since my last lesson,
I have practiced
Spiritual Breathing:

☐ 20+ Times

☐ 11 - 19 Times

☐ 6 - 10 Times

☐ 0 - 5 Times

READING ASSIGNMENT

Start at the top of page 84 and finish out the chapter (page 90).

Questions to answer from the reading assignment:

1. List a Cat's lesson learned and a Dog's additional lesson for the last plague in the ten plagues:

   Cat: _____

   _____

   _____ 501

   Dog: _____

   _____

   _____ 502

2. List a Cat's lesson learned and a Dog's additional lesson from wandering around in the desert for 40 years.

   Cat: _____

   _____ 503

   Dog: _____

   _____ 504

3. Write what the cultural blinders might be on Chinese Christians over the past 40 years.

   _____

   _____ 505

4. What characterized the first 300 years of Christianity?

   _____ 506

5. The past 200 years in America have been characterized largely by blessings. Which one is biblical, the blessings or the persecution of the first 300 years?

_____

_____ 507

6. Some of the missionaries from America knew they only had 2 years to live once they hit the field due to disease. What would the average American today say about their lives? (Circle the ones you feel are appropriate.)

    A. What a wise use of their lives.

    B. What wasted lives.

    C. Fools.

    D. Their lives counted for nothing. 508

7. What would a Dog say about the way they gave up their lives?

_____

_____ 509

8. What types of verses do you usually find in the homes you visit (or your own home)? Circle One:

    A. Verses that deal with God's blessings

    B. Verses that deal with suffering we might have to go through 510

9. We must not assume that the gospel we are experiencing right now is the gospel for all peoples at all times.

    Circle One: True or False? 511

10. We must always be _____ to learning different ways that God chooses to reveal His _____ and to learn from them. 512

1. Read Hebrews 11:24-39.

2. What words would have characterized Moses' life had he chosen to stay and be the son of the Pharaoh's daughter? Circle the ones that apply:

    A. Safe

    B. Easy

    C. Comfortable

    D. Problem Free

    E. Difficult 513

BIBLE STUDY!

3. Moses chose to be mistreated with his fellow Hebrew people. Write down some words that would describe his life in this period.

_____

_____ 514

4. The writer of Hebrews gives a balanced view of what it means to live by faith. In verses 32 – 39, list the situations to which a Cat would love to relate.

_____

_____

_____ 515

_____

5. List the situations to which a Cat overlooks and a Dog pays attention.

_____

_____

_____ 516

_____

6. Would you say most Americans believe in a "safe" gospel?

    Circle One: Yes   No   517

7. Do most Americans relate to verses 35-38?

_____

_____ 518

8. Where do we get such a "safe gospel?"

_____

_____ 519

9. What does verse 38 say of those who followed God?

_____

_____ 520

10. What kept these people going in the midst of such a hard lives (verse 35)?

_____

_____ 521

LESSON 27

CHECK WHICH CIRCLE BEST REPRESENTS YOUR LIFE TODAY:

☐

☐

☐

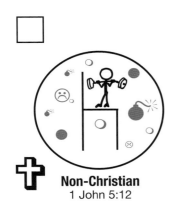

Non-Christian
1 John 5:12

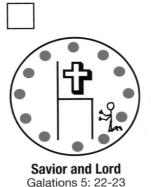

Savior and Lord
Galations 5: 22-23

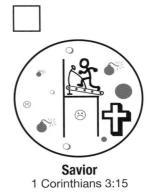

Savior
1 Corinthians 3:15

Since my last lesson,
I have practiced
Spiritual Breathing:

☐ 20⁺ Times

☐ 11 - 19 Times

☐ 6 - 10 Times

☐ 0 - 5 Times

CARTOON

On Relating To Job's Kids

1. The Cat has one goal: to stay alive and be healthy. The thought of relating to Job's kids and possibly dying so someone else could come to know the Lord is not even a remote possibility. Take a wild guess and think about how the Lord might respond to the Cat's way of thinking.

_____

_____

_____

522

_____

CHRIS and SARAH

Chris pulled up to Jim's house and hopped out. One thing he loved about being home-schooled was that he could go visit his other homeschooled friends in the middle of the day. Besides, he wanted to talk to Jim about the other night.

Jim's mom opened the door after Chris knocked. "Why hello, Chris," she said a bit stiffly. "I'll tell Jim you're here."

Her eyes looked him up and down coldly like he might be hiding a bomb behind his back. Chris shifted uncomfortably. Usually, Mrs. Henderson was warm and friendly, albeit a little formal and obsessed with etiquette. He'd never seen her act like this before.

In a few minutes, Jim and Chris were on the court in Jim's backyard. They played back and forth for a few minutes, warming up and joking about each other's weaknesses in the sport.

Chris wasn't a huge fan of this kind of banter, but everyone he knew did it, and it was kind of fun when he could shoot a particularly witty insult. It was just for fun anyway, right?

At one point, Chris glanced back at the house and his eye caught a flash of curtain being dropped quickly. Was he crazy? It looked like Mrs. Henderson had been watching them but hid herself quickly when she saw Chris glance her way.

"Hey, man, is your mom mad at me?" Chris asked as he dribbled the ball.

Jim looked guilty. "Nah, she's not mad at you."

Jim didn't sound convincing enough for Chris to buy it. His gut told him there was a problem and he had a feeling he knew what the problem was.

"It's about last night, isn't it?"

Jim didn't answer for a while. He took a shot, but the ball completely missed. Chris went and got it, giving Jim a moment to collect himself.

"Look, it's nothing personal," his friend finally said, "but she doesn't want me coming to your youth group anymore."

Chris dropped the ball, and it rolled back into the grass.

"What?"

"Yeah, I talked to my parents about what Pastor Jake said, about God wanting us to die sometimes, and they agreed with me. It's not right."

"You're leaving because of that?" Chris asked, trying not to sound incredulous. "Look,

I understand not agreeing with what Jake said, but it's not like he preaches about death every week."

Jim's eyes flashed angrily, "It's not just that, okay? This has been coming on for a while. They've been doing a lot of things at youth group that my parents don't agree with, and I'm beginning to see what they mean."

"Like what?"

"Like taking us out to the homeless park every month. That's a crazy part of the city, and there's no telling what could happen down there. Or how he's always talking about bringing us on missions trips to the Middle East or China. He's putting people in danger all for the sake of growing the church or youth group or whatever. Someone's gonna get hurt."

Chris clenched his jaws. Here it was again. Did Jim just not get it? He was a youth group leader; he and Chris had grown up in the same homeschool group. They had gone to youth retreats and were baptized on the same day. Chris knew how much Jim loved God.

"Lots of people do homeless ministry and go to the Middle East, Jim. It's not like this is a new idea."

His friend looked hurt. "Yeah, well, my dad said there's a reason why we moved out of the city and live in America instead of Iraq. I remember the first day you invited me there. I loved it. Everything was great, but the teaching wasn't like this back then."

He ran to the grass and picked up the ball. "It's not like I really want this. I'm going to miss youth group. I mean, that's when I see most of my friends. I'm gonna miss playing basketball with the guys and checking out the girls. Youth group was fun."

He started dribbling the ball again. He shot, and this time it was nothing but net.

"Our church doesn't teach stuff like that, so I'm probably gonna start going back to my own youth group, though the kids that go there are kind of weird."

He turned to Chris and smiled, "You'll still come over on Thursdays for basketball, right?"

Swallowing and forcing himself to return the smile, Chris replied, "Sure, man, as long

as you stay so easy to beat."

When Chris got home he thought about the decision Jim and his parents had made. Chris hadn't even told his parents about Jake's controversial teaching, but he wondered what it would be like to leave youth group.

He didn't even like to think about it. Youth group was one of the highlights of his week, and Jim was right. Chris would miss seeing his friends. He didn't see the public or private schooled ones any other time of the week except Sunday. He would miss the basketball, the worship music – even with Matt leading it –, the atmosphere, and yes, the girls were pretty.

Those were all the things Jim said he would miss. However, what was making him leave was the teaching—the part about God. Pastor Jake believed that loving and glorifying God was worth more than anything else in this world, even their very lives.

Something was bothering Chris. This hungering for God and wanting to love God, this is what caused such an issue. *Wasn't that supposed to be the most important part of youth group? But what would I miss if I weren't able to go to the youth group?* Chris thought to himself. *Would it be the basketball, the friends, the girls…what?*

God, Chris prayed silently, *Please help me love you more. I know I need to desire you more than anything else. I need your help to do it, because quite honestly, I don't think I'm there yet.*

Lesson 27 Questions: (The suggested answers are on page 51 in the *Answer Key.*)

1. Why do you think Jim's mom gave Chris such a cold welcome?

_____

_____

2. How do you think your parents would react to teaching about relating to Job's kids?

_____

_____

3. What was Jim's main motivation for going to the youth group?

_____

_____

4. What do you think is the motivation that most of your friends have in going to your youth group?

_____

_____

Oh Lord, I need to pass this quiz.

QUIZ!

1. God's goals don't necessarily include

    A. our needs.

    B. our fame and fortune.

    C. our wants and wishes.

    D. All of the above [523]

2. Cats usually relate to the major characters of the Bible and never to the minor characters of the Bible.

        A. True

        B. False [524]

3. The "Winner's Circle Lesson" out of the book of Job is

    A. God may kill you in order for someone else to learn a lesson.

    B. God loves you and wants to take you home early.

    C. God may test you, but in the end everything will work out well.

    D. None of the above. [525]

4. We can learn valuable lessons from the minor characters in the book of Job from

    A. his wife.

    B. his children.

    C. his friends.

    D. All of the above. [526]

5. Cats don't want to relate to Job's kids because

    A. they didn't get to live past the age of 70.

    B. they died.

    C. "A" and "B"

    D. None of the above. [527]

6. The lesson we can learn from David's 70,000 fighting men who died is:

    A. don't follow a bad leader.

    B. someone else can sin and you have to pay a penalty for it.

    C. never fight.

    D. None of the above. [528]

7. Just because you've learned one lesson from a Bible story means you've learned everything there is to know from that Bible story.

    A. True

    B. False [529]

8. We must assume that the gospel we are experiencing right now is the gospel for all peoples at all times.

    A. True

    B. False [530]

9. As you get older and marry and have children, the sins you commit today could have an impact on your children's lives.

    A. True

    B. False [531]

10. Most people reading the Bible will usually read it with cultural blinders on and that will affect what they learn.

    True

    False [532]

What are you going to do differently as a result of what you've learned? **Go to the end of your workbook and write it in for Lesson 27.** [533]

PERSONAL APPLICATION

Go to **www.UnveilinGLORY.com** and click on the left side: Free Online Teaching.

• Once there, click on "Guest."

• In the top right where it says "Choose a Series" choose "Cat and Dog Theology."

• Listen to Cat and Dog Lesson 8.

There is no quiz, no notes to be taken.
Just enjoy and learn!

OPTIONAL
LESSON

LESSON 28

CHECK WHICH CIRCLE BEST REPRESENTS YOUR LIFE TODAY:

☐   ☐   ☐

Non-Christian
1 John 5:12

Savior and Lord
Galations 5: 22-23

Savior
1 Corinthians 3:15

Since my last lesson,
I have practiced
Spiritual Breathing:

☐ 20+ Times
☐ 11 - 19 Times
☐ 6 - 10 Times
☐ 0 - 5 Times

READING ASSIGNMENT

CAT & DOG THEOLOGY

RETHINKING OUR RELATIONSHIP WITH OUR MASTER

LIVING PASSIONATELY FOR THE GLORY OF GOD

Bob Sjogren & Gerald Robison

Start chapter 8 (page 91) and read through until you see the words "Discipline" at the bottom of page 95.

Questions to answer from the reading assignment:

1. On page 91, it says that some Chinese believers "walk for days" to get to meetings. Compare the hunger of those believers to the believers in your church; do you think the believers in your church would walk for days to get to a meeting? Why or why not?

_____

_____

_____ 534

2. In China, God's glory is being revealed at a _____. List some of the things happening to them.

_____

_____ 535

3. How did the pastor ask the Westerners to pray for China?

_____

_____ 536

4. Most Cat prayers are focused on asking God to advance _____ agenda/ kingdom (a safe, soft, comfortable lifestyle) and not to advance _____ kingdom (revealing His _____ to all nations.) [537]

5. Cats make a mistake in assuming that God's glory in their lives will only be revealed in a couple of categories. List the three areas Cats assume God's glory is revealed.

_____

_____

_____ 538

6. Explain the graph in figure 1 on page 92.

_____

_____

_____

_____ 539

7. Why does a Cat assume figure 2 will never be God's will?

_____

_____ 540

8. Dogs know that although a safe, soft, comfortable life _____ point to God's glory, it is the glory that is the _____ priority. Therefore, if _____ is going to result in greater glory, Dogs yield to it so that God's glory can shine in a greater way. 541

9. Regarding the blind man in John 9, God did not say "_____" when he came out blind. No, God _____ him blind so that the _____ of God could be revealed in a _____ way. 542

10. Do a internet search on how Joni Eareckson Tada became paralyzed and list the reason below:

_____

_____

_____ 543

11. List how the Lord has used Joni as a paraplegic.

_____

_____ 544

12. List the reason why the authors believe, that although God could heal Joni instantly, he has left her paralyzed:

_____

_____ 545

13. Asking, "Is life _____ to us isn't a _____ question. Life was never designed to be _____. 546

14. Write down what the authors say life is all about.

Life was designed to be _____

_____

_____ 547

15. We can always ask God for a healing, but we must also realize that if the ailment or infirmity will bring God more glory, God might _____ to allow it to _____ in our lives. 548

1. Read Acts 16:16-34

2. What were the slave owners' motivation in having a slave?

_____

_____

_____

_____

_____ 549

BIBLE STUDY!

3. What did the slave owners do when their slave girl could no longer speak of people's fortunes?

_____

_____ 550

4. What did the officials do to Paul and Silas?

_____

_____ 551

5. Could God have healed Paul and Silas' wounds instantly?

    Circle One: Yes   No   552

6. Which verse gives you the answer that God did not heal their wounds?

_____ 553

7. If you had a dog (as a pet) and while hiking, he saved you from a wild animal, but in the process got very beaten and was bleeding badly because of wounds, would you heal him if you had the power to do so?

    Circle One: Yes   No   554

8. According to the authors, what do they say is the reason God did not heal Paul and Silas?

_____

_____ 555

9. Which verse tells you how God got great glory through this incident and why?

_____

_____ 556

10. What person does the text seem to indicate that God wanted to reach out to through this tremendous testimony?

_____
557

11. What do you think impressed the guard so much that he wanted to be saved?

_____

_____
558

12. Had Paul and Silas been healed instantly, do you think the guard would have been as impressed?

   Circle One: Y   N   559

13. Do you agree or disagree with the following and why? "Sometimes the joy Christians have in the midst of their trials is a greater testimony than the joy they would have if the trials were taken away. Hence God leaves the trials in a believer's life to radiate His glory in a greater way."

_____

_____
560

14. If Paul and Silas had wanted a safe, soft and comfortable life, what kind of an impact would that have had on the growth of the church?

_____

_____

_____

_____
561

LESSON 29

CHECK WHICH CIRCLE BEST REPRESENTS YOUR LIFE TODAY:

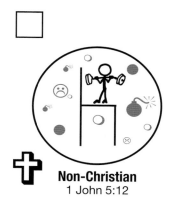

Non-Christian
1 John 5:12

Savior and Lord
Galations 5: 22-23

Savior
1 Corinthians 3:15

Since my last lesson,
I have practiced
Spiritual Breathing:

☐ 20⁺ Times
☐ 11 - 19 Times
☐ 6 - 10 Times
☐ 0 - 5 Times

READING ASSIGNMENT

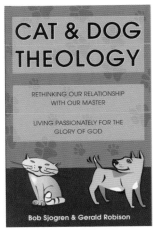

CAT & DOG THEOLOGY

RETHINKING OUR RELATIONSHIP WITH OUR MASTER

LIVING PASSIONATELY FOR THE GLORY OF GOD

Bob Sjogren & Gerald Robison

Start at the bottom of page 95 where it says "Discipline" and finish out the chapter (page 99).

Questions to answer from the reading assignment:

1. Hebrews 12:5,6 clearly tell us that God _____ us is a sign that we will be _____. [562]

2. List what God's primary goal is for us and therefore, what a secondary goal is.

   _____

   _____ [563]

3. In William Branham's story, "The Lamb's Broken Leg," what did the shepherd do to the lamb's leg?

   _____

   _____ [564]

4. What was the lamb doing which required the shepherd to break its leg?

   _____

   _____ [565]

5. What was the ultimate goal in breaking the leg?

   _____

   _____ [566]

6. Why does Matthew 5:10-11 sound strange?

   _____

   _____ [567]

7. In looking at history, we see that God has allowed _____ things to happen to His children in order to _____ His kingdom and reveal His glory. [568]

8. God is so sovereign, that He uses both _____ and _____ for His glory. [569]

Lesson 29

9. Psalm 18:28 says that God can turn our _____ into _____. [570]

10. Explain the motivation described in figure six on page 99.

_____

_____

_____

_____

_____ [571]

11. Write down the definition of "masochistic" below.

_____

_____ [572]

12. Explain how Dogs are not masochistic.

_____

_____ [573]

1. Read Matthew 26:36-68.

2. From verse 39, what was Christ's attitude about going to the cross?

BIBLE STUDY!

_____

_____

_____

_____ [574]

3. From verse 39, what was Christ's ultimate goal in life?

_____

_____ [575]

4. Luke 22:44 tells us that Christ was so distressed about going to the cross that He sweat _____ of _____. [576]

5. Research on the internet "Is it possible to sweat drops of blood" and tell us what you found.

_____

_____

_____

_____

_____ 577

6. The text tells us that Jesus prayed this way three times. It seems to clearly communicate that Jesus did not want to go to the cross. How can that encourage us?

_____

_____ 578

7. What does verse 53 tell us that Christ could have done?

_____

_____ 579

8. Would this have made Jesus' life more safe, soft and comfortable?

   Circle One: Yes   No   580

9. Why did Jesus not call upon His Father to send those angels?

_____

_____ 581

10. If Jesus had not gone through with going to the cross, what would that have meant for the world?

_____

_____ 582

11. Are there ramifications to others if we, as believers, are not willing to suffer?

   Circle One: Yes   No   583

LESSON 30

CHECK WHICH CIRCLE BEST REPRESENTS YOUR LIFE TODAY:

☐   ☐   ☐

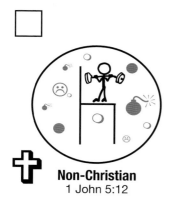 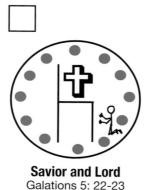 

Non-Christian
1 John 5:12

Savior and Lord
Galations 5: 22-23

Savior
1 Corinthians 3:15

Since my last lesson,
I have practiced
Spiritual Breathing:

☐ 20⁺ Times
☐ 11 - 19 Times
☐ 6 - 10 Times
☐ 0 - 5 Times

CARTOON

How They View Technology

1. Explain why the Cat prayer is incomplete.

_____

_____ 584

2. Explain the difference in the Dog's prayer.

_____

_____ 585

3. Which prayer do you think the Lord would be more pleased with and why?

_____

_____ 586

CHRIS and SARAH

"We're gonna do something a little different this week, guys," Pastor Jake announced as he finished the teaching portion of that night's youth group. "Over the last few weeks we've talked about prayer, what it means to us, and why it's important for us to communicate with God. I'd like to end tonight with everyone breaking up into groups of 5 or 7 people. You can spread out, sit on the floor, whatever. But what I really want you to focus on during the next few minutes is prayer and communicating with our Father and Savior."

Jake explained that it didn't need to be anything fancy. They would just go around the circle and each person could take a turn praying about something going on in their life.

Sarah sighed. These prayer circles were always awkward. Usually she and her friends formed a circle amongst themselves so it didn't get too weird. However, this week a few new kids squeezed into their circle. Actually, Jessica, one of Sarah's friends, invited them in. It was nice of her, but Sarah always felt self-conscious praying out loud. It was easier to do it in front of friends.

Jessica took charge. As a junior, she was the oldest in the group, and everyone usually followed her lead anyway.

"God, thank you for this time at youth group," she started. "I know not everyone gets to experience the fellowship and teaching we get to have every week, so I thank you for Pastor Jake and all the leaders here. God, as far as what's going on in my life right now, I just bring my crazy schedule before you. I feel like I hardly ever have any time, and it's getting hard to keep up with everything. Please help me with all my commitments. Help me have some time to just relax and hang out with my friends more and come to youth group more often. It's really stressing me out, and I know you don't want me to be stressed out like this all the time. In Jesus' name I pray, Amen."

One of the new kids went after Jessica. She was a shy girl who looked much younger than fourteen, but Sarah knew she must be at least a freshman if she was at youth group. She had a soft voice, and Sarah barely heard a word of her prayer over the worship music playing in the background. It sounded like maybe her grandma was sick and in the hospital.

After the new girl prayed, it was Ashley's turn.

Ashley was good at praying. Her voice was heartfelt, and she seemed really into what she was saying, like no one else was listening to her. Sarah wished she could pray like that. But whenever she prayed out loud, all she could think was whether or not she sounded dumb, because she sure felt it. Ashley asked that God heal her dad's knee and help her get good grades. She asked that her brother's tryouts go well this weekend.

Now it was Sarah's turn.

She took a deep breath and let it out a little shakily. "Lord," she started. No one had used "Lord" yet, so she thought it sounded more unique and authentic. Why were her palms sweating so badly? "Lord," she said again, "I just want to thank you for my friends and my school. I'm glad to finally have friends to hang out with every day and classes I enjoy. Please help me do really well in track next spring and do well at school. Please help me to, um, have better quiet times and be a better Christian. Bless my friends and everyone in this circle, and please bless these prayers. In Jesus' name, Amen." To herself, she added, *And God, please help me with this whole Bryan thing. I want to date him so badly, and I know you can do anything. Is there a way you can bring us together somehow? Could you get my parents to change their "no dating before 16" thinking?*

Sarah breathed a sigh of relief. Not too bad. Thankfully, she remembered to pray for a blessing for everyone sitting around her. *Was that the Holy Spirit?* The guy next to her started praying. She thought about her silent prayer for Bryan and glanced to where he

sat in his own circle of friends, head bowed.

Meanwhile, Chris listened to the prayers in his own circle. Someone wanted a new car. One girl needed a job, and the guy next to her prayed for good grades and for his ankle to heal before basketball tryouts.

It wasn't that these were bad prayers. Chris knew God cared about everything in their lives. However, something was missing. Painfully, Chris was reminded of his conversation with Jim a few weeks ago. Was this all that mattered? Basketball and friends and cars? What about the world outside their schools or their church or their friends? Chris grimaced, feeling a twinge of guilt. He was pretty sure he had never prayed for much beyond those things, except for Stan, the homeless guy he befriended during outreaches. Chris had prayed for him for a while. Besides that, his prayers were mostly limited to himself and what he wanted to get out of life.

All of a sudden, Chris felt sick to his stomach. His mind raced to a question he didn't want to answer: *Have my prayers been this self-centered for so long?*

Lesson 30 Questions: (The suggested answers are on page 51 in the *Answer Key.*)

1. What was Sarah concerned about as they prayed in a group?

   _____

   _____

2. Though Jessica's prayers were not wrong, did they focus on her kingdom or God's kingdom, and why do you think that was?

   _____

   _____

3. Name what was "God-centered" in Sarah's prayer and what was "Sarah-centered."

   _____

   _____

4. Most of the prayers that were prayed in this story weren't incorrect, but they were incomplete. Explain what this means.

   _____

   _____

Oh Lord, I need to pass this quiz.

QUIZ!

1. Cats are absolutely willing to pay whatever price it takes to get to know God's Word, just like the Chinese.

    A. True

    B. False [587]

2. Chinese believers who live for the glory of God ask

    A. that the persecution not stop, but that they be strong through the persecution.

    B. that the persecution would stop.

    C. that God would end the Chinese government.

    D. None of the above. [588]

3. Most Cat prayers are focused on

    A. advancing God's kingdom.

    B. advancing their kingdom.

    C. themselves.

    D. God's glory. [589]

4. Cats assume that God's glory will be revealed in their lives through

    A. getting lots of things.

    B. eliminating trouble from their lives.

    C. having a safe, soft comfortable life.

    D. All of the above. [590]

5. Dogs say, "If suffering is going to bring you more glory, then Lord, bring it on for your name's sake."

    A. True

    B. False [591]

6. According to Hebrews 12:5,6, a sign that God loves us will be that we are

    A. disciplined.

    B. cared for.

    C. gives a car to.

    D. None of the above. [592]

7. The lamb's broken leg story tells us that

    A. God wants to bless us.

    B. God may hurt us for our own good.

    C. God will pursue us to do good even when we go astray.

    D. None of the above. [593]

8. God allows tragic things to happen to His children to expand His kingdom.

    A. True

    B. False [594]

9. Which of the following does God use for His glory?

    A. Good

    B. Evil [595]

10. Cat Christians are concerned for God's glory and their comfort.

    A. True

    B. False [596]

PERSONAL APPLICATION

What are you going to do differently as a result of what you've learned? **Go to the end of your workbook and write it in for Lesson 30.** [597]

Free Day. No optional work!

LESSON 31

CHECK WHICH CIRCLE BEST REPRESENTS YOUR LIFE TODAY:

☐   ☐   ☐

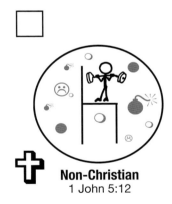

Non-Christian
1 John 5:12

Savior and Lord
Galations 5: 22-23

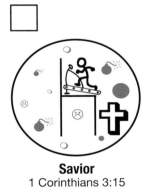

Savior
1 Corinthians 3:15

Since my last lesson,
I have practiced
Spiritual Breathing:

☐ 20⁺ Times

☐ 11 - 19 Times

☐ 6 - 10 Times

☐ 0 - 5 Times

READING ASSIGNMENT

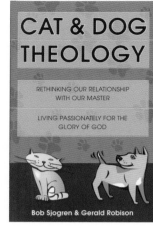

CAT & DOG THEOLOGY

RETHINKING OUR RELATIONSHIP WITH OUR MASTER

LIVING PASSIONATELY FOR THE GLORY OF GOD

Bob Sjogren & Gerald Robison

Start chapter 9 on page 101 and read to the bottom of page 105 and stop when you see the words "Cats so often miss the glory of God..." which begins the last paragraph.

Questions to answer from the reading assignment:

1. Do you think the short-term missionaries would ever have dreamed that they were going to become slaves serving God?

   Circle One: Yes   No   [598]

2. If you knew beforehand that you were going to become a slave, would you still agree to go on a short-term assignment?

   Circle One: Yes   No   [599]

3. Explain the analogy of the $100 bill and how that can help us understand God's glory in a better way.

   _____

   _____

   _____

   _____

   _____
   [600]

4. A Dog's goal is to seek to shine the glory of God through any situation in life, even if it is very _____ —— like becoming slaves to guerrilla forces. [601]

5. Define what the authors mean by "potential glory."

   _____

   _____

   _____

   _____

   _____
   [602]

6. The authors say that when the glory that could have been given to God "evaporates" in front of us, it is the same as "_____ God." [603]

7. Potential glory is most often lost through hard and difficult times. Why?

_____

_____ [604]

8. Name two ways in which God was glorified through the Columbine shootings:

_____

_____

_____

_____ [605]

9. Name two ways in which God was glorified through the shootings in the Baptist church in Fort Worth, Texas:

_____

_____

_____

_____ [606]

10. Though Satan may throw something at us in life that looks tragic, God is completely sovereign and has allowed it into our lives for His _____. [607]

1. Read Acts 4:32 – 5:11.

2. What were the believers doing in verse 32?

BIBLE STUDY!

_____

_____

_____

_____ [608]

3. What did some of the believers do in verses 34 and 35 in order to meet the needs of the church?

_____

_____ 609

4. Did they do this voluntarily or involuntarily? _____ 610

5. Why does it bring God glory when a person voluntarily sells their house and gives the money to others?

_____

_____ 611

6. Where do you think the people slept who had sold their homes?

_____

_____ 612

7. How did people view those who sold their homes to give money to the poor?

_____

_____ 613

8. What do you think were Ananias and Sapphira's motivation in selling their house?

_____

_____ 614

9. Let's assume (the text does not say) that they withheld 30% of the money they got for the house. In the author's terms, Ananias and Sapphira gave God _____ % of the glory He could have had. 615

10. But at the same time, they robbed God of _____ % of His glory. 616

11. Ananias and Sapphira would be called many words today, one of them would be "hypocrites." One definition of a Christian hypocrite is one who is _____ God of His _____ glory. 617

LESSON 32

CHECK WHICH CIRCLE BEST REPRESENTS YOUR LIFE TODAY:

☐   ☐   ☐

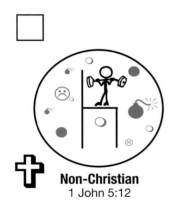

Non-Christian
1 John 5:12

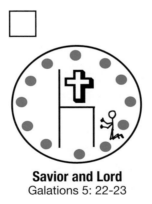

Savior and Lord
Galations 5: 22-23

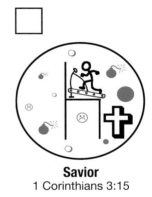

Savior
1 Corinthians 3:15

Since my last lesson,
I have practiced
Spiritual Breathing:

☐ 20⁺ Times
☐ 11 - 19 Times
☐ 6 - 10 Times
☐ 0 - 5 Times

READING ASSIGNMENT

CAT & DOG THEOLOGY

RETHINKING OUR RELATIONSHIP
WITH OUR MASTER

LIVING PASSIONATELY FOR THE
GLORY OF GOD

Bob Sjogren & Gerald Robison

Start at the last paragraph on page 105 and finish out the chapter (page 110).

Questions to answer from the reading assignment:

1. Cats so often miss the glory of God because they are so focused on what _____ get out of it and not what _____ gets out of it. [618]

2. Figure seven on page 106 can be summarized by the words, "The _____ it gets, the _____ glory goes to God." [619]

3. The greater the degree of _____, the greater the _____ for giving our Father glory. [620]

4. Write down what Dogs don't do when they see difficulty coming their way.

   _____

   _____ [621]

5. What do Dogs see when those difficult times come?

   _____

   _____ [622]

6. What does a Cat cry out when those difficult times come into their lives and don't leave?

   _____

   _____ [623]

7. Cats believe that if they are not being _____, then they have no reason to be giving God _____. [624]

8. What can happen in a Cat's attitude toward God if they don't see the potential glory in the difficult times?

   _____

   _____ [625]

9. Explain a Cat and Dog's view of getting a flat tire late at night.

Cat: _____

_____ 626

Dog: _____

_____ 627

10. Describe why the woman killed herself after her daughter became a quadriplegic and tell of the potential glory that was lost.

_____

_____

_____

_____ 628

11. Explain how Cats and Dogs view life differently when the tough times come.

_____

_____

_____

_____ 629

1. Read Exodus 5.

2. The Lord didn't ask Moses to speak to a mayor of a city or to a "Senator" of the nation, who was Moses to address and what was his position?

_____

_____

_____

_____ 630

BIBLE STUDY!

3. When God calls you to do something, you usually think it is for a purpose and there will be results. What was the first response Moses got?

_____

_____
631

4. From Pharaoh's response, it sounds like God had "zero" reputation in both his eyes and in the nation of Egypt. Why do you think God brought about the ten plagues?

_____

_____
632

5. What result did Moses' first conversation with the Pharaoh have on the Hebrew people?

_____

_____
633

6. Do you think the Hebrew people saw this as a tremendous opportunity to bring God glory?

   Circle One: Yes   No   634

7. How did Moses respond to God after the first encounter with the Pharaoh went so wrong (verse 22)?

_____

_____
635

8. Read Exodus 6:1-12.

9. In verse 12, do you think Moses saw this as a tremendous opportunity for glory?

   Circle One: Yes   No   636

10. Even though Moses started out not seeing the big picture, God still used Him to reveal His glory and to establish his reputation around the earth. How does Daniel 9:15 (written 800 years later) confirm this?

_____

_____
637

LESSON 33

CHECK WHICH CIRCLE BEST REPRESENTS YOUR LIFE TODAY:

☐   ☐   ☐

Non-Christian
1 John 5:12

Savior and Lord
Galations 5: 22-23

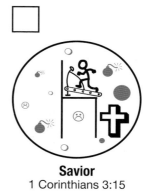

Savior
1 Corinthians 3:15

Since my last lesson,
I have practiced
Spiritual Breathing:

☐ 20⁺ Times

☐ 11 - 19 Times

☐ 6 - 10 Times

☐ 0 - 5 Times

CARTOON

Lord, why did You let this happen?

OK Lord, You allowed this to happen for Your glory. I'm going to trust You through this for Your name's sake.

Crisis Management

1. Explain the Cat's attitude and why they are like this.

_____
_____
_____
_____
_____
_____
_____
_____
_____
638

2. Explain in your own words how Dogs see a crisis.

_____
_____
639

CHRIS and SARAH

God seemed to be answering Sarah's prayers, and life could hardly get better.

Joining the after-school Bible Study was one of the best choices she had made. Not only was it inspiring her to maybe start having Bible study

and prayer times at home, but most importantly it provided the perfect opportunity for her to get to know Bryan better.

She had been shy at first. Unlike some of her friends from church whom she had known since she was little, Bryan was a new friend, and she had liked him for over a year. Fortunately, she was almost positive he liked her as well. They hung out before and after school and had long conversations via Facebook and text. A few times, he put his arm around her while they walked down the hall to class.

Sarah knew people were talking about them. Bryan was a popular junior at school, and she could hardly believe he had even noticed her. As long as her parents didn't find out, she'd be okay. It's not that she and Bryan were dating—talking, maybe, but Sarah wasn't even sure about that. What she was sure about was the fact that she wasn't allowed to date until she turned 16. However, she had a feeling her mom and dad still wouldn't approve of Bryan even then.

One day, while thinking about Bryan, she updated her Facebook status with, "God's amazing. He's blessing me so much right now."

She was afraid to say anything too specific, just in case. Besides, Sarah really felt this was God's will. After all, he went to her church. They had become friends through youth group and the Bible Study at school. They weren't doing anything wrong.

One evening at youth group, Bryan motioned for her to sit with him. Sarah almost always sat with her friends a few rows back. She didn't know what to do, but when she caught Jessica's eye, Jessica had seen everything and encouraged her to do it—grinning from ear to ear.

Sitting next to him felt so right, his arm resting casually on the back of her chair. Sarah had trouble focusing on the message until Pastor Jake showed a video near the end of the night.

The images brought Sarah rocketing back to reality: photos of people living in boxes, carrying everything they owned in battered sacks; an elderly woman pushing a cart loaded with junk; a short interview with a man who had lived on the streets for 25 years.

The video stirred something in Sarah. She wasn't sure if it was shock, fear, or compassion. Fidgeting in her seat, she looked at the floor and wished for the video to finish quickly.

"Alright guys," Jake said after the video. "Next weekend is Thanksgiving. We'll be gathered with our friends and families, eating more food than we eat all year around -"

The students laughed.

"- and there's nothing wrong with that. God has blessed us, and that's what Thanksgiving is all about: thanking Him for everything He's given. But next weekend I want to challenge you to thank Him in a new way."

He explained that the evening before Thanksgiving their church was serving a feast—a huge turkey dinner to the homeless in their city. He enthusiastically invited all the students who were staying in town to be there.

On the way home, Chris asked Sarah, "So, what did you think?"

"Hmm – what?" Sarah was startled out of her daydream about someone's blue eyes, "Oh, you mean the message? It was good, I guess."

She felt a twinge of guilt that she couldn't remember any of it. Meanwhile, Chris seemed to sense she was only half-listening.

"I think I'm gonna do the homeless dinner. Wanna come?" he pushed.

"Hm? Oh, um, I don't think so."

"Why not?"

"Why do you want me to come?" she asked defensively.

Chris sighed. He knew Sarah had a crush on Bryan, and he could tell she was having trouble thinking about anything else these days. The homeless dinner could be really good for her.

"I just think it would be cool to do. You know, like Jake said, as a new way to thank God."

"Isn't Thanksgiving about family? Besides, I don't know who will be there."

Opening her phone, Sarah pretended to text to avoid the conversation.

"You mean you don't know if Jessica will be there? Or Bryan?"

Sarah's head jerked up, "What do you mean?" she snapped.

Oh, now I have her attention, Chris thought, annoyed.

"You know what I mean. Your friends don't need to be there for you to have a good time. It's about blessing other people, not being with someone you're 'talking' to."

"I don't want to talk to you anymore!" Sarah retorted.

Chris later realized the conversation could've gone better if he had stopped at the words "good time."

Instead, Sarah was embarrassed and angry that Chris had noticed how much she

liked Bryan. Sighing, she put her phone down and reaffirmed that her relationship with Bryan was neutral.

"We're just friends, Chris. Keep out of my business."

Chris angrily muttered, "I don't think so. Anyone with eyes can see what's going on."

They fought the rest of the way home.

When Sarah got to her bedroom she threw herself on her bed and started tweeting and texting her friends about what a jerk her brother was.

Lesson 33 Questions: (The suggested answers are on page 51 in the *Answer Key*.)

1. How did Sarah define "God's blessings" in what was happening in her life?

_____

_____

2. Did Bryan's invitation to Sarah make her more God-focused or self-focused and why?

_____

_____

3. What did Chris do that was Dogish? What did he also do that was Catish?

_____

_____

4. Would you say Sarah used Social Media to make God look famous or to draw people's attention to herself?

_____

_____

Oh Lord, I need to pass this quiz.

QUIZ!

1. God didn't know what He was doing when the Jesus film team became slaves in Sierra Leone.
    - A. True
    - B. False [640]

2. If Christians knew beforehand that they were going to become slaves going out on a mission trip, they should
    - A. forget about going.
    - B. ask their pastor.
    - C. go through with it.
    - D. None of the above. [641]

3. Revealing God's glory can, at times, be
    - A. difficult.
    - B. messy.
    - C. hard.
    - D. All of the above. [642]

4. It is quite possible for Christians to
    - A. rob God of his glory.
    - B. not realize that potential glory is all around them.
    - C. miss revealing God's glory in amazing ways.
    - D. All of the above. [643]

5. When Satan throws something at us that looks tragic,
    - A. God is caught by surprise.
    - B. God will use it for His glory.
    - C. God has allowed it.
    - D. All of the above. [644]

6. Cats miss the glory of God so many times because

    A. they are so focused on themselves.

    B. they are only worried about what they can get out of it.

    C. they are not concerned about God's glory.

    D. they are seeking God's glory. [645]

7. In many cases, the greater degree of difficulty in life, the greater potential for giving our Father glory.

    A. True

    B. False [646]

8. When Dogs see difficulty coming at them, they run toward it.

    A. True

    B. False [647]

9. Cats usually run away from difficult times for the glory of God.

    A. True

    B. False [648]

10. If a Cat gets into a difficult situation where there is no resolution, they most likely

    A. wait patiently for the glory of God to be revealed.

    B. get angry with God.

    C. Both A and B

    D. None of the above. [649]

What are you going to do differently as a result of what you've learned? **Go to the end of your workbook and write it in for Lesson 33.** [650]

PERSONAL APPLICATION

Free Day. No optional work!

CAUTION! The more your life is changed, the easier it is to spot Cat behavior in those around you. **Please don't ever use this material to judge others.** ("Oh, they are just a bunch of Cats.") Once we start judging others, we too are acting like Cats. **Use this material to encourage yourself and others to live for God's glory.**

LESSON 34

CHECK WHICH CIRCLE BEST REPRESENTS YOUR LIFE TODAY:

☐   ☐   ☐

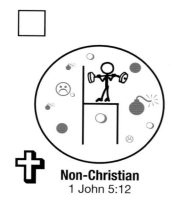

Non-Christian
1 John 5:12

Savior and Lord
Galations 5: 22-23

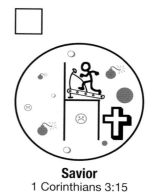

Savior
1 Corinthians 3:15

Since my last lesson,
I have practiced
Spiritual Breathing:

☐ 20⁺ Times

☐ 11 - 19 Times

☐ 6 - 10 Times

☐ 0 - 5 Times

READING ASSIGNMENT

CAT & DOG THEOLOGY

RETHINKING OUR RELATIONSHIP WITH OUR MASTER

LIVING PASSIONATELY FOR THE GLORY OF GOD

Bob Sjogren & Gerald Robison

Start reading chapter 10 (page 111) and finish the chapter (page 116).

Questions to answer from the reading assignment:

1. Cats live the Christian life by living out "proper etiquette". They are basically thanking God for all He's done for them and _____ the favor. [651]

2. Because of this, Cats are trying to live out the Christian life _____ _____ _____ as best they can. Because of this, Cats don't grow to their _____ _____. [652]

3. "Returning the favor" takes away the _____ of the Christian life. [653]

4. Explain the essence of a "Help Me" prayer explaining who receives the credit.

   _____

   _____

   _____

   _____ [654]

   _____

5. When Christ says we can do "nothing" apart from Him, what is He really saying?

   _____ [655]

   _____

6. If you have been struggling to live 70% of the Christian life in your own power and strength, you have _____ God to bring about only 30% of the _____ in your life. 70% of the potential spiritual growth in your life _____ _____. [656]

7. What key verse does the concept of "Cause Me" prayers come from and what are the key words in the King James Version?

   _____

   _____ [657]

   _____

8. "Cause Me" prayers allow God to get _____% of the glory. [658]

9. Break down the verse of Colossians 1:29:

   A. "I labor" means: _____

   _____

   _____

   _____ 659

   B. "His energy" means: _____

   _____ 660

10. What was the prayer that Bob still prays based on Deuteronomy 30:6?

   _____

   _____ 661

11. How does the "Cause Me" prayer apply to Bob's marriage?

   _____

   _____ 662

12. Christians usually tend to rely on their _____ strength when they are in a routine in life; when they've done what they are doing a thousand times before. It is at this point when they _____ trust in God, but trust in their own efforts. 663

13. What is a Dog's response to God after He (God) has you over for dinner?

   _____

   _____ 664

14. In America, you would wear out your welcome if you did that to a friend. But that doesn't happen with God. Because the more you come to God, the more _____ He gets! 665

15. Look up Ezra 6:22 and Psalm 21:6 in the ESV and comment on how they tie in with "Cause Me" prayers and joy.*

   _____

   _____

*This answer is missing in the Answer Key. To see the correct answer, please go to the website (www.CatandDogTheology.org) and click on the red box: "Click Here For Updates And Corrections" to find the answer.

BIBLE STUDY!

1. In 1 Corinthians 3:1-3, Paul speaks about "brethren" (a term Paul usually used to address Christians) as being "worldly" (NIV) or "fleshly" (ESV.) These are people who seemed to be true believers, but were living out the Christian life. Do you think there were Jews like that back in the O.T. days?

    Circle One: Yes   No   [666]

2. Read Psalm 50:1-15.

3. What does God say He is going to do to them in verse 7?

    _____ [667]

4. In verse 8, what were the Jews doing?

    _____

    _____ [668]

5. Were these Jews looking very spiritual?

    Circle One: Yes   No   [669]

6. What can we learn from someone involved in lots of spiritual activity?

    A. They are definitely spiritual.

    B. They are trying to be spiritual.

    C. We should encourage them but check up on what they're doing at the same time.

    D. All of the above. [670]

7. In verses 9-13, what does God say He does not need?

    _____

    _____ [671]

8. What does the first half of verse 14 tell you they didn't seem to be doing?

_____

_____ 672

9. What does the second half of verse 14 seem to indicate that they were not doing?

_____

_____ 673

10. God asked the Jews back in those days who were "playing games with God" to do three things. List them.

A ._____ 674

B. _____ 675

C. _____ 676

11. Note that last one, "Call upon Him in the day of trouble." God says two things will happen when we call upon him in the day of trouble. List them:

A. _____ 677

B. _____ 678

12. "Honoring God" is another way to say "_____ God." 679

13. God is saying, "When you come to Me (breakfast, lunch, dinner, breakfast, lunch dinner, etc) you are bringing Me glory. You honor Me, you glorify Me when you come to me with problems. Therefore, come to me with _____ the situations you face in life. 680

LESSON 35

CHECK WHICH CIRCLE BEST REPRESENTS YOUR LIFE TODAY:

☐   ☐   ☐

Non-Christian
1 John 5:12

Savior and Lord
Galations 5: 22-23

Savior
1 Corinthians 3:15

Since my last lesson,
I have practiced
Spiritual Breathing:

☐ 20⁺ Times

☐ 11 - 19 Times

☐ 6 - 10 Times

☐ 0 - 5 Times

READING ASSIGNMENT

CAT & DOG THEOLOGY

RETHINKING OUR RELATIONSHIP WITH OUR MASTER

LIVING PASSIONATELY FOR THE GLORY OF GOD

Bob Sjogren & Gerald Robison

Start chapter 11 (page 117) and finish out the chapter (page 121).

Questions to answer from the reading assignment:

1. The seventy years we have here on earth are _____ compared to eternity. [681]

2. Yet, Cats _____ the majority of their time, energy, and money on making these seventy years as safe, happy and comfortable as possible. They are not at all concerned for _____ (except to get there!) [682]

3. To a Dog, true life begins after you _____. [683]

4. Explain the author's attempt at comparing this life to trying out for a team.

_____

_____

_____

_____ [684]

5. Write a brief summary in your own words of the following verses, Psalm 102:11, 144:4 and 103:15.

_____

_____ [685]

6. How does 1 Peter 2:11 say we should live on this earth?

[686]

_____

7. In the 1950s, Jim Elliot was a famous missionary in South America who was killed by the Auca Indians—the very people he was seeking to bring to Christ. Fill in his quote:

"He is no fool… _____

_____ " [687]

8. Rewrite Jim Elliot's quote in your own words.

_____

_____ 688

9. Write Matthew 6:19-20 in your own words below.

_____

_____ 689

10. What did the authors want you to learn about God's promises from the book of Job?

_____

_____ 690

11. How does Hebrews 11:13 agree or disagree with what the authors are trying to teach us from the book of Job?

_____

_____ 691

12. Do the authors say that it is wrong to enjoy this life?

Circle One: Yes   No   692

BIBLE STUDY!

1. Read James 4:13-17.
2. What is James basically saying is wrong in verse 13?

_____

_____

_____

_____ 693

3. Once we realize how simple it is to expect future things to happen without considering God, it becomes a bit embarrassing. List three things you think are going to happen tomorrow whether God acts or not:

_____

_____
                                                                                      694
_____

4. According to verse 14, do we really know that these things are going to happen?
   Circle One: Yes   No   695

5. Why do you think that he compared our lives to a mist? What is characteristic of a mist?

_____
                                                                                      696
_____

6. With our lives being like a mist, it means that we could die (circle the correct one[s])

   A. Tomorrow

   B. Next week

   C. Next year

   D. 10 years from now

   E. 50 years from now   697

7. Do you think the kids who were killed at Columbine High School (page 104 in *Cat and Dog Theology* book) were thinking about dying the day they went to school?

   Circle One: Yes   No   698

8. The text says that assuming we are going to do certain things in the next day or week or year is in reality _____ . 699

9. James 4, verse 16 tell us that this arrogance is _____. 700

10. What should we commonly be saying (either out loud or in our hearts) when someone says "See you tomorrow?"

_____
                                                                                      701
_____

LESSON 36

CHECK WHICH CIRCLE BEST REPRESENTS YOUR LIFE TODAY:

☐   ☐   ☐

Non-Christian
1 John 5:12

Savior and Lord
Galations 5: 22-23

Savior
1 Corinthians 3:15

Since my last lesson,
I have practiced
Spiritual Breathing:

☐ 20+ Times
☐ 11 - 19 Times
☐ 6 - 10 Times
☐ 0 - 5 Times

CARTOON

God-Centered Marriages

People-Centered Marriages

1. How could a Cat's desire for a "happy marriage" contradict a "holy marriage?"

_____

_____

_____
702

2. How could a Dog's desire for a holy marriage contradict a "happy marriage?"

_____

_____

_____
703

CHRIS and SARAH

Sarah did end up feeding the homeless at the Thanksgiving dinner. Her dad made her go after Chris told him about the opportunity the youth had. While she thought she would hate it, the following week she felt good about herself. She hadn't been mugged, and the homeless people weren't as dirty and scary as they were in the video – except the guy who spoke really loud and clearly didn't remember where he was or what he was doing. Or maybe even who he was. It gave Sarah the creeps.

One evening, Sarah borrowed her father's laptop once again and posted photos on Facebook of herself at the homeless Thanksgiving outreach. Bryan messaged her: "Hey, u up?"

She smiled. He was a night owl, too. Hopefully her dad wouldn't mind her having it a little longer. "Yeah, what's up?"

"Nice photos – is that guy wearing a fur coat or was his hair really that long?"

She smiled. She loved flirting and being flirted with. Their conversation lasted past midnight, and she fell asleep with her head in her arms next to her dad's laptop.

The next morning, Sarah dragged herself to Spanish class. Her mom wouldn't let her drink coffee yet, and while Sarah usually thought that was dumb, today she was especially mad about it. She had stayed up way too late talking to Bryan.

As soon as she walked into class, Sarah sensed something was wrong. Then she saw the white board at the front of class, and her stomach sank. The test.

Mr. Chase had reminded them about it every day this week, and she had planned to study for it last night before she went to bed. *Boys—they're worth all the trouble they give you. Oh well…* she thought to herself.

Sarah started praying right away, thanking God that He was going to help her through this test. She always prayed before tests. It was her way of showing her dependence upon God.

Nevertheless, a nudge in her spirit made her feel as if there was something wrong. She paused. If this whole Bryan thing was really God's will, wouldn't God help her with this test? Wasn't Sarah just being a good friend last night, and hadn't they even talked a lot about the homeless ministry? Bryan had never tried it before, and he was curious. In the future, they may even serve together. Surely that would please God.

Of course He could help her ace this test. God could do anything, and besides the big fight with Chris, Sarah felt like she'd been especially good lately – she had even tried quiet times a few days a week. That had to count for something. Didn't Pastor Jake say God blesses those He loves? Sarah knew God loved her.

Lord, please help me, she prayed as Mr. Chase handed out the test. While she was at it, she added, and please bless me with Bryan. I really want us to be together.

A few days later, her test results came back. She hadn't expected to pass with flying colors, although she had entertained the idea – *wasn't God able to do anything?*

What she didn't expect was a D-.

Mr. Chase asked to speak with her after class. Sarah was normally a fastidious student, and the D- minus had him concerned. He asked if there was a problem with her test, if she had found trouble with the material, etc. When she said no, he asked if everything was okay at home.

"Yes, sir. Everything's fine at home. We're all fine." Sarah didn't want to talk about how she and her mother were at each other's throats most of the time. That was the whole reason why she was in a private school. However, Mr. Chase didn't need to know that.

"Did you study for the test?"

Now what should she do? She didn't want to tell him about Bryan and about staying up all night flirting. "Um, a little, but I guess I could have studied a bit more," she said sheepishly.

"Yes, I could agree with you on that one. Well, since everything seems to be all right I'll let this one slide, though the grade still stands. Be better prepared on your next test. Okay, young lady?"

"Yes, sir," Sarah left in a daze. She had just had a conversation with her Spanish teacher, but she had hardly listened to a word. All she could think was how much God had let her down. This had been his chance to show her how great he was, how he an-

swered prayers. Why didn't he answer hers? Did he even care about her grades? Up until now, she had assumed he did. Obviously, she had been wrong.

Frustrated, she pulled out her phone. Students weren't allowed to use phones during school hours, but she'd become more reckless about sneaking it out lately. Everyone else did, so why shouldn't she? Still fuming about the test, she tweeted, "What's the point of praying if God doesn't even listen?"

Lesson 36 Questions: (The suggested answers are on page 52 in the *Answer Key*.)

1. Why did Sarah assume God would help her with the test?

   _____

   _____

2. What was Sarah's understanding of God's blessing at this point?

   _____

   _____

3. God's primary way of blessing us is in our relationship with Him. How did Sarah's expectation of God's blessing differ?

   _____

   _____

4. What was God more worried about, Sarah's grades or her attitude toward Him— and how did she do?

   _____

   _____

Oh Lord, I need to pass this quiz.

QUIZ!

1. Many Cat Christians are trying to say "Thanks" to God for all He's done for them (return God's favor) by
    A. living a good life.
    B. trying to please God in what they do.
    C. doing nothing.
    D. playing the "Christian game." [704]

2. Most Cats never grow to their full potential because they are trying to live most of the Christian life in their own power and strength.
    A. True
    B. False [705]

3. "Cause Me" prayers are
    A. very biblical.
    B. crazy.
    C. giving God 100% of the glory.
    D. unbiblical. [706]

4. If we are praying "Cause Me" prayers, we can sit on the couch all day because everything is up to God.
    A. True
    B. False [707]

5. God even wants us to pray
    A. "Lord, cause me to love you. I can't do it in my own power or strength."
    B. "Lord, cause me to be holy."
    C. "Lord, cause me to hunger for your word."
    D. "Lord, cause me to glorify you in everything I do, say and think." [708]

6. Coming to God with all of our problems (time and time again)
    A. burdens God.
    B. is a pain to God.
    C. honors God.
    D. glorifies God. [709]

7. According to this lesson, living approximately 90 years on this earth is
    A. an extremely long time.
    B. nothing compared to eternity.
    C. a curse. [710]

8. Based on this chapter, the authors want you to think that in a very real way
    A. life begins at birth.
    B. life begins after you die.
    C. life begins when you finish high school.
    D. life begins when you get married. [711]

9. You are a fool to give up what you have now for future eternal rewards.
    A. True
    B. False [712]

10. From the book of Job, we learn that God's promises will always be fulfilled
    A. here on this earth.
    B. in the context of eternity.
    C. when there are "na-sayers." [713]

PERSONAL APPLICATION

What are you going to do differently as a result of what you've learned? **Go to the end of your workbook and write it in for Lesson 36.** [714]

Free Day. No optional work!

OPTIONAL LESSON

LESSON 37

CHECK WHICH CIRCLE BEST REPRESENTS YOUR LIFE TODAY:

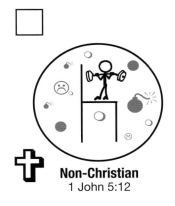

Non-Christian
1 John 5:12

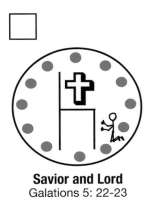

Savior and Lord
Galations 5: 22-23

Savior
1 Corinthians 3:15

Since my last lesson,
I have practiced
Spiritual Breathing:

☐ 20+ Times
☐ 11 - 19 Times
☐ 6 - 10 Times
☐ 0 - 5 Times

READING ASSIGNMENT

CAT & DOG THEOLOGY

RETHINKING OUR RELATIONSHIP
WITH OUR MASTER

LIVING PASSIONATELY FOR THE
GLORY OF GOD

Bob Sjogren & Gerald Robison

Start reading at the top of page 123 to the bottom of page 140 where you see the words "Selective Theology."

Questions to answer from the reading assignment:

1. Describe how the authors say we have violated Deuteronomy 4:2.

_____

_____ 715

2. It is possible to _____ on Cat Theology and have your Christianity become _____.716

3. List the #1 priority of a Cat which is usually reflected in most prayer requests in Church and Sunday Schools.

_____

_____ 717

4. When Cats are praying for their lives and health, they rarely mention _____ _____.718

5. According to the authors, why would "Health and Wealth Theology" (Prosperity Theology) be wrong?

_____

_____ 719

6. List the second priority of a Cat.

_____

_____ 720

7. What is one of the first things Cats will ask themselves when challenged to do missions overseas? It's not, "Is this God's will" but rather…

_____ 721

8. There is nothing wrong with a comfortable lifestyle and enjoying the fruits of one's labor _____ it becomes a higher priority than the glory of God. [722]

9. List the fourth priority of a Cat:

_____

_____ [723]

10. What was wrong with the pastor's outlook on life when he would not let his people become involved in reaching out to the 75 different language groups in a single apartment complex on Sunday morning?

_____

_____ [724]

11. Way on down the list of priorities for a Cat is the _____ of _____ and _____ _____. Neither are a priority in the life of a Cat. [725]

12. List the first thought and priority of a Dog.

_____

_____ [726]

13. When a Dog is faced with a life-threatening disease (like cancer), what will a Dog's prayer sound like?

_____

_____ [727]

14. When it comes to missions, Dogs realize that God's _____ glory will shine when all nations are reached! Therefore they make it a very _____ priority. [728]

BIBLE STUDY!

1. To see a total "Dog" in the Old Testament, read 1 Samuel 13:1 - 14:20.

2. Who were the Israelites fighting?

_____

_____ 729

3. The Philistine army were as numerous as the _____ on the

_____. 730

4. Saul's army went from 3,000 fighting men down to 600. Why do you think they were not attacking?

_____

_____ 731

5. Circle which answer you think best describes why Jonathan left "quietly".

    A. It slipped his mind and he forgot to tell anyone.

    B. He knew his Father was taking a nap.

    C. He felt that they would have discouraged him from going.

    D. He was a rebel and wouldn't have listened to them anyhow. 732

6. In chapter 14, verse 6 (NIV), Jonathan calls the Philistines "uncircumcised fellows." What does that (and the rest of the verse) tell you about how Jonathan saw his enemies?

_____

_____

_____

_____ 733

7. What does the word "perhaps" (NIV) communicate about Jonathan's certainty on the outcome of the battle?

_____

_____ 734

8. Though he wasn't sure about the outcome, what does the rest of verse 6 tell us about what he was sure about?

_____

_____ 735

9. What would be the difference in Jonathan's strength if he had stayed at the bottom of the hill or if he had climbed to the top of the hill?

_____

_____

_____

_____ 736

10. Jonathan chose the worse of the two options as a sign that the Lord would give favor ("If they call us up hill, it is a sign the Lord has given them into our hands"). How did this choice reflect the glory of the Lord?

_____

_____

_____ 737

11. If Jonathan had been a Cat, how would the story have been different?

_____

_____

_____ 738

12. Circle which lessons we can learn from this story.

   A. Sometimes choosing the hardest of the options can bring God more glory.

   B. Dogs are more likely to be world-changers than Cats.

   C. It's good to sneak out at night and not tell your parents where you are going. 739

LESSON 38

CHECK WHICH CIRCLE BEST REPRESENTS YOUR LIFE TODAY:

☐   ☐   ☐

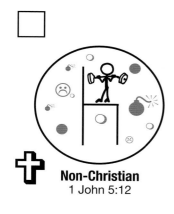

Non-Christian
1 John 5:12

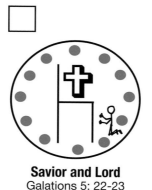

Savior and Lord
Galations 5: 22-23

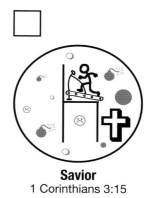

Savior
1 Corinthians 3:15

Since my last lesson,
I have practiced
Spiritual Breathing:

☐ 20+ Times
☐ 11 - 19 Times
☐ 6 - 10 Times
☐ 0 - 5 Times

READING ASSIGNMENT

Start reading at the bottom of page 140 with the words "Selective Theology" and finish out the chapter (page 142).

Questions to answer from the reading assignment:

1. The way many Cats can justify getting a divorce is based on what simple assumption?

   _____ 740

2. Note that in a Cat's reasoning for a divorce, there is no concern about how it affects God's _____. 741

3. God _____ want us happy. But it is our happiness in Him that He is concerned about, not merely our happiness _____. 742

4. When you have a people-centered theology and you ask yourself the question, "What harm is homosexuality doing?" the answer is _____. 743

5. If it doesn't _____ God, we shouldn't be doing it, no matter how _____-_____ it looks. 744

6. Explain "Annihilation Theology" in your own words.

   _____

   _____

   _____

   _____ 745

7. In Annihilation Theology, Cats focus on people and their feelings and needs. But what Cats fail to realize, is that it is not about the sins you have done, it is about the glory you have _____. 746

8. Because God's glory is _____, hell must be _____. 747

9. If hell was not _____, it would mean that God's glory is _____. 748

10. Explain universalism below.

_____

_____

_____ 749

1. Read Luke 16:19-31.

2. Who/what do the rich usually tend to trust in?

_____

_____

_____ 750

3. Since the poor can't trust in themselves and they have no money, what is the only thing left for them?

_____ 751

4. What word does the rich man use to describe his present state?

_____ 752

5. What word in verse 26 indicates how long the rich man was going to be in agony?

_____ 753

6. What does the rest of the verse say is the result?

_____

_____

_____ 754

7. How does 2 Thessalonians 1:5-10 agree with this?

_____

_____ 755

8. How does Matthew 25:41 agree with the time period of punishment?

_____

_____ 756

9. Once the rich man knew that the state he was in was going to be eternal, what did it motivate him to do?

_____

_____ 757

10. What was Abraham's reply to the rich man's argument?

_____

_____ 758

11. What does this story tell you that is common to both the rich and the poor?

_____

_____ 759

LESSON 39

CHECK WHICH CIRCLE BEST REPRESENTS YOUR LIFE TODAY:

☐

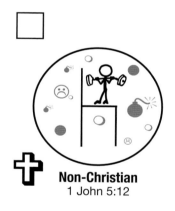

Non-Christian
1 John 5:12

☐

Savior and Lord
Galations 5: 22-23

☐

Savior
1 Corinthians 3:15

Since my last lesson,
I have practiced
Spiritual Breathing:

☐ 20+ Times
☐ 11 - 19 Times
☐ 6 - 10 Times
☐ 0 - 5 Times

1. Spend 45 minutes reviewing Lesson #1 of "YouTeach Cat and Dog Theology" titled, "Thinking Outside The Box." You are going to begin teaching this in two weeks. You may listen to the MP3 playing it from your CD. There are a couple of things to note:

A. The mp3 is not to be played in conjunction with the slides. The mp3 is only for you to learn from. Don't use it for teaching.

B. Each time you teach, you might want to teach the first half and have someone else (your mom? a friend?) teach the second half.

C. **Copy the slides to your hard drive**. Do **not** try to play it while the CD is in the CD-ROM drive. That will make it very slow.

2. Pray that:

A. God will draw those to your group that He wants to hear the message.

B. God will prepare the hearts of those who are going to come.

C. You will be totally dependent upon Him to speak through you.

D. God will speak through you mightily during this teaching time.

E. If you haven't already, call and confirm and see what friends/family can be at your teaching session.

Free Day. No optional work!

OPTIONAL LESSON

LESSON 40

CHECK WHICH CIRCLE BEST REPRESENTS YOUR LIFE TODAY:

☐

Non-Christian
1 John 5:12

☐

Savior and Lord
Galations 5: 22-23

☐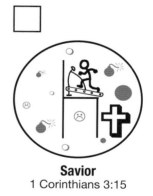

Savior
1 Corinthians 3:15

Since my last lesson,
I have practiced
Spiritual Breathing:

☐ 20⁺ Times
☐ 11 - 19 Times
☐ 6 - 10 Times
☐ 0 - 5 Times

READING ASSIGNMENT

CAT & DOG THEOLOGY

RETHINKING OUR RELATIONSHIP WITH OUR MASTER

LIVING PASSIONATELY FOR THE GLORY OF GOD

Bob Sjogren & Gerald Robison

Start reading chapter 13 (page 143) and finish out the chapter (page 149).

Questions to answer from the reading assignment:

1. Cats always _____ life to be _____. [760]

2. Explain what God did to Jabez.

_____

_____

_____ [761]

3. Summarize what happened to the little girl in 2 Kings 5.

_____

_____

_____

_____ [762]

4. Which do you think was the bigger miracle, Naaman's healing of leprosy, or the young girl's heart attitude and why?

_____

_____

_____ [763]

5. Summarize what happened to Stephen.

_____

_____ [764]

6. If you, like Stephen (Acts 6:8), want to be _____ of God's power and grace, it makes you a perfect candidate for being _____. [765]

7. Asking "Which life was God fair to?" is the _____ question. Life was never designed to be _____. [766]

8. Life was _____ to be a series of opportunities (events) to point to and radiate _____ _____ . [767]

9. R. C. Sproul says, "For the Christian, every _____ is ultimately a
_____ or God is a _____." [768]

10. How does Jeremiah 32:40 agree or disagree with this?

_____

_____

_____ [769]

1. Read Habakkuk 1:1-11.

2. Habakkuk was a prophet who lived about 700 years before Christ. He lived during a time when there was great injustice—when the unrighteous outnumbered the righteous. What does verse 2 tell you that Habakkuk was doing?

_____

_____ [770]

3. Did Habakkuk feel that God was answering his prayer?

_____ [771]

4. List the problems that Habakkuk complains about.

_____

_____

_____

_____ [772]

5. Does it look good or bad for God and His ways?

Circle One: Good   Bad   [773]

6. In verses 5-11, God responds. He tells Habakkuk, not to look to his own people for the answer, but rather to look for the answer by looking at the _____. [774]

7. God was going to use the _____ to bring about the answer. [775]

8. Do you think Habakkuk considered the Babylonians better or worse than his own people the Jews?

Circle One: Better   Worse   [776]

9. In verses 5-11, God speaks about how the Babylonians are a fierce army that will sweep over the whole earth. What do you think God is basically saying to Habakkuk?

_____

_____ [777]

10. Habakkuk is crying out for help and God says, "OK, you want help? I gotcha covered. I'm going to have the Babylonians go and conquer your people." Do you think that was the answer Habakkuk was looking for?

Circle One: Yes   No   [778]

11. A lesson we can learn from this first half of chapter one is that sometimes God does _____ answer our prayers in the way we would like. [779]

12. A simple application of the first half of Habakkuk chapter one is that if we are crying out to God because America has turned away from God (separating the Church from the State, killing the unborn children, etc.), God may hear our prayers and instead of bringing revival, He may have another nation (such as China) go to war with us, _____, and then we as a nation may do some great repentance and get our act right with the Lord. [780]

LESSON 41

CHECK WHICH CIRCLE BEST REPRESENTS YOUR LIFE TODAY:

☐   ☐   ☐

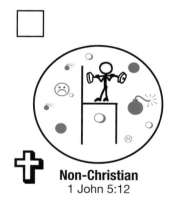

Non-Christian
1 John 5:12

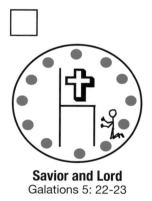

Savior and Lord
Galations 5: 22-23

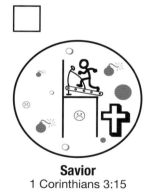

Savior
1 Corinthians 3:15

Since my last lesson,
I have practiced
Spiritual Breathing:

☐ 20+ Times
☐ 11 - 19 Times
☐ 6 - 10 Times
☐ 0 - 5 Times

READING ASSIGNMENT

CAT & DOG THEOLOGY

RETHINKING OUR RELATIONSHIP WITH OUR MASTER

LIVING PASSIONATELY FOR THE GLORY OF GOD

Bob Sjogren & Gerald Robison

Begin reading chapter 14 (page 151) and end at the top of page 155 where it says "Evangelical Humanism."

Questions to answer from the reading assignment:

1. Write a simple definition of humanism.

_____

_____ 781

2. Humanism has so permeated our culture, that it has _____
_____ into our Christianity creating two types of
_____ _____. 782

3. Liberal Humanism says the chief end of Christianity is the _____ of
_____ while here on the earth. 783

4. Write down what a humanist would say about each of the following entities:
   A. Christ's death: _____

   _____

   B. God's goodness: _____

   _____

   C. The Angels: _____

   _____

   D. The Church: _____

   _____ 784

5. What was good and what was bad about how the mother got her sons to read the Bible on the top of page 153?

   _____

   _____

   _____

   _____ 785

6. What are the authors saying about why many Cat Christians give their lives to the Lord?

_____

_____ 786

7. Many Cats are saying, "Lord, give me what I want and then I will _____

_____. 787

8. Asking God for health and wealth is not necessarily wrong. But it can become wrong when the primary focus is on _____ rather than _____ and His glory.788

9. On page 154, there is a story about how church elders dealt with their pastor's wife leaving him. What was faulty with their conclusion?

_____

_____ 789

10. Is life all about being happy?

      Circle One: Yes   No   790

1. Read 1 Samuel 15.

2. What was Saul told to do by the Lord?

      BIBLE STUDY!

_____

_____

_____

_____ 791

3. What is written to show you that God was very specific in what He wanted?

_____

_____ 792

4. In verse 8, what does Saul do to the king and what should he have done?

_____

_____ 793

5. What else did King Saul do in verse 9 that was wrong?

_____

_____ 794

6. Would you call what King Saul did "partial obedience" or "full obedience"?

_____ 795

7. In verse 10-11, how does God define "partial obedience?"

_____

_____ 796

8. What is Saul's reason for keeping the sheep and cattle?

_____

_____ 797

9. Isn't it interesting to note that a "spiritual answer" can be completely
_____? 798

10. Summarize as best you can verses 22 and 23.

_____

_____

_____ 799

11. Saul gives the real reason why he allowed the animals to be kept alive. What was it?

_____

_____ 800

12. Who was Saul worried about impressing, God or people?

Circle One: God   People   801

13. How does verse 30 show that Saul is still worried about impressing people and not obeying the Lord.

_____

_____

_____

_____ 802

14. At the heart of humanism is people. Life is all about people. For Saul, as a king, life was all about impressing the people he was leading, _____ the Lord. 803

LESSON 42

CHECK WHICH CIRCLE BEST REPRESENTS YOUR LIFE TODAY:

☐   ☐   ☐

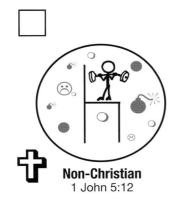

Non-Christian
1 John 5:12

Savior and Lord
Galations 5: 22-23

Savior
1 Corinthians 3:15

Since my last lesson,
I have practiced
Spiritual Breathing:

☐ 20⁺ Times
☐ 11 - 19 Times
☐ 6 - 10 Times
☐ 0 - 5 Times

1. Spend another 45 minutes reviewing Lesson #1 of "YouTeach Cat and Dog Theology" titled, "Thinking Outside The Box." Try to do it without the notes. You are going to begin teaching. Go over each slide making sure you know what to say.

Remember:

A. The mp3 is not to be played in conjunction with the slides. The mp3 is only for you to learn from. Don't use it for teaching.

B. Each time you teach, you might want to teach the first half and have someone else (your mom? a friend?) teach the second half.

C. Make sure the slides are copied to your hard drive.

2. Pray that:

A. God will draw those to your group that He wants.

B. God will prepare the hearts of those who are going to come.

C. You will be totally dependent upon Him to speak through you.

D. God will speak through you mightily during this teaching time.

3. Call and confirm and see what friends/family can be at your teaching session.

Free Day. No optional work!

OPTIONAL LESSON

LESSON 43

CHECK WHICH CIRCLE BEST REPRESENTS YOUR LIFE TODAY:

☐   ☐   ☐

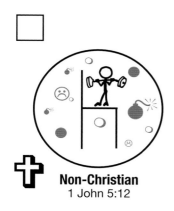

Non-Christian
1 John 5:12

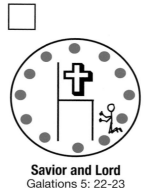

Savior and Lord
Galations 5: 22-23

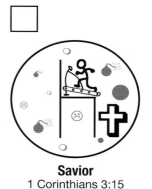

Savior
1 Corinthians 3:15

Since my last lesson,
I have practiced
Spiritual Breathing:

☐ 20⁺ Times
☐ 11 - 19 Times
☐ 6 - 10 Times
☐ 0 - 5 Times

READING ASSIGNMENT

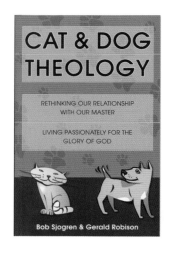

CAT & DOG THEOLOGY

RETHINKING OUR RELATIONSHIP WITH OUR MASTER

LIVING PASSIONATELY FOR THE GLORY OF GOD

Bob Sjogren & Gerald Robison

Begin reading from the top of page 155 ("Evangelical Humanism") and finish out the chapter (page 160).

Questions to answer from the reading assignment:

1. Would most evangelicals reject Liberal Humanism?

    Circle one: Yes   No   [804]

2. What does Evangelical Humanism say is the chief purpose of Christianity?

    _____

    _____ [805]

3. What do Liberal Humanists and Evangelical Humanists have in common?

    _____

    _____ [806]

4. What is the difference between the two?

    _____

    _____ [807]

5. Why would Satan want us to focus on saving people from hell as the first and fore-most thing of our lives?

    _____

    _____ [808]

6. Evangelical Humanists, many times without knowing it, motivate people into missions through _____. "People are going to go to hell _____ you step out into the mission field." [809]

7. For some Evangelical Humanists, reaching people has become an _____ in itself, not a _____ towards the overall goal of glorifying God. [810]

8. How could an Evangelical Humanistic pastor end up ruining his life while focused on saving people from hell?

_____

_____

_____

_____ 811

9. One missionary child was once reported saying, "I wish I had been born a Muslim, my father would have spent more time with me." Comment on this in light of what we're studying in this passage.

_____

_____

_____

_____ 812

10. Evangelical Humanism has put the _____ _____ on the throne. It looks so Christian, so spiritual, so good, but it offends a _____ God. 813

11. Because many Evangelical Humanists are on a _____ mission and not a _____ _____, they really don't have any _____ _____ to tell others. 814

12. Write down what a Dog says is the chief end of Christianity.

_____

_____ 815

BIBLE STUDY!

1. Read John 6.

2. In verse 26, the masses were seeking Jesus, not for who He was, but for what reason?

_____

_____ 816

3. Would these people be considered Liberal humanists or Evangelical humanists, and why?

_____

_____ 817

4. What does this tell you about why many Cats primarily seek God?

_____

_____ 818

5. If you were able to listen to a Cat's prayer life, would you find a Cat praying more about what their needs/wants are, or more about who God is?

    Circle One: Needs/Wants   Who God is   819

6. In verse 41, the same people who were so amazed at Him are now grumbling at Him. Cats can so quickly grumble when they hear things they don't like. How can this apply to Cats who switch churches multiple times in the same city?

_____

_____

_____ 820

7. Jesus gives a very difficult teaching to understand about His flesh and blood. After most of the crowd was grumbling and wanting to leave, he spoke to them again. If he had said, "Hey wait, this is just a figure of speech. Don't leave. All you'll have to do is eat some bread and drink some wine while thinking of me. That's all I meant." For whom would he be living?

821

_____

8. But instead of softening the answer in His own town's synagogue, He drills it home even harder.   As a result, many leave. Why does this show that He is focused more on His glory being revealed than the needs of people?

_____

_____

_____ 822

9. What does He then do to the twelve disciples that were closest to Him?

_____

_____ 823

10. This clearly shows that Jesus is not _____ about how many are following Him. He is willing to let them go. He completely and whole heartedly trusts in God and is focused on glorifying Him, even if it means He ends up all alone. [824]

11. If a pastor, who was a Liberal humanist, was worried about the needs of the people in his congregation, what would his messages focus primarily on?

_____

_____ 825

12. If a pastor, who was an Evangelical humanist, was focused on saving people from hell, what would just about every sermon include?

_____

_____ 826

LESSON 44

CHECK WHICH CIRCLE BEST REPRESENTS YOUR LIFE TODAY:

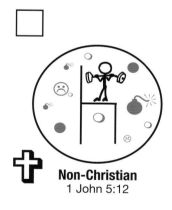

Non-Christian
1 John 5:12

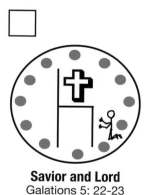

Savior and Lord
Galations 5: 22-23

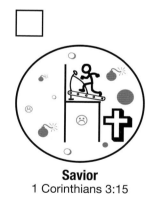

Savior
1 Corinthians 3:15

Since my last lesson,
I have practiced
Spiritual Breathing:

- ☐ 20⁺ Times
- ☐ 11 - 19 Times
- ☐ 6 - 10 Times
- ☐ 0 - 5 Times

READING ASSIGNMENT

Begin reading on page 161 and stop when you see the words "Spring of Living Water" on page 171.

Questions to answer from the reading assignment:

1. Up to this point in the book, the authors have been saying, "It's _____ about you." Now they are saying something very different. It's _____ about you!" [827]

2. By delighting primarily in God, you will find your _____ _____. [828]

3. Put in your own words, why would Larry Crabb say that God is in the business of "shattering dreams."

   _____

   _____

   _____

   _____ [829]

4. Explain what it means that God doesn't want you to have second best and explain what "first best" is.

   _____

   _____

   _____

   _____ [830]

5. Write in your own words what the authors mean when they say, "It's not about you."

   _____

   _____

   _____

   _____ [831]

6. _____ in the Bible does it say that God doesn't want you _____.   In fact, it says just the _____. [832]

7. When the Bible says we are to "die to ourselves," what is it basically saying?

_____

_____ 833

8. Name some of the areas we can find our joy in more than God.

_____

_____ 834

9. We are trying to find our joy in so many things _____ than God, but once we find them, they _____ us for only a short while because they _____. 835

10. When we are so focused on the "abundant life" in the things of the world, God usually ends up only getting the _____ time in our lives.   Meeting with Him is not our _____ priority. 836

11. Explain how Christianity is like dinner at a Mexican restaurant.

_____

_____

_____

_____

_____

_____ 837

Bible Study!

No Bible Assignment. Spend 15 minutes in final preparation for teaching your friends Lesson One of the YouTeach series. Make sure the slides are copied to your hard drive.

CAUTION! The more your life is changed, the easier it is to spot Cat behavior in those around you. **Please don't ever use this material to judge others.** ("Oh, they are just a bunch of Cats.") Once we start judging others, we too are acting like Cats. **Use this material to encourage yourself and others to live for God's glory.**

LESSON 45

CHECK WHICH CIRCLE BEST REPRESENTS YOUR LIFE TODAY:

☐   ☐   ☐

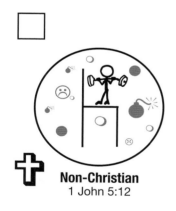

Non-Christian
1 John 5:12

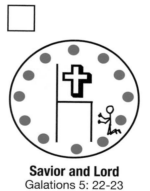

Savior and Lord
Galations 5: 22-23

Savior
1 Corinthians 3:15

Since my last lesson,
I have practiced
Spiritual Breathing:

☐ 20+ Times
☐ 11 - 19 Times
☐ 6 - 10 Times
☐ 0 - 5 Times

1. If you are privately schooled, follow your teacher's instructions.

1. If you are homeschooled, meet together with your group of at least two people. (They can be younger than you.) If you are nervous, tell them. They'll understand and it will make them feel better as well!

2. Start off in prayer asking God to speak through you.

3. Begin teaching Lesson #1 of "YouTeach Cat and Dog Theology" titled, "Thinking Outside The Box" from your hard drive. You can do this in a couple of ways.

    A. First, you can simply go slide by slide, reading from the notes that specify what you are to say.

    B. Or, you can simply show the slides and say what comes to your heart on each slide. (You will need to be extremely familiar with each slide in order to do this.)

    C. You can teach with your mom or dad, alternating slides. (You parent can do all of the even slides, you do all of the odd slides.) Or, you can do the first half, they can do the second half.

Free Day. No optional work!

OPTIONAL LESSON

LESSON 46

CHECK WHICH CIRCLE BEST REPRESENTS YOUR LIFE TODAY:

☐   ☐   ☐

Non-Christian
1 John 5:12

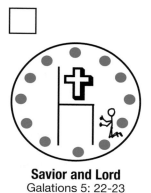

Savior and Lord
Galations 5: 22-23

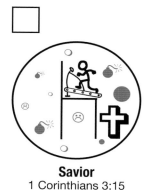

Savior
1 Corinthians 3:15

Since my last lesson,
I have practiced
Spiritual Breathing:

☐ 20+ Times
☐ 11 - 19 Times
☐ 6 - 10 Times
☐ 0 - 5 Times

READING ASSIGNMENT

CAT & DOG THEOLOGY

RETHINKING OUR RELATIONSHIP WITH OUR MASTER

LIVING PASSIONATELY FOR THE GLORY OF GOD

Bob Sjogren & Gerald Robison

Start reading on page 171 at "Spring of Living Water" and finish out the chapter (page 175).

Questions to answer from the reading assignment:

1. Contrary to cisterns that leak, the spring of living water never has to be _____. [838]

2. Because God is infinite, there is an infinite amount of God that we get to _____ and _____. We will _____ get to a point in heaven where we say, "OK, this is getting _____." [839]

3. Write in your own words what Jesus means when He says that He never wants us to thirst again?

_____
_____
_____
_____ [840]

4. Finding our joy primarily in God alone is not a _____ _____. [841]

5. Cats rarely have the _____ to wait upon God. [842]

6. Why do the authors say Proverbs 2:1-5 is so challenging?

_____
_____
_____
_____ [843]

7. Write in your own words what it means to seek God like "pirates seeking a hidden treasure."

_____
_____
_____
_____ [844]

8. Describe "Soul Waiting" in your own words.

_____

_____ 845

9. What are Cats non-verbally communicating to God when they don't wait on Him?

_____

_____ 846

10. John Piper in his book *Hunger for God* challenges us to _____ from whatever pleases us _____ than God. [847]

11. What is something you think Christians your age should fast from?

_____

_____ 848

1. Read Psalm 42.

2. Find the definition of the verb "pant" and write it down.

_____

_____

_____

_____

_____ 849

BIBLE STUDY!

3. If a deer is extremely thirsty and looking for a stream from which to drink (panting for water), how much of its "being" is consumed with finding the water?

_____ 850

4. In the second half of verse one, the author of this Psalm uses the word "soul." Without using a dictionary, or asking someone for help, write in your own words what you believe a person's "soul" represents.

_____

_____ 851

5. Write in your own words what the author of this Psalm is trying to communicate in the second part of verse 1 and in verse 2.

_____

_____

_____

_____ 852

6. What does verse 3, 5, 9, 10 and 11 communicate about where the author of this Psalm is spiritually?

_____

_____ 853

7. In verse 4 it says he "pours out my soul." How long do you think that could have taken him and does it sound like "UPS" (Unrelenting Patient Search)?

_____

_____ 854

8. What in verse 3 indicates as to whether this "dry spell" was a quick one or a very long lasting one?

_____

_____ 855

9. What is the only thing verses 5 and 11 says he has going for him?

_____ 856

10. Does this Psalm ever give any indication as to whether the Psalmist ever gets out of his "depressed state"?

Circle One: Yes   No   857

11. How can this encourage believers?

_____

_____ 858

LESSON 47

CHECK WHICH CIRCLE BEST REPRESENTS YOUR LIFE TODAY:

☐   ☐   ☐

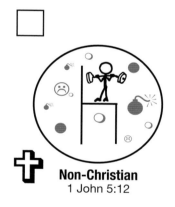

Non-Christian
1 John 5:12

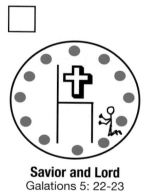

Savior and Lord
Galations 5: 22-23

Savior
1 Corinthians 3:15

Since my last lesson,
I have practiced
Spiritual Breathing:

☐ 20+ Times
☐ 11 - 19 Times
☐ 6 - 10 Times
☐ 0 - 5 Times

READING ASSIGNMENT

Start reading chapter 16 (page 177) to the bottom of page 182.

Questions to answer from the reading assignment:

1. Dogs are constantly holding _____ _____ throughout the day, because in everything they do, they are _____ to God. [859]

2. For Cats, worship is a _____ of their lives. [860]

3. List the times when Cats worship:

   _____

   _____ [861]

4. A Cat's worship is focused primarily on what _____ _____ _____ for them. [862]

5. When Dogs worship, they focus primarily on _____ _____ _____ rather than what He's done for them. [863]

6. Explain how you can worship God by looking at a flower.

   _____

   _____ [864]

7. Explain why an Evangelical humanist doesn't have time to "smell the roses."

   _____

   _____ [865]

CAT & DOG THEOLOGY

RETHINKING OUR RELATIONSHIP WITH OUR MASTER

LIVING PASSIONATELY FOR THE GLORY OF GOD

Bob Sjogren & Gerald Robison

8. Explain the "door analogy" on the top of page 182 and relate that to God (and us) getting joy.

_____

_____

_____

_____

_____

_____ 866

9. If you see a couple taking an evening walk holding their kids' hands, what do you think God is thinking at that very moment about them?

_____

_____ 867

10. If God is getting joy out of that moment, what would keep us from getting that same joy?

_____

_____

_____

_____

_____ 868

BIBLE STUDY!

1. Read Psalm 148.

2. Why are most Christians comfortable with what is written in verses 1 and 2?

_____

_____

869

_____

3. Why are most Christians uncomfortable with verses 3 and 4?

_____

_____

870

4. What type of animal do you think verse 7 says should praise God?

_____

871

5. After all the animals, the stars, the moons, the angels, the lightning, the storms (etc.) are commanded to praise him, finally the writer gets down to people. We are last on the list. Do you think there is any significance to that, and if so, what is it?

_____

_____

_____

872

_____

6. Go to www.youtube.com and type in "Louie Giglio Mashup of Stars and Whales Singing God's Praise" and listen to stars worshiping God. (15 minutes).

LESSON 48

CHECK WHICH CIRCLE BEST REPRESENTS YOUR LIFE TODAY:

☐   ☐   ☐

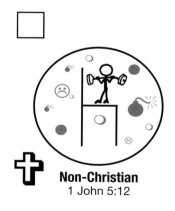

Non-Christian
1 John 5:12

Savior and Lord
Galations 5: 22-23

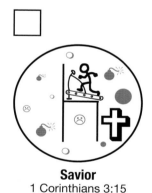

Savior
1 Corinthians 3:15

Since my last lesson,
I have practiced
Spiritual Breathing:

☐ 20+ Times

☐ 11 - 19 Times

☐ 6 - 10 Times

☐ 0 - 5 Times

CARTOON

What Cats and Dogs Really Want Out Of Life

1. Why do you think the word "Santa" is in the cartoon and why do you think the list is very long?

_____

_____

_____

2. Why is the Dog's list short and what is communicated in that half of the cartoon?

_____

_____

_____

CHRIS and SARAH

Sarah slammed her bedroom door and threw her backpack onto the bed.

She heard her mom yell through the closed door, "Don't you slam your door, young lady! We're not finished talking."

Her mom turned the doorknob, but Sarah had already locked it. This is why her mom didn't home school Sarah. They just didn't get along. It was plain and simple.

"Sarah? Unlock your door this instant. Sarah Melanie, I mean it. Open this door!"

Sarah ignored her. She had been listening to her mom lecture her for almost half an hour, and she was done with it. She needed some space, some quiet, somewhere she could think without her parents all in her business. Grabbing her phone and an extra hoodie, Sarah opened her bedroom window, slipped out, and headed toward the old tree house.

Ever since her D-, life had spiraled down. Other grades started slipping. Bryan had started acting weird around her after Christmas. He wasn't as friendly, didn't put his arm around her while they walked – in fact, she hardly saw him at all between classes. What had she done wrong? Did he still like her? It was driving her crazy, and that's why her grades were bad.

Sarah didn't expect her parents to understand how she felt. They thought as long as she was still going to church and youth group, everything was fine.

And the truth was, Sarah still enjoyed doing church things. Her friends were the same; Pastor Jake was still cool and dynamic. Sarah just didn't see God the same way Jake did. He didn't answer her prayers. She never felt His presence anymore. What was the point?

Suddenly, Sarah heard footsteps on the path below the tree house. It was her dad. He was carrying a flashlight and soon found her. "Sweetie, it's time to come down. We need to talk."

She rolled her eyes and climbed down the ladder, preparing herself for another lecture. *Would it ever end?*

Turns out, Sarah got more than a lecture. She was grounded for locking her mother out of her room and disappearing without telling anyone. It wasn't until two weeks later she was allowed to leave the house for anything but school. And then she was only allowed to go with the family to Chris' basketball game.

It wasn't just any basketball game. Chris' small homeschool team had made it to the district finals. Sarah sulked the entire game until the last few minutes. When the game was tied with 45 seconds to go, she started realizing what was happening and started cheering for Chris. She even gave God another chance. Dear Lord, please help Chris' team win and help Chris finish strong.

Right after she finished praying, Chris' teammate got a rebound and saw Chris heading down for a fast break. He threw the ball half way down the court—only to get it intercepted by the other team. Sarah was stunned. Where had that guy come from? She hadn't seen him at all. Chris' team could have taken the lead.

Now there were only 30 seconds left. The other team patiently waited for a back door

opportunity. It came when Chris tried to go for a steal and was faked out. His man cut to the basket, got the ball, and scored an easy lay-up. Chris' team was now down by two.

Chris' coach called a time out. Ten seconds left. Sarah prayed even harder for Chris' team. Certainly God would answer this prayer—it wasn't even about her.

As the team huddled around the coach, he called for a fake drive to draw the opposing team in—especially Chris' defensive man. Chris was to stay on the perimeter and wait for a pass. After they reviewed the play twice, the ref blew his whistle; time to get back. Chris prayed as he took his place.

The play worked like magic! They drove the ball past the half court in two seconds. They quickly set up the play and executed it flawlessly. Everyone went for the drive and collapsed to block it. But there was no shot. The ball was kicked out to Chris, who was sitting wide open on the three-point line. Making this would win the game!

Sarah prayed a third time. Chris got the ball, squared his body up and took the shot. Right after it left his hands the buzzer screamed "game over." It was all up to the ball now.

From Sarah's angle the shot was heading straight for the bucket. She started screaming, but when it hit, it didn't go through. Rather, it bounced straight up off the back of the rim. It seemed like an eternity before it came down and then hit the outside of the front of the rim and bounced out. Chris' team had lost by two.

Chris and Sarah were both devastated. On their way home, their parents tried to be encouraging, reminding Chris that there was always next year. But Chris knew better. Their best players were seniors. They'd be gone next year, and Chris knew the rest of them didn't have a chance.

The next evening was youth group, and Sarah was allowed to leave the house and ride with Chris. They were both pretty sullen. Sarah was still mad about… everything? God wasn't answering her prayers—even for her brother. It was hard for Chris to communicate with Sarah these days, so the car ride over was pretty silent, and at church they separated without a word to go sit with their friends.

"Tonight, some of you aren't going to like what I have to say," was how Jake opened the teaching.

Oh, great, Sarah thought while crossing her arms. *I'm not in the mood for another "God-might-kill-you" lecture, Pastor Jake.*

In his teaching, Jake described three people from the Bible whom God used to demonstrate His glory. One was a man named Jabez, who asked God to bless him. God did. Another was a Jewish girl who was taken into slavery and helped bring God's glory and power to a leader of a foreign country. The last example was Stephen – a godly man who was martyred for his faith in God.

Chris listened to Jake's story with curiosity. *Where was Jake going with this?*

"I want to challenge you through these examples. Each of these people was probably God's child, someone who loved God and was used in powerful ways to spread His word. But they didn't all get a blessed life – at least not in the way we usually define blessing. Not everything went their way. In fact, two them got a really screwed up deal.

"So I want to challenge you with this idea: Life isn't designed to be fair. Life was designed to be a series of opportunities to point to, reflect and radiate the glory of God! Makes sense, right? How many of us get everything we think we should? When life doesn't go the way we think it should, we tend to think God has let us down. But I challenge you to try and look at the situation with your spiritual eyes and ask, 'How can I give God glory out of this?' It could also be that the situation is meant to bring you closer to God."

As Jake spoke, Sarah watched her brother. She knew the basketball game had devastated him. He'd been depressed ever since. However, now he looked different. His face wasn't as sullen. His shoulders weren't slumping. He looked… peaceful.

Something stirred inside Sarah. Her life had felt unfair for weeks – but what purpose could God possibly have in it? What was the point? Why couldn't God just bless her like he did the first guy in Jake's example?

It isn't fair! She thought.

But the instant the thought crossed her mind, she felt a twinge of guilt.

Lesson 48 Questions: (The suggested answers are on page 52 in the *Answer Key.*)

1. If Sarah represents God, how did her interaction with her mom make God look and why?

_____

_____

2. If God is the "spring of living water," with what was Sarah filling up her "cistern" (where was her primary joy/focus)? Where should it have been?

_____

_____

3. Sarah gave God "another chance" by praying for Chris in his basketball game. What was God's "chance" and how was it conditional?

_____

_____

4. What did Chris agree to that Sarah didn't and how did it affect their lives?

_____

_____

1. (From week 13) Cat Theology has violated Deuteronomy 4:2 because it has

    A. added to God's law.

    B. taken away from God's law.

    C. added and taken away from God's law.

    D. None of the above. [875]

2. (Week 13) The first thing a Cat asks himself about going overseas to be a missionary is,

    A. "Is it safe?"

    B. "Will I make a lot of money?"

    C. "Is it God's will?"

    D. "Is it adventurous?" [876]

3. (Week 13) The phrase "God wants us happy" is

    A. not correct.

    B. correct, but incomplete.

    C. unbiblical.

    D. None of the above. [877]

4. (Week 14) God designed life to be fair.

    A. True

    B. False [878]

5. (Week 14) Life was designed to be

    A. safe, soft, easy and comfortable.

    B. a series of opportunities to reflect, radiate and point to God's glory.

    C. fun.

    D. All of the above. [879]

6. (Week 14) The chief end of Christianity is

    A. the happiness of people while they're on this earth.

    B. the happiness of people after they die.

    C. to glorify God. [880]

7. (Week 15) Having your primary focus be on saving people from hell is very healthy.

    A. True

    B. False [881]

8. (Week 15) God is in the business of shattering every dream

    A. you'll ever have.

    B. that is not of Him.

    C. from now on.

    D. None of the above. [882]

9. (Week 16) It is very easy to sin by not making God our greatest joy and delighting more in

    A. sports.

    B. our accomplishments.

    C. our friends.

    D. our families [883]

10. It is a good idea to "fast/discontinue using" whatever pleases us more than God.

    A. True

    B. False [884]

PERSONAL APPLICATION

What are you going to do differently as a result of what you've learned? **Go to the end of your workbook and write it in for Lesson 48.** [885]

OPTIONAL LESSON

Go to **www.UnveilinGLORY.com** and click on the left side: Free Online Teaching.

• Once there, click on "Guest."

• In the top right where it says "Choose a Series" choose "The Dangers of Cat Theology."

• Listen to the "M" "E" lesson.

LESSON 49

CHECK WHICH CIRCLE BEST REPRESENTS YOUR LIFE TODAY:

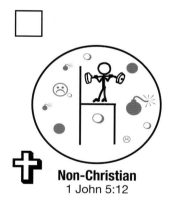

Non-Christian
1 John 5:12

Savior and Lord
Galations 5: 22-23

Savior
1 Corinthians 3:15

Since my last lesson,
I have practiced
Spiritual Breathing:

- ☐ 20⁺ Times
- ☐ 11 - 19 Times
- ☐ 6 - 10 Times
- ☐ 0 - 5 Times

READING ASSIGNMENT

CAT & DOG THEOLOGY

RETHINKING OUR RELATIONSHIP WITH OUR MASTER

LIVING PASSIONATELY FOR THE GLORY OF GOD

Bob Sjogren & Gerald Robison

Start reading at the top of page 183 (where it says "Delight in What God Delights In") and finish out the chapter (page 186).

Questions to answer from the reading assignment:

1. Why did Bob never really enjoy his kids as an Evangelical humanist?

_____

_____ 886

2. When Bob was freed out of Evangelical humanism, what changed in his thinking when he was with his children?

_____

_____

_____

_____ 887

3. What do the authors say God is doing when a young man takes a girl out on a date and treats her with respect, or the seasons come and go as they are supposed to, or two people reconcile?

_____ 888

4. Explain in your own words why, when God is smiling at something, we should smile with Him.

_____

_____

_____

_____ 889

5. Name some of the things around your house where you can see God's glory.

_____

_____ 890

6. Life should be one big _____ _____. ⁸⁹¹

7. What do Dogs do differently from Cats when life is one big worship service? The answer is _____ _____. ⁸⁹²

8. Dogs do everything with a whole new _____. ⁸⁹³

9. Name the two attitudes a Cat and Dog have while doing the dishes.

Cat: _____

_____ ⁸⁹⁴

Dog: _____

_____ ⁸⁹⁵

10. What one word is common in "A Dog's Glossary of Terms" on page 203?

_____ ⁸⁹⁶

11. Which definition in the glossary sticks out to you the most and why?

_____

_____

_____

_____ ⁸⁹⁷

1. Read Luke 10:1-21.

2. Where were the 72 disciples supposed to go?

_____

_____

_____

_____

_____ ⁸⁹⁸

BIBLE STUDY!

3. What was Jesus trying to communicate when He used the words "lambs" and "wolves?"

_____

_____ ⁸⁹⁹

4. What is similar in the messages to be given to towns that accept them and towns that don't?

_____

_____ 900

5. What attitude did the 72 have when they returned?

_____ 901

6. Why were they this way?

_____

_____ 902

7. Though they had great joy, Jesus said, "Don't rejoice in this." What did He tell them to rejoice in?

_____

_____ 903

8. Luke 10:21 is one of the only places in Scripture where it speaks of Jesus having great joy. Why do you think He was happy?

_____

_____ 904

9. What do you think the average person thinks would make someone "wise and learned?"

_____

_____ 905

10. If the Father gave insight only to the "wise and learned," what would the average person think they would have to do before they could be used by God?

_____

_____ 906

11. Because the "little children" understood this, what does this tell us about who can be used by God?

_____

_____ 907

LESSON 50

CHECK WHICH CIRCLE BEST REPRESENTS YOUR LIFE TODAY:

☐

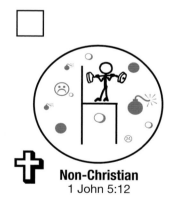

Non-Christian
1 John 5:12

☐

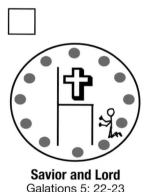

Savior and Lord
Galations 5: 22-23

☐

Savior
1 Corinthians 3:15

Since my last lesson,
I have practiced
Spiritual Breathing:

☐ 20+ Times
☐ 11 - 19 Times
☐ 6 - 10 Times
☐ 0 - 5 Times

READING ASSIGNMENT

CAT & DOG THEOLOGY

RETHINKING OUR RELATIONSHIP WITH OUR MASTER

LIVING PASSIONATELY FOR THE GLORY OF GOD

Bob Sjogren & Gerald Robison

Start reading chapter 17 (page 187) and read to the top of page 192 where you see the words "The Story of the Bible."

Questions to answer from the reading assignment:

1. If you were Corrie Ten Boom, how would you reply if you found out that you had five more years of tremendous suffering, but God was willing to take you home early?

_____

_____ 908

2. How did Corrie reply?

_____

_____ 909

3. What do the authors say happens when Christians worship with people from other cultures in their foreign culture?

_____

_____ 910

4. Since the writing of the book, there has been a change in terminology. We used to say (as the book has written), "God gets more glory." This made it seem as if God was "growing in glory" which is impossible. God is already infinitely glorious and cannot be any more glorious than He already is. Now we say, "God reveals more glory." This hopefully communicates better that God isn't become any more glorious, rather we see His glory in a greater way. Like clouds clearing so you can see the sun (which is always shining), so too as we worship with people from other nations, we see God's glory in a greater way. His glory is the same, but our seeing it is enhanced. Please circle "Yes" if you understand this, or "No" if you do not.   Yes   No   911

5. Why was God specific as to wanting people from "every" tongue, tribe and nation?

_____

_____ 912

6. What words in Genesis 1:28 seem to communicate that this is what God has wanted to reveal from the very beginning?

_____

_____ 913

7. What happens over centuries of time when a people scatter across the earth?

_____

_____ 914

8. The authors believe that God intended to create _____ so He could bring it back together in _____ to reveal His _____ _____. 915

9. Since reaching the world is tied directly into wanting to reveal God's greatest glory, missions is no longer a _____, it is a desire. 916

10. What does John Piper say about missions in the quote?

_____

_____ 917

11. What does John Piper say will abide forever?

_____

_____ 918

1. Read Acts 2:1-13.

2. The gift of tongues is a very controversial topic. In this text we are not going to look at the controversy that surrounds it, but rather look at the context in which it was birthed and see if we can relate it at all to God's _____ glory. 919

3. When this gift was given, who was in Jerusalem at the time and where were they from?

_____

_____ 920

4. What did these people hear?

_____

_____ 921

5. Galileans were not known for being learned men. In today's terminology, they are known for being "rednecks" with an undeniable Northern accent. Why were the people so amazed that they were Galileans?

_____

_____ 922

6. After the people were amazed and perplexed, what did they ask themselves?

_____

_____ 923

7. Because they heard about the wonders of God in their native tongues, do you think this was more convincing to them that this message really was true?

    Circle One: Yes   No   924

8. If their lives changed, what language do you think they would use going back home and sharing with others?

_____ 925

9. Do you think non-Jewish people would be hearing this message as well?

    Circle One: Yes   No   926

10. Where will the gospel have spread as a result of these "tongues" that were given?

_____

_____ 927

11. Circle which lessons you think we can learn from this passage:

    A. Tongues and missions have a direct link.

    B. God intended to show favor to the Gentiles as well as the Jews.

    C. Tongues is purely a prayer language and must only be used in that way. 928

LESSON 51

CHECK WHICH CIRCLE BEST REPRESENTS YOUR LIFE TODAY:

☐

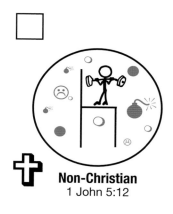

Non-Christian
1 John 5:12

☐

Savior and Lord
Galations 5: 22-23

☐

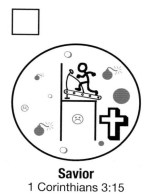

Savior
1 Corinthians 3:15

Since my last lesson,
I have practiced
Spiritual Breathing:

☐ 20⁺ Times

☐ 11 - 19 Times

☐ 6 - 10 Times

☐ 0 - 5 Times

CARTOON

Mission Conference Speakers

1. How is the Cat acting like an "Evangelical humanist?"

_____

_____

_____

_____ 929

2. Where is the focus of the Dog pastor's message and is he making them feel guilty?

_____

_____

_____

_____ 930

The day after Jake's "Life's Not Fair" talk, the dishwasher broke. Chris and Sarah got stuck with washing the dishes by hand after dinner.

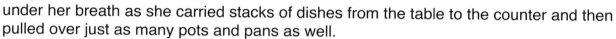

CHRIS and SARAH

"Of course, Mom couldn't have just made spaghetti," Sarah muttered under her breath as she carried stacks of dishes from the table to the counter and then pulled over just as many pots and pans as well.

Chris must have heard her because he said, "Yeah, if the dishwasher's broken, we should just go into survival mode. Nothing but paper plates and frozen pizza."

Sarah shot him a dirty look, but didn't respond otherwise. She was angry—not only at God, but at Chris. *How can Chris be so happy so quickly after losing the state championship?* She thought to herself. It was only two nights ago. All she wanted was to have Bryan as her boyfriend, and his new coldness had ruined her life. She would have been devastated for years had she missed the final shot of the game.

Seeing her look, Chris sighed. She seems mad at the world, he mused. Stepping up to the sink, he squirted soap on the sponge and grabbed a plate. There was definitely something wrong with Sarah. She hardly ever spoke to him or their parents anymore, and when she came home, she retreated immediately into her bedroom and only came out for dinner. She was trying to hide her emotions, feelings, and most importantly, her anger toward God behind her bedroom door. Her thinking was, "If no one comes in, no one will know." But it was way too obvious to everyone the moment she stepped out.

It was beginning to bother Chris. While she had always gotten on his nerves, now he was genuinely worried about her. He knew she had dedicated her life to God at the youth retreat. However, he didn't see anything about her life that showed him she was growing or had any joy.

Suddenly, something occurred to Chris. When his dad had told him to wash the dishes, he had been annoyed. However, he reflected on Pastor Jake's message and asked, "How can I use this for God's glory?" And now he realized this was the perfect opportunity to hang out a little with Sarah. She hadn't been able to hide in her room after dinner like she usually did. Now he just needed to find something to talk about.

He blurted out the first thing that came to mind.

"So, anything new at school?" *Great, now I sound like Dad,* he thought.

Sarah shrugged. "No, not really," she replied and kept drying dishes.

Chris tried again. "What about Bible Club?"

"I haven't been there in a while. Remember, I'm still grounded."

More silence. It screamed at Chris. Chris scrambled for something else. Then he remembered a subject she might like to talk about. "You talk to Bryan lately?"

He regretted it as soon as the words left his mouth. He didn't really want to know about her crush, and he remembered how livid she had been the last time he brought up the subject.

Surprisingly, Sarah didn't act mad. Instead she sighed. "Not really. I don't talk to him a lot anymore. I don't know what's going on with him."

Did Chris see her eyes watering up? "Maybe he's just busy," Chris offered quietly.

"Yeah, maybe."

They talked on and off while the pile of dirty dishes grew smaller. At one point they started bickering, but Chris felt the tug he had begun to recognize as the Holy Spirit. He tried to change the conversation.

Realizing that his attempts at conversations with Sarah weren't really going anywhere, he thought, "Well, if I can't glorify God in how I talk to her, maybe I should just glorify God on my own." And with that, he started humming his favorite Christian songs, and for the first time, he actually enjoyed the chore.

Sarah noticed the change in his attitude, and she got even madder. How can he be so happy doing dishes? Why isn't he still mad over the state championship? Why is life so unfair? She wallowed in her own private pity party.

Seeing her anger, he tried one last time to make her laugh—even crack a small smile, but nothing worked.

As soon as the last dish was washed, she dropped the dish towel on the counter and retreated to her bedroom, mumbling something about checking Facebook. Chris finished wiping up the counters and retreated to his bedroom, too.

Most evenings around this time he was on Facebook, too. However, tonight the laptop stayed closed, and Chris got on his knees to pray for his sister.

"Lord," he prayed, "Something's not right with Sarah. I'm not sure what it is. It seems like she's always in such a bad mood, and she's always hiding out in her room. And she always seems mad – at me, at Mom and Dad, at everyone. Jesus, I think she basically needs You. But I don't know how to pray for that because she already knows You, yet she has no joy. She goes to church, but she lives like a non-Christian. There's no fruit in her life that Pastor Jake talks about. She doesn't read Your Word. She doesn't pray any more. She never talks about You. God, I'm stuck. I don't know what to pray, but I lift her up to You…."

Lesson 51 Questions: (The suggested answers are on page 52 in the *Answer Key*.)

1. How was Corrie Ten Boom's attitude different from Sarah's and similar to Chris'?

    _____

    _____

2. Which circle (#1, #2 or #3) represented Sarah's life at this point, and (besides herself) who was on the throne of her life?

    _____

    _____

3. What changed in Chris' attitude that allowed him to enjoy doing the dishes?

    _____

    _____

4. Explain (as best you can) why Sarah was jealous of Chris' attitude?

    _____

    _____

    _____

    _____

QUIZ!

1. God has feelings and can get great pleasure out of what He sees going on in your life.

    A. True

    B. False [931]

2. God wants life to be

    A, one big worship service.

    B. all about us.

    C. all about saving others from hell.

    D. None of the above. [932]

3. Cats and Dogs do everything the exact same (the dishes, school, chores, etc.) except

    A. Cats have more fun.

    B. Dogs do it as a form of worship.

    C. they fight while doing it.

    D. Dogs do it with a different mindset. [933]

4. Cats

    A. never do the dishes.

    B. never stop to see God's glory.

    C. never want to glorify God.

    D. None of the above. [934]

5. We should seek to try and see God's glory in everything around us.

    A. True

    B. False [935]

6. God doesn't want people from every tongue, tribe and nation. He'll be happy settling for people from most of them.

    A. True

    B. False [936]

7. God first gave us a hint of wanting to reveal His greatest glory in
   - A. Genesis 1:28
   - B. Genesis 12:2,3
   - C. Matthew 28:18-20 [937]

8. The authors believe that God was forced to create diversity because of the pride at the Tower of Babel. Now He wants to bring it back together in harmony to reveal His greatest glory.
   - A. True
   - B. False [938]

9. In one sense, you could say missions is all about
   - A. bringing people their greatest joy.
   - B. trying to make people as happy as possible.
   - C. saving people from hell.
   - D. revealing God's greatest glory. [939]

10. Missions is a temporary necessity. Worship will abide forever.
    - A. True
    - B. False [940]

PERSONAL APPLICATION

What are you going to do differently as a result of what you've learned? **Go to the end of your workbook and write it in for Lesson 51.** [941]

Go to **www.UnveilinGLORY.com** and click on the left side: Free Online Teaching.

• Once there, click on "Guest."

• In the top right where it says "Choose a Series" choose "The Dangers of Cat Theology."

• Listen to the "Refrigerator Theology" lesson.

There is no quiz, no notes to be taken. Just enjoy and learn!

OPTIONAL LESSON

LESSON 52

CHECK WHICH CIRCLE BEST REPRESENTS YOUR LIFE TODAY:

☐   ☐   ☐

Non-Christian
1 John 5:12

Savior and Lord
Galations 5: 22-23

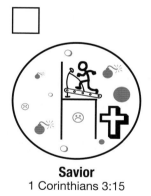

Savior
1 Corinthians 3:15

Since my last lesson,
I have practiced
Spiritual Breathing:

☐ 20⁺ Times

☐ 11 - 19 Times

☐ 6 - 10 Times

☐ 0 - 5 Times

READING ASSIGNMENT

Begin reading on page 192 with "The Story of the Bible" and finish out the chapter (page 197).

Questions to answer from the reading assignment:

1. The goal of bringing every ethnic group into God's presence is the _____ of the Bible. [942]

2. Just as every book has an _____, a _____ and a _____, so does the Bible. [943]

3. The Introduction is found in Genesis chapters _____ - _____. [944]

4. Prior to the Tower of Babel, there was no "_____-_____" mentality. Because of this, God had the opportunity to reveal His _____ but not His _____ _____. [945]

5. Because mankind was being rebellious, God did in one _____ what should have taken centuries to do. He took their one _____ and broke it down into many different _____. [946]

6. What God did at the Tower of Babel was to create _____ so he could bring it back together in _____ to reveal His _____ _____. [947]

7. The story starts in a two-fold promise to _____ where God commits to bless him and to have him be a blessing to _____ the peoples on the face of the earth. [948]

8. God's promise to Abram parallels the _____ _____ of Matthew 28:18-20. [949]

9. Revelation 5:9 tells us that God _____ reveal His greatest glory by reaching all peoples. [950]

10. Missions (reaching all people groups to reveal God's greatest glory) begins in the book of _____ and ends in the book of _____. [951]

1. Read Matthew 24:14.

2. What questions were the disciples asking of Jesus that got Him to say these words?

_____

_____

_____

_____ 952

3. What did Jesus say would have to happen before the end would come?

_____

_____ 953

4. What word is common (showing the extent of the job to be done) in Matthew 24:14, Matthew 28:18-20 and Genesis 12:3?

_____ 954

5. If God did not reach all nations before He came back, He would have broken a promise to Abraham and could be called "what" for all of eternity?

_____ 955

6. If all nations were not reached before He came back, He would reveal
_____ but not His _____ _____ . 956

7. Jesus was very clear, He is not going to come back until all nations are
_____ . 957

LESSON 53

CHECK WHICH CIRCLE BEST REPRESENTS YOUR LIFE TODAY:

☐

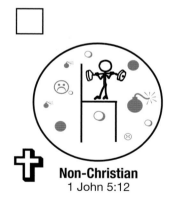

Non-Christian
1 John 5:12

☐

Savior and Lord
Galations 5: 22-23

☐

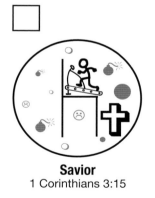

Savior
1 Corinthians 3:15

Since my last lesson,
I have practiced
Spiritual Breathing:

☐ 20+ Times
☐ 11 - 19 Times
☐ 6 - 10 Times
☐ 0 - 5 Times

READING ASSIGNMENT

CAT & DOG THEOLOGY

RETHINKING OUR RELATIONSHIP WITH OUR MASTER

LIVING PASSIONATELY FOR THE GLORY OF GOD

Bob Sjogren & Gerald Robison

Read the Epilogue, pages 199-202.

Questions to answer from the reading assignment:

1. The authors have found that many Christians, pastors and churches have _____-_____ to our message of Dog Theology. [958]

2. Explain the seesaw analogy they use.

_____

_____

_____

_____

_____ [959]

3. The practice of real Dog Theology is a matter of proper _____ and _____. [960]

4. Dog Theology is not the _____ of Cat Theology, it is the _____ of it. [961]

5. Explain the train track analogy.

_____

_____

_____

_____

_____ [962]

6. List the three things the authors say are inappropriate:

_____

_____

_____ [963]

7. Our churches need to be filled with _____. [964]

8. Write down why God commands us to live for His glory.

_____

_____ 965

9. Cats live with _____ in mind. Dogs live with _____ in mind. 966

10. Write out what is a proper and balanced life.

_____

_____

_____

_____

_____ 967

1. Read Acts 18:18-26.

2. In verse 23, what did Paul see as his primary "job description?"

_____

_____

_____

_____

_____ 968

BIBLE STUDY!

3. In which country was Alexandria located?

_____ 969

4. What words are used to describe Apollos?

_____

_____ 970

5. Do you think he was a reserved man and what word gives you an indication of your answer?

_____

_____ 971

6. Although he spoke about Jesus accurately, how was his knowledge limited?

_____ 972

7. Why do you think God (who inspired the Scriptures) put in the word "thorough?"

_____

_____

_____ 973

8. In *Cat and Dog Theology* terminology, we would say that what Apollos knew was not _____ but it was _____. 974

9. Was the preaching of Apollos balanced?

   Circle One: Yes   No   975

10. Circle which lessons we can learn from this text.

   A. We should be listening carefully to what we hear in church and Bible studies to be sure they are balanced and correct.

   B. I should fall asleep in church because what I am going to be hearing will be wrong.

   C. What our pastor is teaching may not be wrong, but it may be incomplete.

   D. Zealous speakers in church may not have the complete picture. 976

LESSON 54

CHECK WHICH CIRCLE BEST REPRESENTS YOUR LIFE TODAY:

Non-Christian
1 John 5:12

Savior and Lord
Galations 5: 22-23

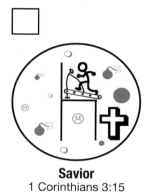

Savior
1 Corinthians 3:15

Since my last lesson,
I have practiced
Spiritual Breathing:

- ☐ 20+ Times
- ☐ 11 - 19 Times
- ☐ 6 - 10 Times
- ☐ 0 - 5 Times

CARTOON

Cats Love To "Protect" Their Church

Speech bubbles: "Let's Go Witnessing in the inner city!" / "Are you crazy? It's not safe. And even if we won people to Christ, they'd never fit in with the people of our church."

1. How does a Cat, in wanting to "protect their church" not allow God to reveal His greater glory through their church?

_____

_____

_____

_____

_____

_____

977

2. What is the Cat's first and foremost concern?

_____

978

CHRIS and SARAH

Two weeks had passed when the student leaders' meeting came up, and Chris was excited about it. At the beginning of the school year, he had joined this group that helped the adults prepare future activities and teachings. Pastor Jake had promised some big news tonight.

When Chris arrived, nearly all of the leaders had assembled. There were Chris' five

or six fellow students – all upperclassmen who were deeply involved in youth group and met twice a month with an adult leader for mentoring. There were about 10 adult leaders of various ages, some married, some single. Most of them were in their twenties and early thirties. Then there were the parent-leaders. This collection of 10-15 parents regularly offered their homes for youth events, helped organize fund raisers, and kept their fingers in almost everything that happened at group.

It started out like any meeting. Jake opened with prayer then addressed each group of leaders, thanking them for their involvement and support of the work God was doing in the youth at this church. He also prayed for the kids in the youth group to get to know God better, to have a passion for Him, and for their youth group to grow.

Then he started describing his plans for the future. He talked about how he loved that the youth in the church were growing in love for God and each other, but he also wanted them to have a heart for the lost overseas. He knew of a big youth missions conference next year, and he wanted the entire youth group to attend. The missions conference would expose them to the spiritual situations in other countries, show them how saving the lost was God's first priority, and teach them the parts of the Bible that were about the Great Commission.

Then Jake grew very serious.

"After the conference, I want to offer several overseas missions trips for the students to chose from. I want them to grow their worldview, see how people live in other countries, serve others there, and hopefully catch a vision for God's heart for the nations.

"It's going to take a lot of work," he continued, "that's why I'm asking for all of your help. But I know it'll be worth it. These kids need to be exposed to other cultures and be a part of God's love and glory reaching the nations."

Chris looked around the room. Some of his fellow students looked excited. Some shifted uncomfortably, and Chris knew why. They were probably having the same thoughts he was. *Another country? Really?* He had always wanted to visit Europe, but that's not usually where missions trips took people. As far as Chris knew, God called people to Africa or China. Maybe someday Chris would serve God overseas, but not there. It was too different from what he was used to.

One of the parents coughed, and Jake looked up expectantly, "Any questions?"

"Yes," one of the dads raised his hand and said, "Jake, when exactly will this conference and trips take place? Frankly, I'm a little concerned about summer plans as they stand now. We're already packed to the limit with my son's baseball travel team and church camp —not to mention our family vacation."

Other parents murmured in agreement.

"Where are you thinking of sending the kids?" one mom asked. "There's a lot of unrest in the world right now. Is it safe?"

Another parent piped up, "And how much is all of this going to cost?"

That provoked a louder murmur. More parents began to voice their concerns. Didn't Jake watch the news? What about terrorists? What about sickness? How long would the trips be? What if they interfered with their kids' summer sports commitments?

Jake handled the questions as well as he could. In the end, the leaders decided to look at the possibility of a missions conference in a year or two, or maybe they would host a special missions night at youth group. There just wasn't enough time right now. Kids already had plans, and there wasn't enough money.

Chris left realizing that Jake had been totally shot down by the parents. Quite honestly, he was relieved. As a student leader, he probably should have led one of those teams, and he wasn't at all interested in going to China or the Philippines or anywhere outside of Europe.

But as he turned the key to start his car, something inside nudged him and he wondered, *Was God really pleased with how this meeting went?*

Lesson 54 Questions: (The suggested answers are on page 53 in the *Answer Key*.)

1. What Dog qualities do you see in Pastor Jake?

   _____

   _____

2. What Cat qualities do you see in the parents? And whose kingdom are they primarily worried about?

   _____

   _____

3. How is Chris being a Cat?

   _____

   _____

4. Do you think God was pleased with how the meeting went and why?

_____

_____

1. Reaching the nations with God's glory is
    A. only found in a few verses in the Bible.
    B. only for those who are called.
    C. the central theme of God's Word.
    D. None of the above. 979
2. According to the authors, just as every book has an introduction, a story and a conclusion, so does the Bible.
    A. True
    B. False 980
3. At the Tower of Babel,
    A. God acted out of anger.
    B. God did in one moment what should have taken centuries to do.
    C. people really made a mess.
    D. None of the above. 981
4. God's promise to Abram in Genesis 12:2,3 parallels the Great Commission of Matthew 28:18-20.
    A. True
    B. False 982
5. Does God ever fulfill His promise to Abram?
    A. Yes.
    B. No
    C. There's no way to tell until we get to eternity. 983
6. Dog theology is the absence of Cat Theology.
    A. True
    B. False 984

7. It is OK to be unbalanced in seeking to bless others and not really worry about getting God's blessing.

    A. True

    B. False [985]

8. Cats live with "now" in mind, Dogs live with "eternity" in mind.

    A. True

    B. False [986]

9. Churches need to have a balance of Cat and Dog Theology.

    A. True

    B. False [987]

10. God commands us to

    A. live for His glory.

    B. live for ourselves. [988]

PERSONAL APPLICATION

What are you going to do differently as a result of what you've learned? **Go to the end of your workbook and write it in for Lesson 54.** [989]

OPTIONAL LESSON

Go to **www.UnveilinGLORY.com** and click on the left side: Free Online Teaching.

• Once there, click on "Guest."

• In the top right where it says "Choose a Series" choose "The Dangers of Cat Theology."

• Listen to the "Selective Application" lesson.

There is no quiz, or notes to be taken. Just enjoy and learn!

Lesson 54

LESSON 55

CHECK WHICH CIRCLE BEST REPRESENTS YOUR LIFE TODAY:

☐

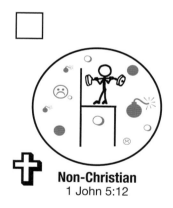

Non-Christian
1 John 5:12

☐

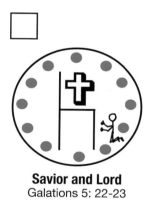

Savior and Lord
Galations 5: 22-23

☐

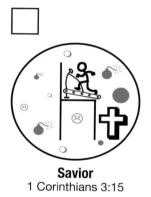

Savior
1 Corinthians 3:15

Since my last lesson,
I have practiced
Spiritual Breathing:

☐ 20+ Times
☐ 11 - 19 Times
☐ 6 - 10 Times
☐ 0 - 5 Times

READING ASSIGNMENT

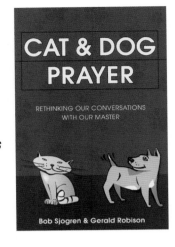

CAT & DOG PRAYER

RETHINKING OUR CONVERSATIONS
WITH OUR MASTER

Bob Sjogren & Gerald Robison

Read The Introduction to *Cat and Dog Prayers* (pages 1-4).

Questions to answer from the reading assignment:

1. Our diet of strict ___-_____ has affected our attitudes, our way of life, our theology and especially our _____. 990

2. What is the reason the authors suggest why most Christians don't find prayer to make a significant difference?

_____

_____ 991

3. Do a quick Google search on "Copernicus" and write a one-sentence statement about what he was the most famous.

_____

_____ 992

4. Read the following quote and explain why Cat Theology influenced even modern science: "'Copernicus' publication on the Revolution of the Celestial Spheres was not published until after he died in order for him to avoid being persecuted by the Church." (from http://burro.astr.cwru.edu/stu/pre20th_europe_church.html)

_____

_____

_____ 993

5. At the bottom of page 2, list some of the things people have prayed for that have resulted in answered prayers.

_____

_____

_____

_____ 994

6. Though we read these things in the Bible, our reality is that we _____ see those things happening now. [995]

7. Many times we feel _____ if we don't pray, but we often feel like _____ _____ when we do. [996]

8. Many times the problem with prayer is in the _____-_____. [997]

9. The book gives a warning that this is not a _____-_____ book. [998]

Bible Study!

1. Reread Daniel 6.

2. Daniel was framed by men who were jealous of Him. They convinced the king to issue a decree they knew Daniel would never keep. Did the king issue it?

   Circle One: Yes   No   [999]

3. In the beginning of verse 10, we read these words, "Now when Daniel learned that the decree had been published…" If those words hadn't been written, and it simply said that Daniel went upstairs to pray, what might the average person think?

   _____

   _____

   _____ [1000]

4. Because those words are there, what does God want us to know about Daniel's prayer time?

   _____

   _____ [1001]

5. In your own words, write down what would have been the focus of your prayers if you would have been in Daniel's situation.

_____

_____

_____

_____ 1002

6. What do you think Daniel prayed regarding the lions?

_____

_____

_____

_____ 1003

7. Daniel's prayer was miraculously answered. Have you heard of many prayers miraculously answered like that in the last year of your life? If yes, what?

_____

_____

_____ 1004

CAUTION! The more your life is changed, the easier it is to spot Cat behavior in those around you. **Please don't ever use this material to judge others.** ("Oh, they are just a bunch of Cats.") Once we start judging others, we too are acting like Cats. **Use this material to encourage yourself and others to live for God's glory.**

LESSON 56

CHECK WHICH CIRCLE BEST REPRESENTS YOUR LIFE TODAY:

☐   ☐   ☐

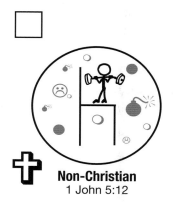

Non-Christian
1 John 5:12

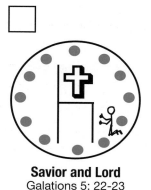

Savior and Lord
Galations 5: 22-23

Savior
1 Corinthians 3:15

Since my last lesson,
I have practiced
Spiritual Breathing:

☐ 20+ Times
☐ 11 - 19 Times
☐ 6 - 10 Times
☐ 0 - 5 Times

READING ASSIGNMENT

CAT & DOG PRAYER

RETHINKING OUR CONVERSATIONS WITH OUR MASTER

Bob Sjogren & Gerald Robison

Begin chapter 1 on page 5 and read through to the middle of page 11 and stop when you read the words, "The Motive Behind Our Prayers."

Questions to answer from the reading assignment:

1. Give a brief definition of what prayer is (page 5.)

_____

_____ 1005

2. There are many types of prayers, but the prayers this chapter will be focusing on are those of _____ . 1006

3. According to page 7, what is typical of a Cat's attitude toward prayer?

_____

_____

_____

_____ 1007

4. Of all of the prayers prayed in the Bible, over _____ % of them were answered positively. 1008

5. List the three reasons given why the authors say most Christians don't pray very much.

_____

_____

_____ 1009

6. The average Christian prays _____ minutes a day, the average pastor prays _____ minutes a day. 1010

7. With life being so busy, parents have a hard time fitting prayer into their schedule. How does this affect kids?

_____

_____ 1011

8. One reason Christians pray so little is that they have very few _____ _____. 1012

9. Instead of looking to God for our needs, list where most Christians look to for their needs.

_____ 1013

10. Getting a positive answer to our request for God to provide depends not only on _____ we are praying for but _____ we are asking for it. 1014

BIBLE STUDY!

1. Read 2 Chronicles 33.

2. Was Manasseh, king of Judah, a good king or a bad king? Circle One:
      Good   Bad   1015

3. In verse 4, the text says he built "altars in the temple of the Lord." Do you think Manasseh was thinking that what he was doing was pleasing to the Lord?

_____ 1016

4. How bad was their evil compared to the nations that had been driven out before them?

_____ 1017

5. What emotions were aroused in the Lord according to verse 6?

_____ 1018

6. In your own words, what do you think the Lord was saying as He "spoke to Manasseh and his people?"

_____ 1019

7. Another king came and defeated Manasseh and the people of Judah.
      Circle One: True   False   1020

8. Who does the text credit for bringing about this devastation of Judah?

1021

_____

9. What does verse 13 say Manasseh did?

1022

_____

10. When Manasseh had everything going his way, he had no time to sincerely seek the Lord.

    Circle One: True   False   1023

11. What got Manasseh's attention that brought him to a point of seriously praying to the Lord?

1024

_____

12. Sometimes the Lord allows us to experience great times of need so that we will turn to God and sincerely seek Him.

    Circle One: True   False   1025

LESSON 57

CHECK WHICH CIRCLE BEST REPRESENTS YOUR LIFE TODAY:

☐   ☐   ☐

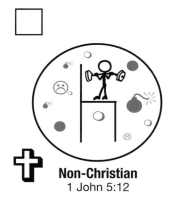

Non-Christian
1 John 5:12

Savior and Lord
Galations 5: 22-23

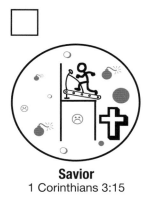

Savior
1 Corinthians 3:15

Since my last lesson,
I have practiced
Spiritual Breathing:

☐ 20⁺ Times
☐ 11 - 19 Times
☐ 6 - 10 Times
☐ 0 - 5 Times

CARTOON

When Pastors Don't End On Time

1. Why do you think the Cat is so upset and pointing to his watch?

_____

_____

_____ 1026

2. What does it look like the Cat-child is doing?

_____

_____ 1027

CHRIS and SARAH

Between Facebook and Twitter, rumors spread about the meeting Jake had with the parents. Some kids were disappointed they wouldn't be allowed go on missions trips next year. However, Sarah was relieved. She wanted to go backpacking across Europe as much as anyone, but the idea of working in the slums in India gave her the creeps. It would be like serving the homeless at Thanksgiving, but 1,000 times worse. She didn't give her life to God to make her feel bad. It was a no-brainer not to go. Besides, they wouldn't have any access to the internet, and she'd be totally cut off from her friends.

But one day at the beginning of Algebra class, Sarah heard the worst rumor of all. Her best friend slipped her a note just before the bell rang, and when Sarah read the words, she almost choked. Her hands started trembling, and she didn't hear a word Mrs. Brewer said the rest of class. The news drove her to Facebook the moment she got home that afternoon.

No, no, no, no, no. Please, God, no, she prayed desperately.

Nevertheless, when she got home she took her dad's laptop without asking. After she went over to his Facebook page, she could only stare at it helplessly. So it was true. Bryan's status had changed from "single" to "in a relationship."

Sarah felt a stinging sensation behind her eyes and blinked furiously. What had happened? Why did he stop liking her? What had she done? Was she not pretty enough? Did she not flirt enough? Maybe she flirted too much? Her mind buzzed with more questions than she could answer. She stared at the screen again.

"In a relationship with Brittany Morris."

Numbly, Sarah found herself clicking on Brittany's name and browsing her profile. She knew the girl by sight at school, but she had never actually spoken to her. Brittany was part of an elite clique Sarah had tried to break into the first year she attended her school. However, it was an unspoken rule that the crowd Sarah was in and the crowd Brittany was in could never mix.

Jealousy and bitterness bubbled inside Sarah. Looking back at the screen, she already hated Brittany. She was cute, tall, and blonde. All of a sudden Sarah fingered her straight auburn hair and felt ugly. Sarah was petite, like her mom. While her eyes weren't as almond-shaped as hers, Sarah resented them. Normally, she liked how different her features were from other kids at school. But Brittany had big blue eyes and blonde hair.

She was Sarah's opposite in every way.

Feverishly, Sarah clicked through the photos of her and Bryan posing together. One looked like it had been taken over Christmas but hadn't been uploaded until now. Had

they really been together that long? Why didn't they announce it sooner? Was it because of… Sarah?

Sarah yanked out her phone. There was already a text message waiting for her. It was from Jennifer.

"hey, just heard about bryan. U ok?"

Her fingers flew across the phone.

"um. Not really. Kinda confused. Call me?"

While waiting for her reply, Sarah texted the rest of her friends and checked Twitter for any more information.

When the phone rang, she took a deep breath, willing her voice to stay calm.

"Hey," she said, trying to sound casual.

"Hey girl," Jennifer's voice was soft. "How ya doing?"

Sarah laughed sarcastically, "How do you think I'm doing? It's like one minute we were talking and everything was great, and then he's cool toward me for a couple of months, and the next minute he's acting all weird. Now this? Did Bryan ever even like me? This is so surreal."

"Oh, Sarah, you know why he's dating her, don't you?"

"What? No --- how do you know? What do you mean?"

"Well, I don't know the whole story, but it's no secret that your parents won't let you date yet. I'm positive he liked you; he told my boyfriend. But he probably knew he couldn't date you."

Sarah felt numb.

"Sarah? You still there?"

"Yeah… I gotta go."

"Um, okay, but call me anytime, alright?"

Sarah flung herself on the bed, and this time she didn't try to stop the tears. It was all her parents' fault. That dumb no-dating-until-you're-16 rule. She'd be 16 in less than six months. Why should a few months matter so much? What other parents still did that? And now it had cost her the guy she'd liked for over a year.

Where was God in all this? Why didn't He answer her prayers? Didn't He want to bless her? Didn't He know seeing Bryan date someone else was killing her?

God, I hate my parents! she ranted inwardly. *And while we're on the topic, You could have stopped all of this. I hate You, too.*

Lesson 57 Questions: (The suggested answers are on page 53 in the *Answer Key.*)

1. What was Sarah's reason for not wanting to go on a mission trip and was it biblical?

   _____

   _____

2. When someone or something other than Christ is on the throne of your life, what can it do to your focus? What did it do to Sarah's focus and how did it impact her last class?

   _____

   _____

3. How did her desire to date Bryan ultimately affect her relationship with her parents?

   _____

   _____

4. When the Bible talks about us loving God, it talks about us loving God "unconditionally." How was Sarah's love for God conditional?

   _____

   _____

Oh Lord, I need to pass this quiz.

QUIZ!

1. A strict "diet" of "Me-ology" can affect
    A. your attitudes.
    B. your way of life.
    C. your prayers.
    D. your theology. [1028]

2. Many times the problem with prayer is in
    A. the words we use.
    B. the "pray-er" themselves.
    C. the glory of God.
    D. the fact that God is too busy to be bothered. [1029]

3. Prayer is simply talking with God.
    A. True
    B. False [1030]

4. The average Christian prays
    A. 3 minutes a day.
    B. 5 minutes a day.
    C. 10 minutes a day.
    D. in the morning. [1031]

5. The average pastor prayers
    A. 3 minutes a day.
    B. 5 minutes a day.
    C. 10 minutes a day.
    D. in the morning. [1032]

6. Kids are affected by how their parents pray.
    A. True
    B. False [1033]

7. Some of the reasons Christians don't pray much is because

    A. they are so busy.

    B. they don't believe prayer really works.

    C. they haven't seen answers to prayers.

    D. All of the above. [1034]

8. In their mind, most Christians today don't need to look to God for their physical needs.

    A. True

    B. False [1035]

9. God looks not only at what we are praying for, but why we are praying for it.

    A. True

    B. False [1036]

10. Prayer

    A. works.

    B. is for the weak.

    C. works for people who have been Christians a long time.

    D. None of the above. [1037]

What are you going to do differently as a result of what you've learned? **Go to the end of your workbook and write it in for Lesson 57.** [1038]

PERSONAL
APPLICATION

Go to **www.UnveilinGLORY.com** and click on the left side: Free Online Teaching.

• Once there, click on "Guest."

• In the top right where it says "Choose a Series" choose "The Dangers of Cat Theology."

• Listen to the "Winner's Circle" lesson.

There is no quiz, no notes to be taken. Just enjoy and learn!

OPTIONAL LESSON

LESSON 58

CHECK WHICH CIRCLE BEST REPRESENTS YOUR LIFE TODAY:

☐

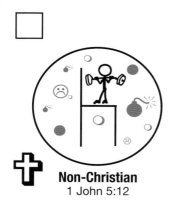

Non-Christian
1 John 5:12

☐

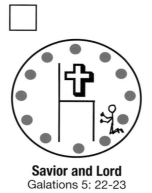

Savior and Lord
Galations 5: 22-23

☐

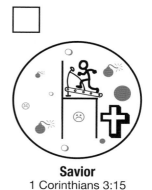

Savior
1 Corinthians 3:15

Since my last lesson,
I have practiced
Spiritual Breathing:

☐ 20⁺ Times
☐ 11 - 19 Times
☐ 6 - 10 Times
☐ 0 - 5 Times

READING ASSIGNMENT

CAT & DOG PRAYER

RETHINKING OUR CONVERSATIONS WITH OUR MASTER

Bob Sjogren & Gerald Robison

Begin reading on page 11 where it says "The Motive behind Our Requests" and finish out the chapter (page 15).

Questions to answer from the reading assignment:

1. Many of the prayers in the Bible people prayed were prayers focused on themselves, yet these were not necessarily _____ or _____. [1039]

2. These prayers that were prayed in the Bible were for deep concerns and _____ needs such as _____, _____, and physical provision. [1040]

3. Go to www.dictionary.com and write the definition for "squander."

_____

_____ [1041]

4. Write James 4:3 in your own words.

_____

_____

_____ [1042]

5. Many Christians are taught that asking God to provide lavishly for our wants is within their _____ as a believer. [1043]

6. The Bible speaks about us as having _____ _____. [1044]

7. Unfortunately the new nature doesn't arrive _____ _____ and doesn't _____ displace the old nature. [1045]

8. Write in your own words what the Bible means in practical terms when it says our old nature has been crucified.

_____

_____

_____ [1046]

9. What questions does your old nature ask in your quiet times?

_____

_____

_____ 1047

10. Circle which lessons we learn from the analogy of "two dogs in a fight."

    A. If I spend more time in front of the TV and gaming, the new nature inside of me will be stronger and win.

    B. If I spend more time in God's Word and prayer, it is a 50/50 chance that I will have a better walk with God.

    C. It's OK to be focused on myself in my prayer time.

    D. I need to focus more on myself and my needs in order to strengthen my new nature.

    E. None of the above [1048]

1. Read 1 Samuel 1:1-19.

2. Although Peninnah had many children, she was jealous of Hannah. Why?

BIBLE STUDY!

_____

_____

_____

_____

_____

_____

_____ 1049

3. Write in your own words what Peninnah did to Hannah to keep her from enjoying her food?

_____

_____ 1050

4. Do you think her words had anything to do with the fact that she couldn't have children?

 Circle One: Yes   No   1051

5. How long did this go on?

_____ 1052

6. What did her bitterness drive her to do?

_____ 1053

7. Would you say her prayer was to some degree "self-centered?"

 Circle One: Yes   No   1054

8. Although praying this prayer, what also did she do that would make the prayer "God-centered"?

_____

_____ 1055

9. Why do you think the Lord did not give her a baby all of those years?

_____

_____

_____ 1056

10. Circle which lessons we can learn from this story.

 A. God can take the meanest words of others and use them for His glory.

 B. We should pray like a drunkard and God will answer our prayers.

 C. Whatever we ask of the Lord should be dedicated to Him.

 D. Our deepest pains should take us to the Lord. 1057

LESSON 59

CHECK WHICH CIRCLE BEST REPRESENTS YOUR LIFE TODAY:

☐   ☐   ☐

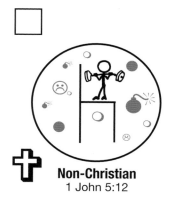

Non-Christian
1 John 5:12

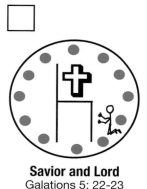

Savior and Lord
Galations 5: 22-23

Savior
1 Corinthians 3:15

Since my last lesson,
I have practiced
Spiritual Breathing:

☐ 20⁺ Times
☐ 11 - 19 Times
☐ 6 - 10 Times
☐ 0 - 5 Times

READING ASSIGNMENT

CAT & DOG PRAYER

RETHINKING OUR CONVERSATIONS WITH OUR MASTER

Bob Sjogren & Gerald Robison

Begin reading chapter 2 on page 17 and end at the bottom of page 21.

Questions to answer from the reading assignment:

1. Because many Cats have never had their selfish prayers answered, what is the only thing left for them to conclude?

   _____

   _____ 1058

2. The authors are trying to give prayer a _____ _____ so that people can pray prayers that do get answered. 1059

3. The Lord's Prayer is a _____ or _____ . He is basically saying, "These are the _____ or _____ that I want you to base your prayers on." 1060

4. To "hallow" means, "to venerate, to regard as holy, to consider sacred." Write the definitions of the following words.

   Venerate: _____

   _____ 1061

   Sacred: _____

   _____ 1062

5. Write your own definition for the word "hallow."

   _____

   _____ 1063

6. We venerate (consider holy, sacred) God's name, not merely because He has complete and ultimate authority, but because we _____ Him. 1064

7. Dogs recognize that not only is God our Father but our _____. 1065

8. What do the authors suggest we need to really think through in light of "Your Kingdom come."

_____

_____

_____ 1066

9. When saying, "Your will be done." Jesus is really speaking of
_____, a willing and desirous submission to Him. 1067

BIBLE STUDY!

1. Read Acts 18:1-14.

2. In verse 6, it says that Jews "became abusive." What do you think may have happened?

_____

_____

_____

_____ 1068

3. Why do you think the Lord appeared to Paul in a vision?

_____

_____ 1069

4. What do you think Paul feared?

_____

_____ 1070

5. As Paul was wrestling in fear, he had a decision to make. He could either keep on preaching to the Jews and Gentiles (facing the possibility of beatings) or he could teach those whom he had already converted and not go out to the harder parts where he would be beaten.

Circle One: True   False   1071

6. Which did he choose?

_____ 1072

7. List what you believe were the top five worst things that have happened to Paul according to 2 Corinthians 11:24-28.

_____

_____

_____

_____

_____ 1073

8. According to Acts 18, would you say the Apostle Paul was committed to "Thy kingdom come, Thy will be done?"

Circle One: Yes   No   1074

9. What was the Lord's first answer to Paul's fear?

_____ 1075

10. Why should that put Paul at ease?

_____

_____

_____ 1076

LESSON 60

CHECK WHICH CIRCLE BEST REPRESENTS YOUR LIFE TODAY:

☐

☐

☐

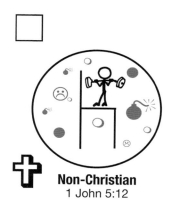

Non-Christian
1 John 5:12

Savior and Lord
Galations 5: 22-23

Savior
1 Corinthians 3:15

Since my last lesson,
I have practiced
Spiritual Breathing:

☐ 20⁺ Times
☐ 11 - 19 Times
☐ 6 - 10 Times
☐ 0 - 5 Times

CARTOON

RECEIVING THE BLESSINGS

RECEIVING THE BLESSINGS

GIVING AWAY THE BLESSINGS

RECEIVING THE BLESSINGS

Cats and Dogs prepare Differently
For The "Game of Life"

1. What is strange about the Cat on the left and what is it trying to communicate?

_____

_____

_____ 1077

2. What would the first few words of a Cat's prayer life be like with this type of attitude?

_____

_____ 1078

Lesson 60

CHRIS and SARAH

The next few weeks were a blur for Sarah. She found herself spending more and more time online, reading everything Bryan and Brittany posted on Facebook and Twitter. The more she read, the faster a hatred sprouted up inside of her toward Brittany.

At the next youth group, Pastor Jake talked about "hallowing" God's name in the context of the Lord's Prayer. She had always wondered what that meant, so she listened—kind of.

That night the thought occurred to her that maybe God let Bryan start dating someone else to motivate Sarah to "hallow" God more—and to even pray more and grow closer to God. She then reasoned that if she grew closer to God, maybe her parents would see the change in her and ease up on her, eventually allow her to date—maybe even before she was officially sixteen!

So Sarah started to try to change her life. She started trying to obey her parents more and trying to wake up earlier for Bible study in the morning. At church and youth group she focused on the worship and prayed desperately for God to bring her and Bryan back together. She started praying about other things too: that God would help her get better grades, stop fighting with Chris and her parents, and that they would get off her back.

She felt a little closer to God, but she was exhausted from trying so hard. When she wasn't praying or studying, she hopped online or on the phone and gossiped with her friends about Bryan and Brittany. Her friends kept telling her that Bryan was a jerk. She agreed outwardly, but inwardly he was still her man. Over the phone, she and her friends thought up new rumors about Brittany to try and get back at her for ruining Sarah's life.

Despite what she and her friends did, Bryan and Brittany kept dating, and Sarah's grades stayed low. Her relationship with her parents was a little better because they could see she was trying so hard. But overall, life was still miserable. Why wasn't God answering her other prayers?

Some of the rumors about Brittany made it to their youth group. Sarah had helped spread them, but only because Brittany didn't go to their church, so what did it really matter?

One evening, Chris came to her bedroom door.

"Got a sec?" he asked.

Sarah shrugged and pulled off her headphones. *What does he want now?*

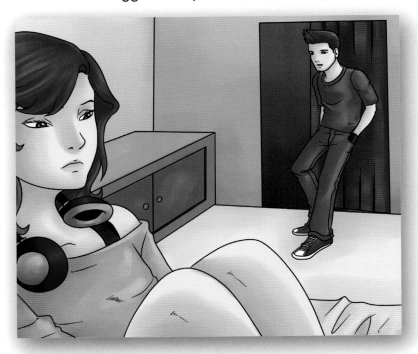

Chris leaned on her door and asked her about some of the rumors he had heard about Brittany.

"Yeah, can you believe it?" she said, hoping Chris would really take her side.

"No, not really," Chris replied, looking hard at her. "Look, Sarah, I heard you talking about her with your friends last week. I think you're the one starting these rumors. You gotta stop spreading these things about her. You don't even know Brittany."

Sarah looked hurt, but she avoided Chris' eyes. "You don't know her either. How do you know they aren't true?"

"Look, I know you don't like Brittany, and I guess I don't blame you. But you can't keep acting like this. Ripping up someone else isn't gonna make you look any better – to Bryan or anyone else."

Now Sarah was angry. Deep down, she knew Chris was right, but she didn't want to give Chris that satisfaction. "Hey, I was just kidding. Don't take it so seriously." She went a little further, "I'm fine with them dating. It's… whatever, it's fine."

Chris didn't look convinced, but he could tell she was done talking to him.

After he left, Sarah prayed about her and Bryan, asking God to change his heart and her parents' hearts so they could be together by the end of the year.   In order for that to happen, he had to sour on Brittany so she prayed for that as well…

Dear Lord, she prayed desperately, *I know I may be asking a lot, but when I turn 16— and maybe even by the end of the school year, could you please have Brittany and Bryan break up? And then could he start liking me again, please? And Lord if You did that, I would so… um, what did Pastor Jake say, "Hallow Your name." I would really praise You and thank You and totally obey my parents and get my grades up, Lord, if you'd just do that please.*

Though Sarah hadn't really seen God answer a prayer in a long time, she wondered if this "hallowing thing" might just be the trick. Soon Sarah began daydreaming of new ways she could flirt with Bryan when he was single again. She just had to have faith.

Then her mind came back to reality, and she thought of Chris. *Ugh. Brothers.* She hopped online to talk with her friends to blow off some steam about him. How dare he think she was the reason for the rumors. After all these years, couldn't he tell when she was just joking?

Aren't brothers supposed to love you? Aren't they supposed to be sensitive to you? What a jerk.

Lesson 60 Questions: (The suggested answers are on page 53 in the *Answer Key.*)

1. How were Sarah's rumors about Brittany violating Ephesians 4:31?

_____

_____

2. How was Sarah's motivation for walking with God "Catish" and how do you think God viewed it?

_____

_____

3. How did Sarah's prayer miss the whole idea of "hallowing God's name" and how was her prayer like a business contract?

_____

_____

4. How was Sarah's attitude toward her brother hypocritical?

_____

_____

Oh Lord, I need to pass this quiz.

QUIZ!

1. James 4:3 tells us that
   A. God wants to answer all of our prayers.
   B. God only answers selfish prayers.
   C. God doesn't answer selfish prayers. [1079]

2. Many Christians are taught that to ask God to lavishly provide for our wants is their right as a believer.
   A. True
   B. False [1080]

3. The Bible says that after we come to know Christ, we have
   A. one nature.
   B. two natures. [1081]

4. Once we become a Christian, our old nature
   A. is nailed to the cross.
   B. dies.
   C. no longer has full control over our lives. [1082]

5. When you go to have a quiet time or pray to God, your old nature excuses itself and doesn't interfere.
   A. True
   B. False [1083]

6. Many Cat Christians have concluded that prayer
   A. doesn't work.
   B. is only for holy people.
   C. should focus on them. [1084]

7. The Lord's prayer is a pattern that we should follow. Praying it word for word is OK, but not mandatory.
   A. True
   B. False [1085]

8. Christians really need to ask themselves a tough question before they pray, and that is,

   A. "Are they really committed to living for themselves?"

   B. "Are they really committed to living for God's kingdom?"

   C. "Are they really praying in the right position?" ¹⁰⁸⁶

9. The opening words of the Lord's prayer ("hallowed be Thy name) refers to

   A. making God famous.

   B. making God look good.

   C. God wanting to focus on us.

   D. lifting up and exalting God and His ways. ¹⁰⁸⁷

10. When we pray "Your will be done," Jesus is really asking,

   A. "Am I Lord of your life?"

   B. "Are you willing to submit to Me?"

   C. "How can I make you happy?"

   D. All of the above. ¹⁰⁸⁸

What are you going to do differently as a result of what you've learned? **Go to the end of your workbook and write it in for Lesson 60.** ¹⁰⁸⁹

PERSONAL
APPLICATION

OPTIONAL LESSON

Go to **www.UnveilinGLORY.com** and click on the left side: Free Online Teaching.

• Once there, click on "Guest."

• In the top right where it says "Choose a Series" choose "The Dangers of Cat Theology."

• Listen to the "God Only Speaks To Me" lesson.

There is no quiz, no notes to be taken. Just enjoy and learn!

LESSON 61

CHECK WHICH CIRCLE BEST REPRESENTS YOUR LIFE TODAY:

☐   ☐   ☐

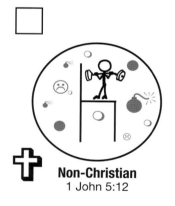

Non-Christian
1 John 5:12

Savior and Lord
Galations 5: 22-23

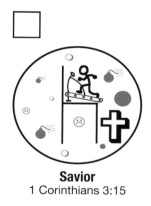

Savior
1 Corinthians 3:15

Since my last lesson,
I have practiced
Spiritual Breathing:

☐ 20⁺ Times

☐ 11 - 19 Times

☐ 6 - 10 Times

☐ 0 - 5 Times

READING
ASSIGNMENT

CAT & DOG PRAYER

RETHINKING OUR CONVERSATIONS
WITH OUR MASTER

Bob Sjogren & Gerald Robison

Start reading at the top of page 22 and read to the middle of page 28 where it says "And Do Not Lead Us Into Temptation."

Questions to answer from the reading assignment:

1. Note that half of the Lord's prayer is completed before our _____, our _____, and our _____ _____ are even mentioned. [1090]

2. Why did the prayer for Brianna fall short?

_____

_____ [1091]

3. Why was Gerald's prayer for his dog at first self-centered?

_____

_____

_____

_____ [1092]

4. Why did God allow the manna to spoil at the end of each day?

_____

_____

_____

_____

_____ [1093]

5. Why do most American Christians not understand the need to trust God on a daily basis?

_____

_____ [1094]

6. Explain the warning in Deuteronomy in your own words.

_____

_____

_____

_____ 1095

7. What three questions do the authors suggest we need to consider when praying?

_____

_____

_____ 1096

8. Why do the Scriptures say that many husbands' prayers aren't answered?

_____

_____ 1097

9. To God, _____ count.   Poor ones can keep your prayers from being heard. 1098

1. Read Matthew 5:21-24.

2. The word "But" at the beginning of verse 22 is telling you that Jesus is trying to say something a bit different from their understanding of the previous words, "Do not murder." Circle which of these you think applies:

    A. The Jewish teachers had taught that nothing except actual murder was forbidden by the sixth commandment, thus they explained away its spiritual implications.

    B. What they understand about the sixth commandment was not incorrect, but incomplete.

    C. Christ was going to tell them that all anger in the heart is murder. 1099

3. Christ contrasts two words, "_____" and "_____." The first is said out of pride (it is a term of contempt), the other is said out of anger. [1100]

4. In essence, Christ is saying, "Though you think saying these words to people is no big deal, to God it is a huge deal and you will be judged simply based on having said these words."

  Circle One: True   False   [1101]

5. This is non-verbally communicating that to God, relationships are _____. [1102]

6. The old phrase, "Sticks and stones may break my bones but words will never hurt me" is totally wrong according to God.

  Circle One: True   False   [1103]

7. After talking about our relationship with others, Jesus then talks about our _____ with God. [1104]

8. According to verse 23, who was the one who has done the "damage" in a relationship, you or your brother?

  Circle One: You   Your brother   [1105]

9. What does the word "reconcile" mean?

  _____

  _____ [1106]

10. Which of the following lessons can we learn from this passage?

  A. If I'm having a quiet time and realize I've hurt someone, I should go ahead with my quiet time and talk to the person later.

  B. If I'm having a quiet times and realize I've hurt someone, I should stop my quiet time and go and take care of it.

  C. Broken/damaged/hurt relationships can directly affect my relationship with God. [1107]

LESSON 62

CHECK WHICH CIRCLE BEST REPRESENTS YOUR LIFE TODAY:

☐

☐

☐

Non-Christian
1 John 5:12

Savior and Lord
Galations 5: 22-23

Savior
1 Corinthians 3:15

Since my last lesson,
I have practiced
Spiritual Breathing:

☐ 20⁺ Times

☐ 11 - 19 Times

☐ 6 - 10 Times

☐ 0 - 5 Times

READING ASSIGNMENT

CAT & DOG PRAYER

RETHINKING OUR CONVERSATIONS WITH OUR MASTER

Bob Sjogren & Gerald Robison

Start reading at the middle of page 28 where it says "And Do Not Lead Us Into Temptation" and finish out the chapter (page 31).

Questions to answer from the reading assignment:

1. Asking God to "lead us not into temptation but to deliver us from evil" is not simply so that we will have a safe, soft, comfortable life. There is a reason we are to pray this. What is it?

_____

_____ 1108

2. We should have great peace in the thought that God never slumbers or sleeps, because He is keeping _____ over us. 1109

3. If the devil does affect us, it is with our Father's _____ and with His _____ goal in mind. 1110

4. What was God's answer to Paul when he asked the Lord to take away his weakness?

_____

_____ 1111

5. List the top two lessons that pop out at you at the top of page 30.

_____

_____

_____

_____ 1112

6. One of the things that will keep us praying like this is realizing that we are a _____ of Satan. 1113

7. Satan wants to ruin your life so that…

_____ 1114

8. You may face tragedy, calamity, distress, adversity, persecution, weakness and more. This doesn't mean that God isn't _____ your _____. [1115]

9. The pattern of prayer that Jesus gave us both starts and ends in _____. [1116]

10. Circle what lessons can we learn from this.

    A. A great way to start off my quiet time is jump right in to interceding for others.

    B. A great way to start off my quiet time is simply to worship and enjoy God.

    C. My needs should be directly related to somehow advancing God's kingdom.

    D. Praying, "Dear Lord, please bless this food we are about to receive" is incomplete.

    E. Praying, "Dear Lord, please bless this food we are about to receive so that we might have strength to continue to further your kingdom" is complete. [1117]

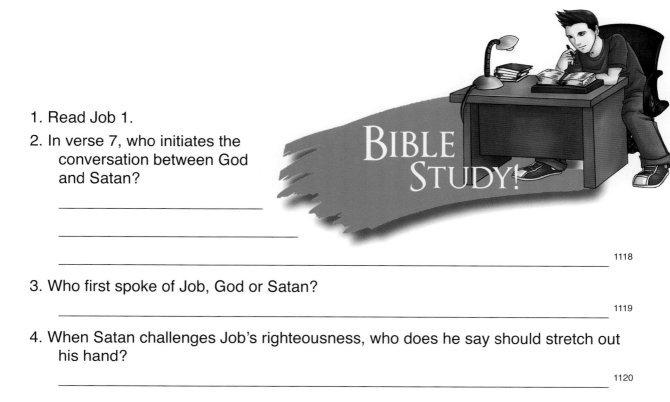

BIBLE STUDY!

1. Read Job 1.

2. In verse 7, who initiates the conversation between God and Satan?

_____

_____

_____ [1118]

3. Who first spoke of Job, God or Satan?

_____ [1119]

4. When Satan challenges Job's righteousness, who does he say should stretch out his hand?

_____ [1120]

5. When God says (NIV), "Very well, then" what is He basically communicating He is going to do in light of Satan's request?

_____
1121

6. But instead of stretching out His hand, what does God do?

_____

_____
1122

7. Name what "instruments" Satan uses to accomplish God's will.

_____

_____
1123

8. When Job says, "The Lord has taken away," who is he blaming for all of the terrible things that have happened in his life?

_____
1124

9. What tells you in verse 22 that Job was not wrong in attributing all of these things to the Lord?

_____
1125

10. Circle which lessons we can learn from this chapter.

    A. Satan cannot do anything unless God gives him permission.

    B. Even when Satan does something, we can attribute it to God's sovereign guidance.

    C. Satan can influence people and storms just like God can.

    D. Satan can act outside of God's will. [1126]

LESSON 63

CHECK WHICH CIRCLE BEST REPRESENTS YOUR LIFE TODAY:

☐   ☐   ☐

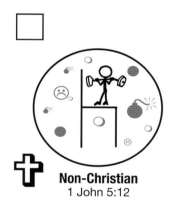

Non-Christian
1 John 5:12

Savior and Lord
Galations 5: 22-23

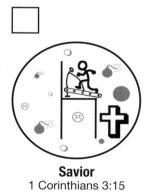

Savior
1 Corinthians 3:15

Since my last lesson,
I have practiced
Spiritual Breathing:

☐ 20⁺ Times

☐ 11 - 19 Times

☐ 6 - 10 Times

☐ 0 - 5 Times

CARTOON

Cat and Dog Youth Minister Prayers

1. How is a Cat youth pastor trying to motivate people into the Kingdom?

_____

_____

_____
1127

2. If youth start coming because it is "cool," how will that motivation keep them going when things get tough and there is persecution—possibly even a threat on their lives?

_____

_____

_____

_____
1128

Lesson 63

CHRIS and SARAH

The week before Easter, Pastor Jake showed another one of his eye-opening videos. It was about West Africa, an area of the world filled with sand, scrubby trees, and unreal poverty. The students saw photos of emaciated children and starving women. They saw tiny huts that housed 10-12 people, and kids playing in water with raw sewage flowing next to it.

It was the kind of video that made everyone uncomfortable. Some students watched with compassion. Some, like Sarah, were moved but obviously confused.

How could there be so much poverty in one place? If there was no food, where were the stores? Didn't governments have food stamps for these situations? Why didn't they get jobs? She found it hard to believe there were still places in the world where people washed their clothes by hand and cooked food over an open fire.

Chris was moved as well. He had seen videos like this before, but this time he felt a stirring inside him. He went home and prayed about it. Jake's video had challenged Chris in two ways, and he was really struggling with one of them.

He had expected the first challenge. After showing the video, Jake told the students about an opportunity to donate money to build wells for some of the remote villages. The wells would provide clean water to families that had to walk miles each day in the desert heat to the nearest wells, families that were dying from disease and dehydration. Chris had heard dozens of these talks in church, and he had even donated to them a few times.

Then Jake said something that struck a cord in Chris' soul. He mentioned that these people were gathering in wooden huts to worship God. Their scrawny faces haunted Chris and even challenged him. In all their poverty, they were worshipping God. They were thanking Him for what they did have.

One evening as Chris sat on his floor, leaning over his open Bible, it occurred to him that these people were much better Christians than he was. All his life he had been told to rely on God. But if he was honest with himself, he had never understood what that meant. Everything he needed was already his. He had never gone hungry or needed to walk for miles to get clean water. All he had to do was go to the fridge or turn on the faucet. He never gave a second thought as to how good he had it.

Chris thought of what he had considered "needs" before seeing the video from Africa. His savings account was packed with money for a new laptop – a laptop he said he "needed" after his turned three years old and some of the hardware was outdated.

He had worked hard for that money, building a small business doing lawn care and landscaping in his neighborhood.

God, maybe this is crazy, he prayed, *but I want to rely more on You with this. And I think you want me to give this money to help build that well. But I want to know that if I give this money away, You will still provide me with either the money or the extra work I need to get a new laptop – but only when I really need it. Please make that so Lord. So, for your glory, I think I'm going to give this money in your name!*

The next week, Chris nearly emptied his savings account. However, when he arrived home, he took a photo Jake had given him of the villagers in the video and tacked it onto his bulletin board.

He tweeted, "So today I emptied my bank account for the well project in West Africa. To God be the glory."

When Sarah saw his tweet, she burst out of her bedroom and went straight to him going ballistic! "Chris, what are you doing? You said you were going to give me your old laptop when you got a new one. You know how I hate borrowing yours and dad's. And now you've given that money away? What were you thinking?"

"I'm still going to give you my old laptop," Chris replied, trying not to get agitated by her. "It's just going to take a little longer than I thought."

"Why in the world did you do that?" she demanded.

"I felt the Lord leading me to do it." He hesitated. He didn't want to sound like he was preaching to her, but she was staring daggers at him with her hands on her hips. Her "I'm not satisfied" look demanded more of an answer. She stood there waiting.

"Okay, so I thought it would give Him glory and that He would be pleased with it."

There. Argue with that.

"Well, aren't you holy, Saint Christopher? Do you think God is pleased that I'm not getting your laptop?"

"Sarah, quit being so selfish. Didn't you hear what the video said? These people have to walk miles through the desert just to get clean water. It's real; it's not just some movie they showed us for fun. Thousands are dying without it, and I just wanted to help. So I prayed and decided to give all my money away for them. Don't judge me."

"Yes, but in doing so, you gave away my laptop. Besides, didn't you see how expensive those wells are? You probably didn't even have enough to build a whole one. What big difference did it really make?"

Chris wanted to literally hit her, but he held off. Trying to control himself, he said, "Sarah, between you having a laptop and them living, it wasn't a hard decision. They needed it more."

"Why don't you ever think of me, Chris? Just once. Just once I wish you'd think of me and put my needs first. I'm your sister. Sometimes I think you care more about all those homeless and poor people than you care about me."

With that, Sarah stomped into her bedroom and slammed the door behind her. She vented her anger at God. "Okay Lord, no boyfriend, no laptop, what's next? I don't even know why I go to church or to youth group any more. You're not blessing me at all."

Lesson 63 Questions: (The suggested answers are on page 53 in the *Answer Key.*)

1. How did the people in West Africa probably rely on God more than Chris did and why?

_____

_____

2. What was Chris non-verbally communicating when he gave away all of his savings for the laptop to help dig the well, and how do you think God felt at that point?

_____

_____

3. What was Sarah non-verbally communicating to God when she reacted to Chris' tweet, and how do you think God felt at that point?

_____

_____

4. What did Sarah think were God's ways of blessing her, and how was she wrong?

_____

_____

QUIZ!

1. In the Lord's prayer, the first thing we are to address are our needs.
   - A. True
   - B. False [1129]

2. Having credit cards has really helped people
   - A. get into debt.
   - B. draw closer to God.
   - C. get farther away from God. [1130]

3. God wants us to trust Him for our daily bread. This means
   - A. not thinking about him as we go to the grocery store is OK.
   - B. He wants us trusting Him each and every day.
   - C. God is against preservatives. [1131]

4. Sometimes a husband's prayer will not be heard because
   - A. they don't live with their wives in an understanding way.
   - B. they don't honor their wives.
   - C. there is sin in their lives.
   - D. All of the above. [1132]

5. Having a poor relationship with someone else can hinder your prayers, whether you are a husband or not.
   - A. True
   - B. False [1133]

6. When Jesus told us to pray, "lead us not into temptation but deliver us from evil" God is communicating
   - A. He wants us to have a safe, soft, comfortable life.
   - B. He wants to use us to expand His kingdom.
   - C. He knows sin can keep us from accomplishing His purposes through us. [1134]

7. Sometimes a weakness in our lives can

    A. draw us closer to God.

    B. be used to keep us humble.

    C. be God's purpose for our lives. [1135]

8. Satan isn't really interested in targeting individuals like you and your friends, he just wants to target pastors.

    A. True

    B. False [1136]

9. The authors suggest that the primary reason why Satan wants to destroy you is

    A. to ruin your life.

    B. keep you from glorifying God.

    C. satisfy his need for hate. [1137]

10. A great way to start off a quiet time is to

    A. jump right in interceding for others.

    B. take a quick nap.

    C. praise God for who He is.

    D. exalt His name. [1138]

PERSONAL APPLICATION

What are you going to do differently as a result of what you've learned? **Go to the end of your workbook and write it in for Lesson 63.** [1139]

OPTIONAL LESSON

Go to **www.UnveilinGLORY.com** and click on the left side:

Free Online Teaching.

• Once there, click on "Guest."

• In the top right where it says "Choose Series" choose "The Dangers of Cat Theology."

• Listen to the "Half the Cross" lesson.

There is no quiz, no notes to be taken. Just enjoy and learn!

a

LESSON 64

CHECK WHICH CIRCLE BEST REPRESENTS YOUR LIFE TODAY:

☐   ☐   ☐

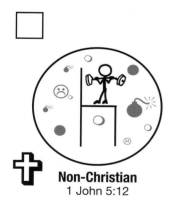

Non-Christian
1 John 5:12

Savior and Lord
Galations 5: 22-23

Savior
1 Corinthians 3:15

Since my last lesson,
I have practiced
Spiritual Breathing:

☐ 20⁺ Times
☐ 11 - 19 Times
☐ 6 - 10 Times
☐ 0 - 5 Times

READING ASSIGNMENT

CAT & DOG PRAYER

RETHINKING OUR CONVERSATIONS WITH OUR MASTER

Bob Sjogren & Gerald Robison

Begin reaching chapter 3 on page 33 and read to the bottom of page 36.

Questions to answer from the reading assignment:

1. What is the analogy between the "Bill and Melinda Gates'" blank check and our prayers?

_____

_____

_____ 1140

2. Jesus didn't say, "Rhetorically or theoretically I say unto you," He said, "Truly, Truly I say to you." What does this mean and why did Jesus repeat "truly" twice?

_____

_____

_____ 1141

3. When we end a prayer with the words, "In Jesus' name, amen" we are guaranteed to get what we've asked for.

　　Circle One:　True　　False　　1142

4. Throughout the New Testament, not _____ _____ ends "in Jesus' name." 1143

5. In the Scriptures, what did a person's name represent?

_____

_____ 1144

6. When Dogs pray "in Jesus' name," what are they basically saying?

_____

_____

_____ 1145

7. Before we utter any words in prayer, we should be making absolutely certain that our request is in _____ with God's will and purposes. 1146

8. What should praying "in Jesus' name" cause us to evaluate?

_____

_____ 1147

9. If Jesus wouldn't make this request, then _____ should we. 1148

BIBLE STUDY!

1. Read Nehemiah 1.
2. Read Deuteronomy 8:10-20 and summarize what put the Israelites into exile?

_____

_____

_____

_____

_____

_____ 1149

3. How long was the exile to be? (See Jeremiah 29:10)

_____ 1150

4. Why do you think Nehemiah wept in verse four?

_____

_____ 1151

5. Because he saw that God's city was in ruins, what did it move him to do?

_____ 1152

6. When he says in verse 8, "Remember the instructions you gave your servant Moses," how is that praying "in Jesus' name?"

_____

_____ 1153

7. What does it mean that Jerusalem was to be "a dwelling place for" God's Name?

_____

_____ 1154

8. If Jerusalem was to be in ruins, how did that reflect upon God?

_____

_____ 1155

9. If Jerusalem was to be modern and new (in splendor), how does that reflect upon God?

_____

_____ 1156

10. In Nehemiah 2:5, Nehemiah asks the king if he can go and rebuild Jerusalem. Do you think this was in line with what God wanted and how does that reflect what we've learned in this chapter about a "blank check?"

_____

_____

_____ 1157

LESSON 65

CHECK WHICH CIRCLE BEST REPRESENTS YOUR LIFE TODAY:

☐   ☐   ☐

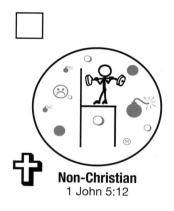

Non-Christian
1 John 5:12

Savior and Lord
Galations 5: 22-23

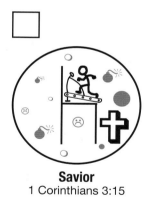

Savior
1 Corinthians 3:15

Since my last lesson,
I have practiced
Spiritual Breathing:

☐ 20⁺ Times
☐ 11 - 19 Times
☐ 6 - 10 Times
☐ 0 - 5 Times

READING ASSIGNMENT

Start at the top of page 37 and finish out the chapter (page 42).

Questions to answer from the reading assignment:

1. In the two prayers that are looked at in this reading, the authors focused on the _____ for each prayer. [1158]

2. Why does Joshua 7:7-9a seem to "meow?"

_____

_____ [1159]

3. Why does verse 9b make it "bark?"

_____

_____ [1160]

4. While Joshua's prayer was for the future of his people, it was ultimately for—and based on—the reputation and name of _____ _____. [1161]

5. How can praying for our needs be both incomplete and right?

_____

_____

_____

_____ [1162]

6. Even though Daniel saw his people in a terrible situation, Daniel still began his prayer in _____ . [1163]

7. Look up the word "reproach" and write the definition.

_____

_____ [1164]

8. Write in your own words what it meant for Israel to be a "reproach" to the nations around them.

_____

_____

_____ 1165

9. Ultimately this prayer was about _____, not just His people. 1166

10. Write down what draws God into acting on our prayers and what God is not drawn to.

_____

_____

_____ 1167

11. Daniel and Joshua prayed big prayers. One asked for _____ for an entire nation. The other asked for the _____ of an entire nation. Both were motivated for God's _____. 1168

BIBLE STUDY!

1. Read 2 Kings 6:8-22.

2. With whom was Israel at war?

_____

_____

_____ 1169

3. Why was the King of Aram so mad?

_____ 1170

4. King Aram sent the "strong force" at night to capture Elisha. Because it was at night, do you think it took God by surprise?

Circle One: Yes   No   1171

5. God had warned Elisha to tell the king of Israel about King Aram's moves, and He knew that King Aram was going after Elisha, but it doesn't appear that God warned Elisha about King Aram's moves against him (Elisha) as a person.   Why do you think God didn't do this?

_____

_____

_____ 1172

6. In verses 15 and 16, list some words that might describe the feelings of Elisha's servants at that point?

_____ 1173

7. What did Elisha know as a result of his faith?

_____

_____ 1174

8. Elisha prayed three amazing prayers. What were they?

_____

_____

_____

_____

_____

_____ 1175

9. In your own opinion, which do you think was the most miraculous and why?

_____

_____ 1176

10. Have you heard of any prayers like this being answered in your lifetime?
    Circle One: Yes   No   1177

11. What ended the wars between the King of Aram and the King of Israel?

_____ 1178

LESSON 66

CHECK WHICH CIRCLE BEST REPRESENTS YOUR LIFE TODAY:

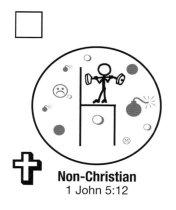

Non-Christian
1 John 5:12

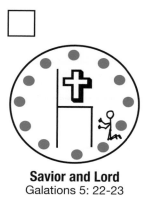

Savior and Lord
Galations 5: 22-23

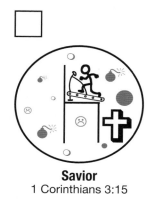

Savior
1 Corinthians 3:15

Since my last lesson,
I have practiced
Spiritual Breathing:

❏ 20⁺ Times
❏ 11 - 19 Times
❏ 6 - 10 Times
❏ 0 - 5 Times

CARTOON

Cats And Dogs On The Athletic Field

1. What do you think was the primary goal of the Cat in playing this sport?

_____ 1179

2. Why do you think the Dog had such a better attitude and was able to encourage the Cat and not feel threatened?

_____

_____

_____

_____ 1180

CHRIS and SARAH

Sarah loved the spring. The world blossomed around her and filled her with new hope. She knew she had been moody and hard to live with the past few months. Thankfully, it was hard to stay that way when the outdoors was drenched in sunlight and new life. Track started, and she threw herself into the practices. Maybe she should just let go of this whole Bryan and Brittany thing for a while. She still had a few months before she turned 16.

Every now and then her family had what they called "popcorn prayers" around the table. After dinner, they would bow their heads and just pray out loud for whatever they felt led to pray. On the evening before Sarah's first track meet—one with seven schools participating—her dad had them do just that.

Sarah knew exactly what she was going to pray.

"Lord, thank you for my family and for the track meet tomorrow. Please help me to run well; protect me and everyone else from injury. In Jesus' name, I pray."

There was a brief silence then Chris spoke up.

"God, thank you for my sister. Thank you that she has this opportunity to play a sport she loves and that she excels in. I pray for You to be greatly glorified through her running. Cause her to be a light for You, to show Your love and glory to the other athletes she interacts with at the meets and at practice. If she wins, may she win for Your glory. If she loses, may she lose for Your glory. Whatever happens, may she run well for You, in Jesus' name."

Their parents prayed about Sarah's meet as well, but she hardly heard a word. She turned Chris' prayer over in her mind. *Running for God's glory? Losing for God's glory? What did God's glory have to do with track?* Wasn't she the one bending over backwards to beat her time and hone her skills? Sure, she knew God could make her better, but how was she supposed to show His love to the other runners? They were just there to compete.

The next day the meet came. As a freshman new to the team, Sarah was stoked and nervous all at the same time. She had been working hard, and her times were getting better. She had almost beaten the senior with whom she competed. As she did her final stretches, she prayed one last time. "Okay, God, this is it. Please help me win."

Before the gunshot had time to hang in the air, Sarah was off and running. Chris and her mom cheered her on. She could hear them screaming even from half way around the track. It was at this point that she realized something very, very bad. She was giving it all she had, and she was only in third place thus far…and losing steam.

Sarah couldn't drive her legs any faster. Unfortunately other girls behind her could. Although first for her school, Sarah ended up in sixth place out of the twenty-one girls representing the seven schools competing.

She wanted to cry. Some of the others who had beaten her approached to congratulate her, but she turned and walked the other direction, not wanting them to see her tears.

On her way home, both Chris and her mom tried to encourage her. However, nothing worked. She simply stared out the window at the daffodils popping out of the ground.

"Hey sis," Chris asked, "Why are you so down?"

"If that isn't the stupidest question I've ever heard!" Sarah replied with all the sarcasm she could come up with. "I just took sixth place in the only event I ran and was hoping I could win. Why else would I be so down?"

"But Sarah," her mom continued, "You were first for your team. That's the first time you've done that. That should encourage you."

"Oh mom," Sarah said without thinking, "Shut up."

"Sarah, don't talk to mom that way," Chris quickly replied.

Their mother looked in the rear view mirror directly at Sarah and gave her a look that said, "I agree with Chris. What are you going to do, young lady?"

"I'm sorry, Mom," Sarah mumbled, but her heart lacked true repentance.

There was a long pause then Chris finally offered, "Sis, did you do your best?"

"Yes," she said, looking out the window and blinking furiously, trying to hold back a fresh wave of tears.

"Well, then did you run for God or for yourself?"

"Run for God? Chris, you come up with some of the stupidest sayings. No, I didn't run for God, I ran for myself. I've run all the practices. I did all the hard work. I pushed it as hard as I could. I didn't see God out there running with me." Her voice trailed off in silence, communicating her desire to drop the topic.

Chris thought to himself. *Well, no wonder she can't lose for God's glory. She was never running for Him anyhow.*

Lesson 66 Questions: **(The suggested answers are on page 54 in the *Answer Key*.)**

1. How did Sarah's first prayer at the dinner table differ from her second prayer right before she ran the event?

   _____

   _____

2. How was Sarah's attitude toward losing pure Cat?

   _____

   _____

3. How could Sarah have been a Dog and shown God's love and glory to those who beat her?

   _____

   _____

4. If Sarah had been a Dog, what should her attitude have been?

   _____

   _____

Oh Lord, I need to pass this quiz.

QUIZ!

1. God puts a limit on what we can ask Him.
    A. True
    B. False [1181]

2. When we end our prayer with the words "in Jesus' name, Amen" we are guaranteed to get what we prayed for.
    A. True
    B. False [1182]

3. When a person prays "in Jesus name," they are basically saying,
    A. "Jesus, I know you want to give me the best life possible."
    B. "Jesus, this is something I know you would ask for."
    C. "Jesus, I know this is primarily to glorify you."
    D. Both B and C. [1183]

4. Our motivation in prayer should be primarily about
    A. advancing our kingdom.
    B. advancing God's kingdom. [1184]

5. If we think that Jesus wouldn't be praying the prayer we want to pray, then
    A. we have an opportunity to teach something new to Christ.
    B. we probably shouldn't be praying that prayer either.
    C. it probably isn't God's will.
    D. All of the above. [1185]

6. Joshua's prayer in Joshua 7:7-9 tells us that
    A. it's not OK to pray for ourselves.
    B. we can pray for ourselves in the context of glorifying His great name.
    C. we should always pray for ourselves. [1186]

7. Praying for our needs

    A. is always wrong.

    B. is always right.

    C. is best done in light of glorifying His great name. [1187]

8. When Daniel was in the midst of the enemy (Babylon) he still started his prayers with

    A. petitions for his nation.

    B. petitions for himself.

    C. praise. [1188]

9. Daniel was worried about the nation of Israel becoming a reproach to the nations around them. This tells us that

    A. we should be concerned about how our lives reflects God to others around us.

    B. we should let the politicians worry about Israel.

    C. we don't need to worry about Israel, Daniel already did. [1189]

10. Joshua and Daniel prayed big prayers. One asked to deliver an entire nation. Another asked God to rebuild an entire nation. What we can learn from this is that

    A. God is tired and we shouldn't bother Him asking for more big things.

    B. we can ask God for BIG prayers just like them.

    C. there is no limit to what we can ask God for.

    D. None of the above [1190]

PERSONAL APPLICATION

What are you going to do differently as a result of what you've learned? **Go to the end of your workbook and write it in for Lesson 66.** [1191]

OPTIONAL LESSON

Go to **www.UnveilinGLORY.com** and click on the left side: Free Online Teaching.

• Once there, click on "Guest."

• In the top right where it says "Choose a Series" choose "The Dangers of Cat Theology."

• Listen to the "Worship" lesson.

There is no quiz, no notes to be taken. Just enjoy and learn!

CAUTION! The more your life is changed, the easier it is to spot Cat behavior in those around you. **Please don't ever use this material to judge others.** ("Oh, they are just a bunch of Cats.") Once we start judging others, we too are acting like Cats. **Use this material to encourage yourself and others to live for God's glory.**

LESSON 67

CHECK WHICH CIRCLE BEST REPRESENTS YOUR LIFE TODAY:

☐   ☐   ☐

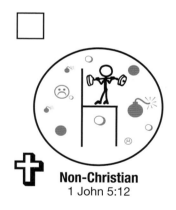

Non-Christian
1 John 5:12

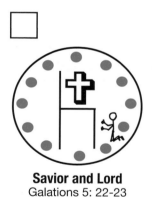

Savior and Lord
Galations 5: 22-23

Savior
1 Corinthians 3:15

Since my last lesson,
I have practiced
Spiritual Breathing:

☐ 20⁺ Times
☐ 11 - 19 Times
☐ 6 - 10 Times
☐ 0 - 5 Times

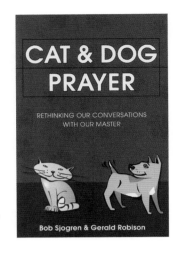

CAT & DOG PRAYER

RETHINKING OUR CONVERSATIONS WITH OUR MASTER

Bob Sjogren & Gerald Robison

READING ASSIGNMENT

Start reading chapter 4 on page 43 and end when you see "Cause Me Prayers" (page 48).

Questions to answer from the reading assignment:

1. Jesus said, "Whatever you ask in My name, that will I do so that you may have a safe, soft, easy and comfortable life right where you are."

   Circle One: True   False   [1192]

2. Write why Jesus wants to answer your prayers according to John 14:13.

   _____ [1193]

3. In John 16:23-24, Jesus speaks of another reason why He wants to answer our prayers, what is it?

   _____ [1194]

4. Do these two motivations contradict each other?

   Circle One: Yes   No   [1195]

5. Write how those two verses do not have to contradict each other.

   _____

   _____ [1196]

6. To a person who has never experienced this kind of joy, it might be difficult for them to understand how you can be joyful in _____ _____ glory. [1197]

7. Prayer is not calling on a celestial _____ _____ to fulfill our wishes. [1198]

8. Explain the Olympics analogy.

   _____

   _____

   _____

   _____

   _____

_____

_____

_____

_____

_____ 1199

9. All of the works that we do in our own power and strength are going to
_____ _____. 1200

10. Much of a Cat's life is _____ _____ because Cats live mostly
out of their own _____. 1201

1. Read Psalm 127.

2. According to verse 1, is it possible
to "build our" lives in vain?

Circle One: Yes   No 1202

3. How does Matthew 7:26,27
agree with this?

BIBLE
STUDY!

_____

_____

_____

_____ 1203

4. How could a city "fall" even if a watchman is watching over it?

_____

_____

_____ 1204

5. From a dictionary, define the word "toil" used in the NIV in verse 2.

_____

_____ 1205

6. Explain what it means to toil for food in vain?

_____

_____ 1206

7. How does 1 Corinthians 15:10 agree with this?

_____

_____

_____ 1207

8. Circle the following ways the Lord can take away your hard earned money, hence you would be laboring "in vain."

   A. You buy something you realize soon after, you really didn't want.

   B. Something breaks down and needs to be fixed.

   C. You unexpectedly go out with friends and have to buy food you weren't expecting to purchase.

   D. Your pet gets sick and you are faced with a big bill. [1208]

LESSON 68

CHECK WHICH CIRCLE BEST REPRESENTS YOUR LIFE TODAY:

☐   ☐   ☐

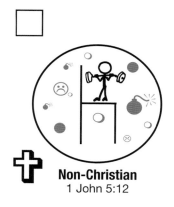

Non-Christian
1 John 5:12

Savior and Lord
Galations 5: 22-23

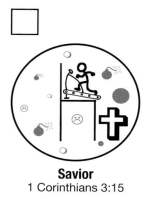

Savior
1 Corinthians 3:15

Since my last lesson,
I have practiced
Spiritual Breathing:

☐ 20⁺ Times

☐ 11 - 19 Times

☐ 6 - 10 Times

☐ 0 - 5 Times

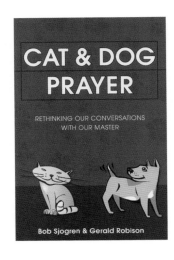

READING ASSIGNMENT

CAT & DOG PRAYER

RETHINKING OUR CONVERSATIONS WITH OUR MASTER

Bob Sjogren & Gerald Robison

Start on page 48 at "Cause Me Prayers" and finish out the chapter (page 53).

Questions to answer from the reading assignment:

1. What does the author say are the two key words in Ezekiel 36:26,27 on page 49?

   _____ _____ 1209

2. What did God clearly not say?

   _____ 1210

3. The true work that needs to be done in our lives is a _____ _____. That is why we can do _____ by ourselves. 1211

4. What does Romans 8:8 say cannot please God?

   _____

   _____ 1212

5. The first reason God wants to do the work Himself is due to the fact that it is a spiritual matter. List the second.

   _____

   _____ 1213

6. Explain the difference between a "Cause Me" prayer and a "Help Me" prayer in your own words.

   _____

   _____

   _____

   _____

   _____

   _____ 1214

   _____

7. If we are praying "Cause Me" prayers, why shouldn't we just be "couch potatoes" and let God do everything?

_____

_____

_____ 1215

8. Fill in the rest of this sentence in your own words. "Lord, I'm going to have my quiet times, but…"

_____

_____ 1216

9. Fill in the rest of this sentence in your own words. "Lord, I'm still going to share my faith, but…"

_____

_____ 1217

10. Fill in the rest of this sentence in your own words, "Lord, I'm still going to put a filter on my computer to keep me away from pornography, but…"

_____

_____

_____ 1218

11. Do the words you pray really matter to God? Why or why not?

_____

_____ 1219

12. The best way you can honor God and glorify Him is to bring Him your

_____ and _____. 1220

BIBLE STUDY!

1. Read the following passages below and write down why the people who prayed these prayers were forced to be 100% dependent upon God.

a. 1 Samuel 1:3-11

_____

_____ 1221

b. Daniel 3:13-23

_____

_____ 1222

c. Daniel 6:1-16

_____

_____ 1223

2. Explain why most Americans don't have the need to pray "Cause Me" prayers when praying for their "daily bread".

_____

_____ 1224

3. In order for Americans to pray "Cause Me" prayers, they really have to be determined in their mind to see life as being totally dependent upon God.

   Circle One: True   False   1225

4. Circle which of the following verses agrees with what is written in question #3.

   A. Acts 17:28

   B. Psalm 42:12

   C. Colossians 1:16,17

   D. Isaiah 45:7 1226

LESSON 69

CHECK WHICH CIRCLE BEST REPRESENTS YOUR LIFE TODAY:

☐   ☐   ☐

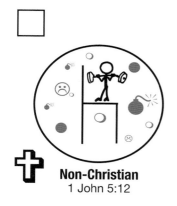

Non-Christian
1 John 5:12

Savior and Lord
Galations 5: 22-23

Savior
1 Corinthians 3:15

Since my last lesson,
I have practiced
Spiritual Breathing:

☐ 20⁺ Times
☐ 11 - 19 Times
☐ 6 - 10 Times
☐ 0 - 5 Times

CARTOON

Responding To God's
Heart For The Nations

1. Why does the Cat not respond to God's heart for the nations?

_____

_____ 1227

2. What will the Dog do if God makes it clear they are to go?

_____ 1228

3. Why is God likely to answer the Dog's prayer?

_____

_____ 1229

CHRIS and SARAH

Two weeks later when Sarah got to the locker room after another meet, she flung her towel at the lockers while screaming in frustration. The towel flopped harmlessly onto the floor, but Sarah lowered herself onto the bench in front of it and fought back the anger and tears bubbling inside.

They were halfway through the season, and her track career might as well be over. After the first meet, she started doing better, but now she was losing most of the races. All this hard work for nothing, she thought to herself. It was too far into the season to try switching events, and her frustration was seeping into other areas of her life.

It didn't help that she had just been grounded again for not doing her chores. She and her mom seemed to be fighting all the time, and just the previous night her dad had to break up the shouting. It was a miracle they let her come to the meet today.

But I might as well have stayed home, she thought bitterly as she remembered her poor performance.

After finishing in the locker room, she headed back towards the track. A few of her friends were competing today, too, and she wanted to cheer them on. But she didn't want to sit with her parents in the bleachers. *No way. If you ground me*, she thought to herself, *there's no way I'm going to sit with you.* She'd go anywhere to avoid sitting with her parents.

A few yards in front of Sarah, a girl was standing alone with her back to her. Sarah's stomach dropped when she recognized the dark frizzy hair and thick-rimmed glasses peeking out from behind her ears.

She had been avoiding Isabel ever since Mrs. Brewer asked her to tutor her. It wasn't that Sarah disliked her. She just wondered if Isabel had heard that Sarah refused to tutor her.

No, I just didn't have time because of Bible Club, Sarah reminded herself. Either way, she was embarrassed. With a jolt, Sarah, realized Isabel was turning around. *What if she tried to talk to her in that broken English? What would Sarah do? What if others saw her talking to Isabel? What would they think?*

Sarah whirled around too and headed toward the parking lot. She could hear the girl's thick-soled shoes clopping on the sidewalk behind her. Was she following her?

Out of the corner of her eye, Sarah spotted Chris' car a few rows over. He had just started it. She quickened her pace. In a few seconds, Isabel's footsteps faded, and Sarah

was only a few feet from the car. She whipped open the door and ducked into the passenger's seat.

"Someone after you?" Chris asked, smirking.

Sarah scowled, then tried to smile naturally. It didn't work, and she could tell.

"No, I just thought… well, never mind."

She peaked up far enough to look through the side door's rear view mirror. She watched the poof of frizzy hair disappear amidst the cars and exhaled, relieved.

She sat up and looked at Chris, "So where you going?"

"Bible study."

Sarah rolled her eyes, "Of course you are."

"What's that supposed to mean?"

"You know what I mean. You're the perfect child. Of course you're going to Bible study."

Chris' eyebrows furrowed, "Hey, I'm not –"

"Oh, yes you are!" She opened the door and climbed out. "Just – just forget it. Have fun at Bible study." She slammed the door and headed back towards the track.

Chris sat in the car for a few minutes, mulling over what his sister had said. How could she think that? There were so many things he wasn't doing right.

Not that he wasn't trying. After he had emptied his savings account, he felt convicted to rely on God even more and started leading an "I am Second" Bible Study group for middle school guys. Chris often wondered what he had gotten himself into when they came to him with tough questions. Nevertheless, it was definitely causing him to rely on God more.

Okay, I guess I can see why she would think that, Chris admitted to himself. It was like he and his sister were running down two roads pointed in opposite directions. While she was getting into fights with their mom for not doing chores, Chris had found himself helping out more around the house. It wasn't that he was trying to show her up. Instead,

he had simply discovered how awesome it felt to serve God. His life had never been better.

Nevertheless, he had his own struggles. He was still fighting jealousy over Matt and his role in the limelight at youth group. He wrestled with some feelings for one of the girls in his co-op Biology class. He felt like his laptop was on its last legs, and he was working like crazy to save up money to replace it. There were plenty of things he could get frustrated about. However, that didn't stop the joy he felt right now. He knew he was doing what he was made to do.

He only prayed Sarah would discover the same thing soon.

Lesson 69 Questions: (The suggested answers are on page 54 in the *Answer Key*.)

1. How was Sarah's relationship with her parents affected by her Cat attitudes?

_____

_____

2. How did Sarah act like a Cat with Isabel?

_____

_____

3. If Sarah had been a Dog, how could she have responded when she heard Chris was going to Bible Study?

_____

_____

4. Explain how Chris' situation shows that Dogs aren't perfect.

_____

_____

Oh Lord, I need to pass this quiz.

QUIZ!

1. John 14:13 tells us that Christ wants to answer our prayers so that

    A. we can have a safe, soft comfortable life.

    B. He can bring glory to the Father. [1230]

2. John 16:23-24 tells us another reason why Christ answers our prayers and that is so that

    A. we can have a safe, soft comfortable life.

    B. our joy can be complete. [1231]

3. Getting joy out of someone else (God) being glorified is

    A. crazy.

    B. biblical.

    C. what God wants for us. [1232]

4. When many Christians pray, they are really hoping that they are praying to

    A. a celestial Santa Claus who will give them all their wishes.

    B. a powerless Being.

    C. Satan. [1233]

5. All of the works we do in the Christian life in our own strength are

    A. going to burn.

    B. going to be rewarded. [1234]

6. Ezekiel 36:26,27 tells us that God wants to

    A. help us become more like Him.

    B. cause us to be obedient to His commands.

    C. Neither A or B.

    D. Both A and B. [1235]

7. The true work that needs to be done in us is a

    A. spiritual matter we can do on our own.

    B. spiritual matter requiring God's help.

    C. spiritual matter only God can do in us. [1236]

8. If we did the work of changing us spiritually,

    A. we would get the glory.

    B. it wouldn't last.

    C. God wouldn't get the glory.

    D. All of the above. [1237]

9. As soon as you prayed the words, "Lord help me," God noticed the word "help" and was let down a little bit.

    A. True

    B. False [1238]

10. Instead of being a "couch potato Christian," we should

    A. act as if everything depended upon us and pray like everything depended upon God.

    B. act as if everything depended upon us and pray like everything depended upon God.

    C. act as if everything depended upon us and pray like everything depended upon God. [1239]

What are you going to do differently as a result of what you've learned? **Go to the end of your workbook and write it in for Lesson 69.** [1240]

PERSONAL
APPLICATION

Free Day. No optional work!

OPTIONAL
LESSON

LESSON 70

CHECK WHICH CIRCLE BEST REPRESENTS YOUR LIFE TODAY:

☐   ☐   ☐

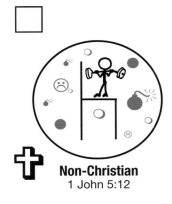

Non-Christian
1 John 5:12

Savior and Lord
Galations 5: 22-23

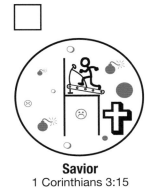

Savior
1 Corinthians 3:15

Since my last lesson,
I have practiced
Spiritual Breathing:

☐ 20+ Times
☐ 11 - 19 Times
☐ 6 - 10 Times
☐ 0 - 5 Times

READING ASSIGNMENT

CAT & DOG PRAYER

RETHINKING OUR CONVERSATIONS WITH OUR MASTER

Bob Sjogren & Gerald Robison

Start reading chapter 5 on page 55 and end at the words "Blessing in the New Testament" on page 61.

Questions to answer from the reading assignment:

1. God is already answering many people's prayer for blessings and they don't even realize it. Why?

_____

_____

_____ 1241

2. What is the Hebrew word for blessing and what does its meaning suggest?

_____

_____ 1242

3. In the book of Genesis, Jacob was blessed by God on _____ specific occasions. 1243

4. In a few words, write what Jacob's life looked like having been triply blessed?

_____ 1244

5. Name five ways the average person would say "By looking at his life, this man was not blessed."

_____

_____

_____

_____

_____ 1245

6. How did Jacob summarize his own life and what specific word did he choose to use?

_____

_____ 1246

7. Would the average Christian American today say that Jacob lived the "abundant life?"

     Circle One: Yes   No   ¹²⁴⁷

8. Name the two ways Jacob made God famous.

_____

_____ ¹²⁴⁸

9. Recognize, that if you ask God to bless you, your days may be

_____ ; _____ _____ may happen to you. ¹²⁴⁹

10. God could be saying to you, "I'm going to answer your prayer by allowing

_____ _____ into your life. But as you focus on Me through it all, you'll make Me _____ in others' eyes." ¹²⁵⁰

11. Believers need to realize that God's blessings may come in

_____ ways, including some that may not be safe, soft, or comfortable but also show God's _____

_____. ¹²⁵¹

1. Read Jonah 1.

2. When the "Word of the Lord" comes to someone, what kind of person does it usually come to?

    A. A person who has a pretty close relationship to God

    B. A heathen who has no respect for God. ¹²⁵²

BIBLE STUDY!

3. Write how Jonah 1, verse 9 helps you answer the above question.

_____

_____ ¹²⁵³

4. Why can we never really "run away" from the Lord?

_____

_____ ¹²⁵⁴

5. How did Jonah's disobedience cost others?

_____

_____ 1255

6. Is it possible that our disobedience can hurt others?

    Circle One: Yes   No   1256

7. How did Jonah describe his God to the men of the ship?

_____

_____ 1257

8. In God's sovereignty, He used Jonah's disobedience to bless what people in this chapter and what verse tells us this?

_____

_____

_____ 1258

9. The rest of the book tells us that Jonah ended up going and preaching to the Ninevites, and they repented. Jonah was not only used by God, but an entire book of the Bible was dedicated to him. Would you say that Jonah was a greatly blessed man of the Lord?

    Circle One: Yes   No   1259

10. Does God sometimes use natural disasters to get people's attention? What in this text helps give us the answer?

_____

_____ 1260

11. Do you think God still uses natural disasters to get people's attention?

    Circle One: Yes   No   1261

12. Circle the following lessons that we can learn from this:

    A. We can run from God's blessings.

    B. Our disobedience can cause others to lose their property and possessions.

    C. The way God may want to bless us is not always an easy way.

    D. Jonah loved God and always obeyed God. 1262

LESSON 71

CHECK WHICH CIRCLE BEST REPRESENTS YOUR LIFE TODAY:

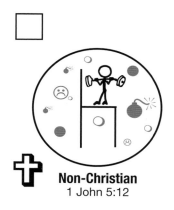

Non-Christian
1 John 5:12

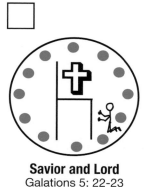

Savior and Lord
Galations 5: 22-23

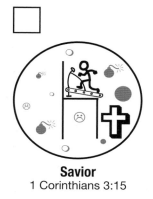

Savior
1 Corinthians 3:15

Since my last lesson,
I have practiced
Spiritual Breathing:

- ☐ 20⁺ Times
- ☐ 11 - 19 Times
- ☐ 6 - 10 Times
- ☐ 0 - 5 Times

READING ASSIGNMENT

CAT & DOG PRAYER

RETHINKING OUR CONVERSATIONS
WITH OUR MASTER

Bob Sjogren & Gerald Robison

Start on page 61 "Blessings in the New Testament" and finish out the chapter (page 68).

Questions to answer from the reading assignment:

1. There are _____ different Greek words used for blessing in the New Testament,. The one that focuses the most on people being blessed is _____. [1263]

2. Write the main idea behind the Greek word "*makarios*."

_____

_____

_____

_____ [1264]

3. Why is having peace and joy in the midst of difficulties such a great witness?

_____

_____ [1265]

4. Explain why this "standing ovation" was a strange blessing.

_____

_____

_____ [1266]

5. Cats need to realize that when they ask God to bless them, it may mean that God will allow them to be _____. [1267]

6. Would you like to be a "chosen instrument of God?"

   Circle One: Yes   No   [1268]

7. What did it mean for Paul to be a chosen instrument of God?

_____

_____ [1269]

8. Though Paul went through severe beatings and great trials, how was he blessed by God?

_____

_____ 1270

9. Rewrite Job 5:17 in your own words.

_____

_____

_____ 1271

10. What does Proverbs 14:21 mean?

_____ 1272

11. We should be saying, "God, fill me with joy no matter what _____ come our way so that we might make you _____ in the eyes of others!" 1273

BIBLE STUDY!

1. Read Acts 5:12-41.

2. What made the high priest put apostles in jail?

_____

_____

_____ 1274

3. How do you think the apostles were feeling having been thrown in jail?

_____

_____ 1275

4. How do you think the apostles were feeling having been released by an angel?

_____

_____ 1276

5. What was Peter's defense as to whether or not they should be preaching the message God had given them?

_____

_____ 1277

6. Being thrown in jail and having an angel rescue you is one thing, but now the disciples probably were even more fearful than ever. What in verse 33 tells you this?

_____

_____ 1278

7. The disciples were put outside to wait. It might have been 10 minutes, it might have been up to an hour. We have no idea. But what do you think they were feeling during that time knowing the leaders wanted them killed?

_____

_____ 1279

8. They were not put to death, but what did happen to them?

_____ 1280

9. What was their emotional response after having been flogged?

_____ 1281

10. Is that a natural response or a supernatural response?

Circle One: Natural   Supernatural   1282

11. What does this tell you about the joy we are to have even when we are going through tough circumstances?

_____

_____ 1283

LESSON 72

CHECK WHICH CIRCLE BEST REPRESENTS YOUR LIFE TODAY:

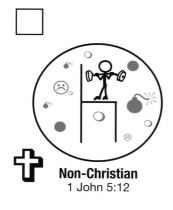

Non-Christian
1 John 5:12

Savior and Lord
Galations 5: 22-23

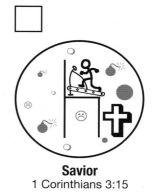

Savior
1 Corinthians 3:15

Since my last lesson,
I have practiced
Spiritual Breathing:

- ☐ 20⁺ Times
- ☐ 11 - 19 Times
- ☐ 6 - 10 Times
- ☐ 0 - 5 Times

CARTOON

Lord, this isn't fair. My life will be ruined. Get me out of this mess!

Oh Father, this is hard. But don't take it away until I learn the lesson You have for me.

Responding To Trials

1. What does the Cat think life should be to them?

_____

_____

_____

_____
1284

2. Why does the Dog want to see happen before the trial is taken out of their lives?

_____

_____

_____
1285

CHRIS and SARAH

The horn honked outside and Sarah pulled on her backpack.

"Jessica's here. Bye, Mom!" she shouted. Her mother didn't answer, but Sarah didn't care. She could hardly wait to get out of the house. Summer was almost here, this was the first really hot weekend of the year, and it was a great time to leave home.

Jessica had invited Sarah to spend the weekend at her family's lake house, and the two high schoolers were ready for a girls' weekend. Sarah breathed a sigh of relief as

Jessica pulled out of the driveway. She felt like she had been walking on ice for weeks, being extra thoughtful and obedient to her mom. Eventually, her parents agreed to let her have this weekend, and she wasn't too proud to admit home was more enjoyable when she didn't fight all the time.

When they arrived at the house, the girls unloaded their bags and walked around to the back door. Jessica set her bag on the pavement and pulled keys out of her pocket. Suddenly Sarah noticed their car was the only one in the driveway.

She turned to her friend, "Aren't your parents here?"

Grinning mischievously, Jessica opened the front door and led the way inside. "Actually, no. They're on a four-day business trip half-way across the country."

She waltzed down the hall, tossed her bags into the master bedroom, and dove into the pillows on the king-sized bed.

"My friend, you and I are completely on our own for the entire weekend! Can you say girls' night?!?"

She squealed and jumped off the bed. "I'm starving. Are you?" she called, heading toward the kitchen.

Slowly, Sarah sat on the bed, bags still in hand. She distinctly remembered Jessica telling Sarah's parents the whole family would be here. That was part of the reason her parents had given her permission. Jessica was Sarah's best friend and she trusted her, but why would Jessica lie to her parents?

Then again, Sarah's parents were pretty strict, and she had a feeling they wouldn't like her and Jessica here for a whole weekend by themselves. She also had a feeling Jessica knew that when she lied to them.

Should I call my mom? Pulling out her cell phone, Sarah stared at the keys. A girls' night with Jessica sounded fantastic, and she'd been looking forward to this for weeks. But…

"You still in here?" Jessica appeared at the doorway.

"Huh? – Um, yeah, I was just…"

She glanced at her phone, feeling a little guilty. Jessica noticed.

"Are you worried about my parents not being here?"

"No! It's just --- I thought I had heard you say they were, and then…"

Sighing, Jessica sank onto the bed next to Sarah.

"Look, you're right. I was afraid your parents would say no. But I promise, it's going to be awesome! We're almost adults. They have to start letting us be on our own eventually."

Sarah liked what she heard but knew she shouldn't be convinced.

"Besides," that mischievous grin flashed across Jessica's face again, "I have a surprise for you I know you'll love. But you have to wait until tomorrow for it. Until then," she bounced off the bed and headed back to the kitchen, "do you want chocolate or vanilla ice cream for dinner? I rented a couple movies I know you've been dying to see."

Ice cream and movies? How bad could it be?

"Chocolate, " Sarah grinned as she closed her phone, "chocolate is always better."

The weekend was fun. They spent most of Friday night eating junk food and watching movies Sarah's parents wouldn't let her see. Admittedly, Sarah felt a little guilty. But Jessica was right. She had been dying to see these movies, and now she could finally talk about them with all of her friends. Besides, her parents did have to let her grow up some time.

The next morning, Jessica let Sarah borrow one of her bikinis so they could lie out on the deck. Sarah's parents were strict about swimsuits, too, so all she had was a conservative one piece. However, Jessica assured Sarah that her petite figure looked fantastic in a two-piece.

After lunch, they sat on the dock and dipped their feet in the water. Suddenly, Sarah heard heavy footsteps behind them. The girls whirled around.

"Just in time!" Jessica grinned and jumped up.

Sarah's heart dropped into her stomach. Jessica's boyfriend, Gary, was standing behind them, and next to him was Bryan.

"I told you I had a surprise for you, Sarah!" her friend called.

Although she tried to stand, Sarah felt glued to the dock and a little self-conscious in her friend's swimsuit. Before she realized it, Bryan was sitting next to her.

"Hey," he said.

She smiled, "Hey."

"Really great to see you. When Gary told me you would be here, I jumped at the chance to come over."

"Yeah, um, great to see you, too."

Sarah floated on cloud nine the rest of the afternoon. There was swimming, laughing, teasing, and Jessica and Gary took the rowboat out for a while, leaving Sarah and Bryan alone on the dock. He held her hand and reaffirmed how glad he was to see her and how much he had missed hanging out. Why hadn't he seen her at Bible study?

For a moment, Sarah thought of Brittany and how she had stolen him from her. Are they still together? She realized she hadn't heard anything about them breaking up.

Then Bryan jumped off the dock and into the water, pulling her in after him. With a shriek and splash, she screamed, "Oh my God, this water is freezing!" Bryan put his arms around her to warm her. Suddenly, all thoughts of Brittany washed out of Sarah's mind.

When the sun dipped below the horizon, they lit up the fire pit and made s'mores. Gary came out of the house and set something heavy on the table. "Alright, anyone ready for the real party to begin?"

Playfully, Jessica hit his arm.

"Gary, you didn't tell me you were bringing any."

"YOLO!" He grinned and opened a beer, passing it to Jessica. He passed one to Bryan too, and Sarah saw no hesitation as he took it.

Meanwhile, Sarah's heart was pounding. She had never tried beer before. Red flags waved inside her head – like they had most of the day – but when Bryan offered her a bottle, she looked at Jessica. "YOLO?" she said hesitantly.

Jessica burst out laughing. "You Only Live Once, my dear!"

Sarah reached out and took the beer. Right, you only live once. Make the best of it! These were her friends, and they had obviously done it before. How bad could it be? This whole weekend had been amazing. Jessica wouldn't steer her wrong.

Sarah didn't like the taste of the beer, but pretended she loved it. There was no way she was going to be a dork and not fit in with her friends.

Afterwards, Sarah had a hard time remembering what happened. They polished off the alcohol Gary had brought and whatever else they found in the lake house. There was a lot of laughing. Eventually, Bryan had to help her inside where they all collapsed on the couch and Jessica put in a movie.

Sarah didn't know what movie they watched. The last thing she remembered that night was curling up in Bryan's arms.

Lesson 72 Questions: (The suggested answers are on page 54 in the *Answer Key*.)

1. What in the story shows how Cats can easily reject the prompting of the Holy Spirit?

_____

_____

2. What in the story shows how Cats can rationalize away responsibility to their parents?

_____

_____

3. How did Jessica violate Colossians 3:9 in this story?

_____

_____

4. How was Bryan being totally people-centered, acting like a Cat?

_____

_____

Oh Lord, I need to pass this quiz.

QUIZ!

1. For many people, God is answering their prayers and they are not even aware of it.

    A. True

    B. False [1286]

2. Jacob was blessed three times by the Lord Himself

    A. but his life did not look blessed to the average person.

    B. but he endured terrible hardships.

    C. Both A and B

    D. None of the above. [1287]

3. Christians need to be aware that if they ask God to bless them

    A. God will always do it.

    B. their days may be unpleasant.

    C. seemingly bad things may happen to them.

    D. they will always get a positive answer. [1288]

4. God's blessings

    A. always come in comfortable ways.

    B. always make your life easier.

    C. Both A and B

    D. None of the above. [1289]

5. The New Testament Greek word *"makarios"* for blessing is used in a context that is communicating

    A. great peace and joy only when things go your way.

    B. being so satisfied in God that no matter what the circumstances might be, you can still have peace and joy.

    C. God will bless you with lots of money. [1290]

6. A lesson of blessing that we can learn from the Apostle Paul is that when you are chosen by God you

    A. will always be blessed financially.

    B. may be called to be persecuted. [1291]

7. Paul was beaten multiple times and went through great trials, yet scripturally he was greatly blessed by God.

    A. True

    B. False [1292]

8. When you are corrected by God

    A. you are greatly blessed.

    B. you are in big trouble.

    C. you should be ashamed. [1293]

9. If you are kind to the poor

    A. you should expect rewards.

    B. you are blessed.

    C. Both A and B.

    D. None of the above. [1294]

10. All Christians should be praying,

    A. "Lord, fill me with joy no matter what circumstances come my way so that I may make you famous in the eyes of others."

    B. "Lord, keep me from all pain and sorrows and hardships."

    C. "Lord, I want to be saved." [1295]

PERSONAL APPLICATION

What are you going to do differently as a result of what you've learned? **Go to the end of your workbook and write it in for Lesson 72.** [1296]

Free Day. No optional work!

OPTIONAL LESSON

LESSON 73

CHECK WHICH CIRCLE BEST REPRESENTS YOUR LIFE TODAY:

☐   ☐   ☐

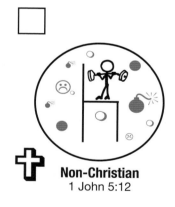

Non-Christian
1 John 5:12

Savior and Lord
Galations 5: 22-23

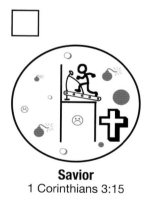

Savior
1 Corinthians 3:15

Since my last lesson,
I have practiced
Spiritual Breathing:

☐ 20+ Times
☐ 11 - 19 Times
☐ 6 - 10 Times
☐ 0 - 5 Times

READING ASSIGNMENT

CAT & DOG PRAYER

RETHINKING OUR CONVERSATIONS WITH OUR MASTER

Bob Sjogren & Gerald Robison

Begin reading Chapter 6 on page 69 and end at the bottom of page 75 where you see the words "Prodigal Son."

Questions to answer from the reading assignment:

1. Cat Christians can be _____ to how God is actually blessing them. [1297]

2. How did the fairy answer the man who asked for a wife who would be 30 years younger?

   _____
   _____ [1298]

3. What is the lesson we learn from the joke?

   _____
   _____ [1299]

4. What were the Israelites really communicating to the Lord in Numbers 11:4 when they asked for meat to eat?

   _____
   _____ [1300]

5. The Israelites were supernaturally surviving in hostile conditions, and just like those Israelites, Cats aren't _____ with merely _____. [1301]

6. Many Christians are not happy with what God has given them because they are listening to the _____ of others around them. [1302]

7. What did the blessing of meat that God gave to the Israelites actually end up being?

   _____ [1303]

8. In Numbers 11:20 (NIV), the Scriptures say that the meat they were going to eat would be loathsome to them. Write down the definition of "loathsome."

   _____ [1304]

9. What did Psalm 78:18-19 communicate about Israel's request?

_____

_____ 1305

10. It is possible that we can ask God for things and by so doing that, we are actually rejecting Him.

   Circle One: True   False   1306

11. In Malachi 2:2 we find out that God may actually _____ our blessings. 1307

1. Read Acts 5:1-10.

2. What does verse 4 tell us about Ananias and Sapphira?

_____

_____

_____

_____ 1308

BIBLE STUDY!

3. Being a landowner, do you think they were "rich" in comparison to most people back in that day?

_____ 1309

4. In Ephesians 4:28, Paul talks about why God allows us to do hard work (and as a result be able to purchase things). What is that purpose?

_____ 1310

5. What do you think God intended for Ananias and Sapphira to do with the wealth they gained from selling the land?

_____ 1311

6. They kept a certain percentage of the money for themselves. Do you think that is what God was so upset about?

_____ 1312

7. What does Acts 5:8 tell you about what Ananias and Sapphira had to be talking about before they separated that morning?

_____

1313

8. Do you think God was more upset over the fact that they kept some of the money or agreed to lie about it?

_____

1314

9. What does Proverbs 6:17,18 tell you about what God hates in relation to the actions of Ananias and Sapphira?

_____

1315

10. How did the blessing that God gave to Ananias and Sapphira turn out to be cursed?

_____

_____

1316

LESSON 74

CHECK WHICH CIRCLE BEST REPRESENTS YOUR LIFE TODAY:

☐   ☐   ☐

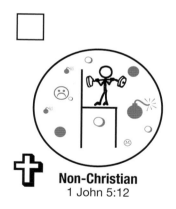

Non-Christian
1 John 5:12

Savior and Lord
Galations 5: 22-23

Savior
1 Corinthians 3:15

Since my last lesson,
I have practiced
Spiritual Breathing:

☐ 20⁺ Times

☐ 11 - 19 Times

☐ 6 - 10 Times

☐ 0 - 5 Times

READING ASSIGNMENT

CAT & DOG PRAYER

RETHINKING OUR CONVERSATIONS WITH OUR MASTER

Bob Sjogren & Gerald Robison

Begin reading page 75 at "Prodigal Son" and finish out the chapter (page 80).

Questions to answer from the reading assignment:

1. What is the key thing that the authors want you to remember about the prodigal son?

_____

_____

_____ 1317

2. Cats need to be very careful of what they pray for because they might be asking for something that actually takes their _____ _____ from God. 1318

3. How does Proverbs 18:22 describe finding a wife?

_____ 1319

4. Solomon got a "good thing" from the Lord in his wives, but those "good things" turned bad on him. How is 1 Kings 11:2 an example how this can happen?

_____

_____ 1320

5. Although many of the things a Cat may first pray about may not be bad at all, Cats need to be careful because they have the _____ of seducing a Cat's heart away. 1321

6. God is looking for believers who can _____ the blessings. 1322

7. Explain in your own words what it means to "survive" the blessings.

_____

_____

_____ 1323

8. Sometimes believers go to God or other believers more spiritual than them because they want God or others to think they are _____ themselves. 1324

9. Many people go to God not at all interested in what God wants them to do, but asking God to _____ what they _____ to do. [1325]

10. What is the second reason given at the bottom of page 78 as to why God may give believers what they are asking for "in keeping with their great idolatry?"

_____

_____ [1326]

11. Cats need to be careful. They can _____ themselves right out of God's _____. [1327]

BIBLE STUDY!

1. Read Luke 18:18-30.

2. A "ruler" by definition, is one who rules. Do you think this young man owned lots of things and was in charge of many people?

Circle One: Yes   No   ¹³²⁸

3. Guess at what kind of possessions he could "lose" if things didn't go his way?

_____
1329

4. Very few rulers are concerned about what they will own in the afterlife. They are too preoccupied with the things of this life. But why did this ruler come to Jesus?

_____
1330

5. Did Jesus' first answer differ from what the Old Testament speaks about?

_____
1331

6. Do you think he had really kept all of the commands from his youth?

Circle One: Yes   No   ¹³³²

7. By saying he had kept all of the commands, how do you think he was trying to get Jesus to think about him?

_____
1333

8. Jesus saw right through his pseudo-righteousness and challenged him to do what?

_____
1334

9. Though he was outwardly righteous, what was the greatest love of his life?

_____
1335

10. He seemed to be a spiritual man wanting to get into heaven. Do you think he asked God to bless him with the great wealth he had?

Circle One: Yes   No   ¹³³⁶

11. If he did ask God to bless him, how is this like the prodigal son?

_____

_____
1337

LESSON 75

CHECK WHICH CIRCLE BEST REPRESENTS YOUR LIFE TODAY:

☐   ☐   ☐

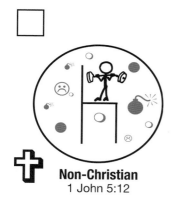

Non-Christian
1 John 5:12

Savior and Lord
Galations 5: 22-23

Savior
1 Corinthians 3:15

Since my last lesson,
I have practiced
Spiritual Breathing:

☐ 20⁺ Times

☐ 11 - 19 Times

☐ 6 - 10 Times

☐ 0 - 5 Times

CARTOON

Cat and Dog Grandparenting

1. How are the Cat grandparents not surviving the blessings of grandchildren?

_____

_____

_____

_____ 1338

2. The Dog grandparents have been blessed with children and grandchildren, but what is their attitude toward them?

_____

_____

_____ 1339

CHRIS and SARAH

Sarah was flying high. Despite fighting hangovers Sunday morning, the teenagers made it to church on time. When her parents asked if she was feeling okay, she just mumbled that she had a headache from staying up too late but that she had a great time.

On the way home, She told them about the swimming, the s'mores, the tanning—but nothing about the guys or drink-

ing. Something inside her said, "Tell her more." But Sarah suppressed it. *I'm not lying*, she insisted to the voice. *That's the important thing. I'm just not telling the whole truth.*

The following week, Bryan paid more attention to her than he had for months, and Sarah's latest Algebra test came back with an A.

It's finally happening, she thought as she waited for her parents to pick her up after school. Things were finally going to work out the way she wanted. *God, how could I have ever doubted You?* Sarah prayed silently. *You were working it out all along. Now everything will get better.*

She wondered when Bryan would break up with Brittany, and they could finally be together. Impatiently, Sarah glanced at her watch. Normally, her mom arrived at 3:15. It was almost 4 PM. Suddenly, she heard footsteps behind her.

"Sarah."

Turning, she saw Mrs. Harris, one of the assistant principals. "There's been an accident. Can you come with me, please?"

Chris had been hit by a drunk driver on his way home from feeding the homeless that morning. A friend picked Sarah up from school, and the next day, Chris came home from the hospital with a broken leg and a few broken ribs. At Sarah's request, she stayed home and helped her mom get Chris settled. Although Chris usually made her feel like the bad child, Sarah realized she never wanted to come this close to losing him again. She spent most of the day bringing him water, pain meds, and pillows.

Sarah had just left the room when Chris' phone vibrated on the table next to him. Wincing, he picked it up and checked the text.

"Just heard about what happened at Jessica's last weekend – did u know?"

Confused, he typed quickly, "no, what?"

"oh man… sarah and bryan got drunk and slept together."

Chris almost dropped his phone. A sick feeling settled deep in his stomach, and his head started hurting worse than his leg.

Really, God? I know Sarah has a huge crush on this guy. But how could she sleep with him? He's already got a girl friend? This can't be true…can it?

It occurred to him that if rumors were already spreading, it was only a matter of time before their parents heard about it.

Suddenly, Sarah was at the door.

"Need anything?"

He looked up, startled, "Um, uh – yeah," looking at her, the feeling in his stomach worsened. There was no way he could confront her about it, "Can… can you get Mom please?"

When she left, Chris took a deep breath and tried to not to succumb to the throbbing in his head. What had his little sister done?

That night, Sarah's parents sat down with her and asked her point-blank exactly what had happened last weekend.

Sarah's cheeks flushed, and her eyes filled with tears, "No, no it wasn't like that. Gary just brought out the beer, and everyone else seemed so comfortable with it… I… I didn't think it would hurt anyone. We just fell asleep watching a movie. I swear that's all that happened. No one slept with anyone."

Her mother's almond eyes were glassy too, but she looked like she could ground her until she was 60.

"Sarah, your brother was just hit by a drunk driver, at nine in the morning no less, after feeding breakfast to the homeless. That could've been any one of you if you had decided to drive that night. It most certainly can hurt someone."

"But we didn't go anywhere, Mom," Sarah insisted.

"Not to mention you're under age, my dear," her father added calmly. "God's Word says to obey the laws your government gives you. Drinking isn't allowed until you turn 21, which is a long way off. Do you want to be pleasing to God or not?'"

Sarah didn't answer and hid her face with her hands, sobbing. She hated all these Christian rules. And did they even believe that she didn't sleep with Bryan? How were they going to punish her now? Would she ever get out of this house? Would she ever see Bryan again?

After a long silence, her father ran his hands through his hair and spoke, "Sarah, your mother and I are going to have to take some drastic steps on this one. You openly disobeyed us--"

Sarah lifted her head and burst, "I didn't openly disobey you, Dad. Jessica told me her parents were going to be there too. I wouldn't have gone…" she hesitated. *Was she speaking the truth? If Jessica had told her ahead of time her parents were gone, would Sarah have gone anyway? Oh whatever, I just need to salvage this situation.*

"I wouldn't have gone if I'd known her parents weren't there—and you wouldn't have let me go anyway. So don't blame me."

"Sarah," her father spoke lovingly but firmly, "When you found out her parents weren't there, did the thought ever occur to you to give us a call and let us know?"

She paused, unsure of the best answer. Then she sighed and quietly admitted the truth, "Yes."

"And why didn't you?" her father asked.

"Well, I... um... she said all we were going to do was eat ice cream for dinner and watch movies. So I thought, 'What's so bad about that?' And then she was like, 'They've got to let us grow up some time,' and I guess I kind of agreed. So I guess I just convinced myself it was alright."

"Okay, Sarah," he nodded, "that is when you rejected the prompting of the Holy Spirit. And that my dear, is when you disobeyed us, so the blame does fall completely on you. I agree you went up there thinking her parents were there, but when you found out they weren't, you should have called."

He continued, "Two things have happened here, Sarah. The first is that you broke Ephesians 5:3, a law in God's Word which is designed to protect you: 'Let there not even be a hint of sexual immorality among you.' The reason we would have driven up and brought you back was for fear that something like this might happen. Your reputation— of which you only have one—has been severely damaged. We want you to represent Christ, to be holy and blameless. And, even though you've been falsely accused, it's going to take a long time for you to rebuild your reputation. If you had obeyed us, none of this would have happened.

"But secondly, what is far greater and more damaging, is the fact that your mother and I have lost our trust in you."

His words sunk deeply into Sarah's soul. Her dark eyes widened. "I'm so sorry," she whispered. "I'm so sorry." When her parents exchanged looks, Sarah could tell they were silently deciding her fate.

"We know you're sorry, Sarah," her dad finally said, "but it's going to take some time before we give you back the freedoms you've been enjoying. You had these freedoms because we trusted you. Now that trust has been broken, so these freedoms are going to be taken away again for a whole month. After that, we'll see if you're making good decisions that will allow us to trust you again. If so, we can slowly start giving those freedoms back. Sweetie, please know we don't do this out of bitterness or resentment. We do this to protect you, and we hope that it will help you grow in your relationship with the Lord... because this is really all about Him."

His words rang with the finality of a judge's gavel.

"Yes, sir," Sarah forced out of her mouth. "May I go to my room now?"

Feeling his own pain and wondering if he had failed her as a father, he sighed. "Yes, you may," he said quietly.

After Sarah cried herself dry, she curled up in her blanket and mulled over what her parents had said: her damaged reputation, how she couldn't just blame someone else, a whole month of being grounded. Eventually, her mind focused on the deepest hurt. *A month at home I can handle; a damaged reputation I can handle; but he said they can't trust me anymore. Oh my God, what have I done? Anything but that, they're my family.*

Lesson 75 Questions: (The suggested answers are on page 55 in the *Answer Key.*)

1. How was Sarah thinking like a Cat when she assumed God was finally working things out for her?

   _____

   _____

2. Why would a Cat have a hard time believing God would let Chris—who is serving God faithfully—be in a car accident?

   _____

   _____

3. Name three ways Sarah acted like a Cat and tried to get out of the blame.

   _____

   _____

4. Would you say your parent's trust in you is the greatest blessing you have in your relationship with your parents? Why or why not?

Oh Lord, I need to pass this quiz.

   _____

   _____

   _____

   _____

QUIZ!

1. Cat Christians can be blind to how God is blessing them.
   A. True
   B. False [1340]

2. The lesson we learn from the fairy joke is

    A. always ask for what you want.

    B. God loves women more than men.

    C. God may answer your prayers in a way you aren't expecting.

    D. None of the above. [1341]

3. One of the lessons we can learn from the Israelites wandering around in the desert is

    A. never be satisfied with just surviving.

    B. be thankful for what you've got, even if it isn't "everything you'd like." [1342]

4. Psalm 78: 16-18 tells us that if we are not satisfied with what God gives us,

    A. we are putting God to the test.

    B. sinning.

    C. Both A and B.

    D. None of the above. [1343]

5. Many Cat Christians are not happy with what God has given them because they are listening to the greed of the others around them.

    A. True

    B. False [1344]

6. We need to be very careful about what we are asking God for because without realizing it, by asking for certain things, we may be actually rejecting God.

    A. True

    B. False [1345]

7. It is actually possible for God to

    A. die.

    B. curse our blessings.

    C. Both A and B

    D. None of the above. [1346]

8. The prodigal son teaches us that the very thing we ask God for

    A. will be scrutinized by God.

    B. He will not give us.

    C. could be the very thing that takes us away from God.

    D. All of the above. [1347]

9. The phrase "God is looking for people who can survive the blessing" means

    A. He wants people to trust Him for big pay raises they can spend on themselves.

    B. He wants people to be willing to give up the big job and money for the sake of His great name.

    C. He wants people to trust Him for greater blessings in their personal life.

    D. He wants people to be willing to give up what is rightfully theirs for Him. [1348]

10. Our mindset in life (as well as prayer) should be

    A. "God, what can you do for me?" not "What can I do for you?"

    B. "God, what can I do for you?" not "What can God do for me?" [1349]

What are you going to do differently as a result of what you've learned? **Go to the end of your workbook and write it in for Lesson 75.** [1350]

PERSONAL APPLICATION

Free Day. No optional work!

OPTIONAL LESSON

LESSON 76

CHECK WHICH CIRCLE BEST REPRESENTS YOUR LIFE TODAY:

☐

☐

☐

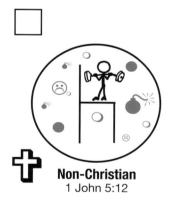

Non-Christian
1 John 5:12

Savior and Lord
Galations 5: 22-23

Savior
1 Corinthians 3:15

Since my last lesson,
I have practiced
Spiritual Breathing:

☐ 20+ Times
☐ 11 - 19 Times
☐ 6 - 10 Times
☐ 0 - 5 Times

READING ASSIGNMENT

CAT & DOG PRAYER

RETHINKING OUR CONVERSATIONS
WITH OUR MASTER

Bob Sjogren & Gerald Robison

Begin reading chapter 7 on page 81 and read to the top of page 86 where it says "Relationship, Not Just Recognition."

Questions to answer from the reading assignment:

1. Many Christians get _____ by the length of time it takes to get their prayers _____. [1351]

2. Abraham's servant was not a Jew. He was a Gentile. Yet how did God answer his prayer?

   _____ [1352]

3. Joseph, who was a Jew and one of God's key men for establishing his reputation among the nations, also prayed that the cupbearer would speak of his name to the Pharaoh. How long did it take that prayer to get answered?

   _____ [1353]

4. How many years did it take Abraham's prayer for a son to get answered, assuming he was 40 years old when married and started praying for a son?

   _____ [1354]

5. Assuming the first generation of Hebrews were enslaved by the Egyptians after Joseph's death, how many years did it take for their prayers to get answered to be free?

   _____ [1355]

6. Some of those Hebrews never saw the answer to their prayers in their

   _____. [1356]

7. List the six reasons why God may say, "Wait."

   _____

   _____

   _____

   _____

   _____ [1357]

BIBLE STUDY!

1. Read Genesis 15.

2. In verse 13, someone who was associated with Abraham was to get the Promised Land. Who was it?

_____

_____ 1358

3. These people were promised this land, but how long will it be before they actually get into it? (See verse 13.)

_____ 1359

4. During those 400 years, what else in verse 13 tells what basically happened to the Israelites?

_____ 1360

5. How do you think the first generation felt about this promise?

_____

_____ 1361

6. Assuming one generation is 40 years, how many generations were enslaved?

_____ 1362

7. Do you think anger may have been involved in the 7th, 8th and 9th generations?

      Circle One: Yes   No   1363

8. Circle which of the following you think they may have been thinking:

     A. God, this isn't fair.

     B. I kind of like being a slave.

     C. God, why aren't you blessing us?

     D. God, why can't we go to the Promised Land now? 1364

9. What does verse 16 tell you about why they weren't allowed in?

_____ 1365

10. Circle the following lessons you think can apply:

A. Sometimes our prayers are answered, but not in our lifetime.

B. God's purpose for them as slaves was purposeless.

C. We need to realize that it is not about us, it is about God.

D. Sometimes our lives can be hard in order to make God look good. [1366]

CAUTION! The more your life is changed, the easier it is to spot Cat behavior in those around you. **Please don't ever use this material to judge others.** ["Oh, they are just a bunch of Cats."] Once we start judging others, we too are acting like Cats. **Use this material to encourage yourself and others to live for God's glory.**

LESSON 77

CHECK WHICH CIRCLE BEST REPRESENTS YOUR LIFE TODAY:

☐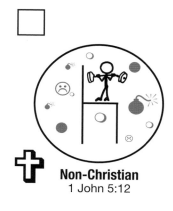

Non-Christian
1 John 5:12

☐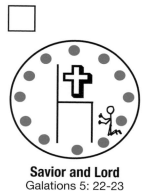

Savior and Lord
Galations 5: 22-23

☐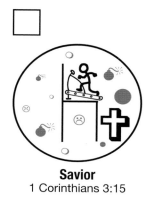

Savior
1 Corinthians 3:15

Since my last lesson,
I have practiced
Spiritual Breathing:

☐ 20⁺ Times

☐ 11 - 19 Times

☐ 6 - 10 Times

☐ 0 - 5 Times

READING ASSIGNMENT

CAT & DOG PRAYER
RETHINKING OUR CONVERSATIONS WITH OUR MASTER
Bob Sjogren & Gerald Robison

Start on page 86 where it says "Relationship, Not Just Recognition" and finish out the chapter (Page 93).

Questions to answer from the reading assignment:

1. The first reason God would have us wait is due to the fact that He is first and foremost _____ about our _____ with Him. [1367]

2. When you love someone, what is the purpose of spending time with that person?
   _____
   _____ [1368]

3. In "Praying God's Word," what does Beth Moore say?
   _____
   _____ [1369]

4. Use your prayer time to delight in God, to get to know Him, to become _____ with Him. Don't simply _____ through your prayer list. [1370]

5. Dogs will pray, "Lord, if there are _____ I need to learn, do _____ answer my prayers until I've learned those lessons." [1371]

6. What is the reasoning as to why a Dog would pray this prayer?
   _____
   _____ [1372]

7. Note, even though our prayers may be prayed _____, God's answer may still be "no." [1373]

8. List the first two "LSD Prayers" Bob has prayed for 30 years.
   _____
   _____ [1374]

9. Cats find it easy to praise God _____ their prayers are answered. [1375]

10. Dogs persist in praise _____ they get a response. [1376]

11. List what a Cat and Dog focus on in their prayers and what the difference is.

_____

_____

_____

_____ 1377

BIBLE STUDY!

1. Read Psalm 100.

2. What is the first thing the Psalmist tells you to do?

_____

_____

_____ 1378

3. Who does he tell to do that?

_____ 1379

4. Do you think "all the earth" just refers to people or to everyone and everything on the earth? (Hint: the same Psalmist wrote Psalm 148.)

Circle One: People   Everything/Everyone   1380

5. What are the attitudes we are commanded to have in verse 2?

_____ 1381

6. If God were a mean, cruel, callous, vindictive God, would we naturally come into His presence with singing and gladness?

Circle One: Yes   No   1382

7. In verse 3 when the Psalmist says, "Know that the Lord, He is God," what is that insinuating about who God is?

_____

_____ 1383

8. What do verses 3 and 5 tell us about why we should be doing all of these things?

_____ 1384

9. Notice not one request is asked in this Psalm. What really is the focus?

_____ 1385

10. He is not only good and kind to us, but who else does verse 5 tell us will know the kindness and goodness of God?

_____ 1386

LESSON 78

CHECK WHICH CIRCLE BEST REPRESENTS YOUR LIFE TODAY:

☐

Non-Christian
1 John 5:12

☐

Savior and Lord
Galations 5: 22-23

☐

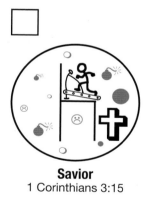

Savior
1 Corinthians 3:15

Since my last lesson,
I have practiced
Spiritual Breathing:

☐ 20+ Times
☐ 11 - 19 Times
☐ 6 - 10 Times
☐ 0 - 5 Times

CARTOON

How Cats and Dogs Wait On God

1. Why is the Dog being still before God?

_____

_____

_____

_____

2. What is being communicated by the Cat's side of the cartoon?

_____

_____

_____

_____

CHRIS and SARAH

Wincing slightly, Chris shifted his leg down from the coffee table and onto the floor. The days following the accident had been brutal, to say the least. He had passed in and out of a fog of pain killers, infuriated at how helpless he was and how dependent he was on other people. However, when his mind cleared up, he sat down and confronted God about the accident. *Why did God let it happen?*

"Lord, I need some answers, because I'm a bit confused," Chris prayed honestly. "I've been serving you in just about every way I can. I know you're pleased with the homeless ministry. I know you like me mentoring the middle school boys, and I know you like me going to youth group each week. Between those and sports and school, I don't have any free time. My life is booked solid. What more can I do for you? Why did you let this accident happen?"

Chris waited patiently, yet there seemed to be no answer.

A few days later, he remembered something Pastor Jake had said. It was a quote from Jeremiah 32:40: "I have made an everlasting covenant to never stop doing good to you." Okay, God, he thought, is this just my memory coming in to play or is this from you? And if it's from you, how was a broken leg and broken ribs good for me? Chris still couldn't figure it out.

While stranded at home, Chris discovered he had lots of time with the Lord. He seemed to grow closer to Him each day. His prayer times lasted longer and longer, and God's Word opened up to him in ways he'd never seen before.

One Friday, after spending an hour and a half praying in the den, it hit him.

Oh my gosh. Have I really been that blind and clueless? His mind raced over the past year. He felt convicted, devastated, and yet completely overjoyed that God had finally given him the answer.

Father, he prayed, *forgive me. Thank you, thank you, thank you for this broken leg. You really have made an everlasting covenant to never stop doing good to me.*

Half an hour later Sarah came home from school. As usual she joined him in the den, dropping her backpack on the floor and sinking onto the couch next to Chris. Between the broken leg and her grounding, they spent a lot of time together now. And as much as they would have hesitated to admit it, they had grown closer than ever.

"What a day," she sighed.

"People still bothering you about what happened?"

Sarah rubbed her temples, "Yeah… seems like there's a new rumor every day. I mean, it doesn't bother me as much as it used to. The truth is out there. It just… it's like what Dad said. It's gonna take a long time to rebuild my reputation. I wish I knew what to do about it now."

Sarah glanced at her brother. "Hey, you okay peg-leg?"

Although Chris was sitting in the same position he had for weeks, he looked different. The frustration was wiped off his face and in its place was a strong, confident peace. Sarah had noticed recently how annoyed he was at being stranded at home, plucked out of all his activities. However, he no longer looked annoyed.

"Yeah…" Chris answered slowly, "Yeah, I'm actually really great."

Sarah was puzzled and really didn't know what to say. "So your ribs and leg are feeling a lot better, huh?"

"No. It has nothing to do with that, Sis," he grinned, "I think today God showed me why I needed this accident."

"You needed it?" Sarah's dark eyes widened in disbelief.

"Yeah, I know that sounds weird," said Chris.

She grinned mischievously, "Are you sure you're not taking too many pain meds?"

"No," Chris laughed and leaned over, putting his arm around her. His hug was real and genuine, and Sarah liked it. Whatever had gotten into Chris, it must have been big.

"Okay, you got me. What happened?" She settled down to listen.

"You know how before the accident I was so busy with life – feeding the homeless, holding the Bible study for the guys, going to youth group, doing homework, sports… right?"

"Uh, yeah. I hardly saw you and I live here," Sarah replied.

"When I was doing all that stuff, I hardly had time to fit in a quiet time. My life was so busy meeting the needs of others, God took second place."

Sarah's brow furrowed, "But how can God take second place when you're doing His work?"

"Weird, right? But I finally realized that doing His work isn't the same as seeking Him. I was so busy trying to please God I forgot that it was first and foremost about my relationship with Him."

"And this accident…?" Sarah looked to Chris to fill in the blank.

"This accident took all of the serving God stuff away. All I could do was meet with Him. And that's what I've been doing these past weeks. I'm spending time with Him in

prayer and actually reading His Word. Sis, it's like a light bulb went off in my head. Life isn't about serving God as much as it is about loving God! Somehow before now, it wasn't God that I wanted. I wanted His blessings: what I thought I could get by doing stuff for Him."

Sarah felt a tug on her heart, and she wondered if it was the Holy Spirit. She had felt it more frequently the last few weeks.

"What do you mean you didn't want God? Nobody wants God more than you. You're always doing things for Him," Sarah said.

"No," Chris shook his head and ran his hand through his auburn hair. How do I put this into words… "I think there's a huge difference between serving God and loving God. I served God because I thought that if I did all of these things for him, I would get his acceptance. And as he accepted me, I'd be blessed by him. Now I realize that I don't have to serve God to get all of that – it simply comes because God is love! All I really need to focus on is my love for God. Serving will come naturally, but it has to take second place to my relationship with God. Serving God had *actually become* my God. Now, I just want God, period."

The tug on Sarah's heart grew more insistent, and suddenly she was filled with the same overwhelming feeling she had experienced at the youth retreat last fall. She knew what it meant. She began to cry.

Surprised, Chris hesitated, "Um… what's wrong?" Here he was sharing his heart, the greatest news ever, and she was crying.

There was a long pause. Finally, Sarah spoke, "I don't think I've ever wanted God either. I don't really have quiet times. And when I do meet with Him, it's all about what God can do for me. I've wanted Him to get me good grades. I've wanted Him to help me win races. I've wanted Him…" another pause, "I've wanted Him to get me with Bryan—and look what it's done to me." She burst into sobs. Her pain was so deep she found it hard to breathe. The words dug into her heart, and she gasped, "Oh my God. I'm so selfish. I'm just using God. I don't really want Him. I just want what He can do for me."

Hiding her face, she turned away from Chris, feeling so sinful, and curled up into the cushions, sobbing like a baby.

Taking a deep breath, Chris reached out and grabbed her, pulling her close to him. He then put his arm around her, saying a quick, silent prayer for wisdom. Sarah sank into his hug.

"Hey… it's okay, sis," Chris said. "God loves you for who you are, not what you've done. He is love. He is kind. He is gracious. He is merciful. He died and paid the price for all your selfishness. He's forgiven you. It's all gone. Don't let it pull you down. And he'll love you more than a thousand Bryans ever will." He didn't know what else to say, so he just held her and let her cry.

Eventually, her sobbing turned into crying, which later died down to whimpering. When she stopped, they were quiet for a long time.

Finally, Sarah broke the silence, "Um, Chris?"

He looked down at her, seeing the tears still trickling down her cheeks.

"Will you teach me how to live my life to the Lord? I feel like a total baby and I'm making a mess trying to live this Christian life on my own. I don't think I even know Him, but I really do want to know Him more than anything."

Chris hugged her even tighter, "Sure, I'd be honored."

Lesson 78 Questions: (The suggested answers are on page 55 in the *Answer Key*.)

1. Summarize in your own words what Chris learned through his "accident."

_____

_____

2. Why was Jeremiah 32:40 still true even though Chris almost lost his life?

_____

_____

3. What kind of things does the average Christian teenager look to God for today? And how can they sometimes become a god in and of themselves?

_____

_____

4. In what ways was Sarah honest with herself to bring her to the point that she probably didn't even know the Lord?

_____

_____

Oh Lord, I need to pass this quiz.

QUIZ!

1. God wants us to know that our prayers will always be answered quickly.

    A. True

    B. False [1389]

2. Some prayers get answered

    A. instantaneously.

    B. after a long period of time.

    C. Both A and B.

    D. None of the above. [1390]

3. We should always expect God to answer our prayers in our lifetime.

    A. True

    B. False [1391]

4. Sometimes our prayers can take hundreds of years to be answered.

    A. True

    B. False [1392]

5. God may say wait because

    A. God wants a relationship with you, not just recognition.

    B. God might want us to learn a deep lesson.

    C. God might be waiting for us to pray humbly.

    D. God might want us to learn to be persistent.

    E. The answer could be delayed by spiritual battle.

    F. Praise during the waiting time brings God even greater glory [1393]

6. God is far more interested in you getting to know the Deliverer than simply being delivered.

    A. True

    B. False [1394]

7. Dogs pray,

    A. "Lord, don't answer my prayer if there are things I need to learn first."

    B. "Lord, please make my life safe, soft and comfortable."

    C. "Use this to advance Your kingdom, not my kingdom." [1395]

8. Some prayers need to be prayed over and over and over again.

    A. True

    B. False [1396]

9. Cats find it easy to praise God

    A. before their prayers are answered.

    B. after their prayers are answered.

    C. at any time. [1397]

10. Dogs persist in praise

    A. even before their prayers are answered.

    B. after their prayers are answered.

    C. even if they get a "no" to their prayer request.

    D. All of the above. [1398]

PERSONAL APPLICATION

What are you going to do differently as a result of what you've learned? **Go to the end of your workbook and write it in for Lesson 78.**[1399]

Free Day. No optional work!

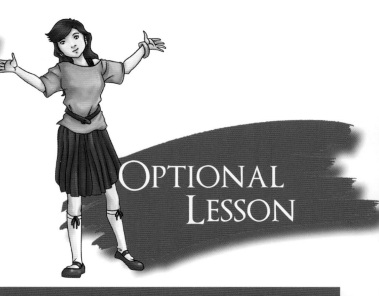

OPTIONAL LESSON

LESSON 79

CHECK WHICH CIRCLE BEST REPRESENTS YOUR LIFE TODAY:

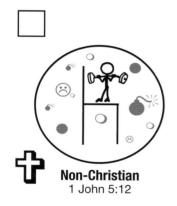

Non-Christian
1 John 5:12

Savior and Lord
Galations 5: 22-23

Savior
1 Corinthians 3:15

Since my last lesson,
I have practiced
Spiritual Breathing:

- ☐ 20⁺ Times
- ☐ 11 - 19 Times
- ☐ 6 - 10 Times
- ☐ 0 - 5 Times

READING ASSIGNMENT

CAT & DOG PRAYER

RETHINKING OUR CONVERSATIONS WITH OUR MASTER

Bob Sjogren & Gerald Robison

Start chapter 8 on page 95 and read to the middle of page 99 where it says "A Revelation of Greater Glory."

Questions to answer from the reading assignment:

1. List the four reasons why God sometimes answers our prayers "no."

_____

_____

_____

_____

_____ 1400

2. What did Moses do that was sinful?

_____

_____ 1401

3. God says that Moses did not _____ Him and therefore was not treated as "holy" in the sight of Israel. 1402

4. Since sin in our lives can keep our prayers from being answered, should we go around inspecting every area of our lives looking for sin?

Circle One: Yes   No   1403

5. Whose job is to convict of us sin and what scripture tells us that?

_____ 1404

6. Our view of what God is up to can be very _____ or _____. 1405

7. Great men of God (Moses, Elijah and Jonah) asked God for something and God said, "_____." What they were asking for was _____ of God's _____. 1406

8. Cat Christians rarely think about the _____ _____-they tend to only relate to their _____ and _____. 1407

1. Read 1 Kings 19.

2. In this context, Elijah has just defeated all of the prophets of Baal both spiritually and physically. After this great victory of multiple prophets, who is he afraid of?

_____ 1408

BIBLE STUDY!

3. This woman was the daughter of the King of Tyre and the wife of the King of Israel. She brought with her idolatry and the worship of Baal to Israel, and they were polluted with her ways. She was a powerful woman who "ruled behind" her husband, the king. What did she vow to do?

_____

_____ 1409

4. What was his response and what did he do?

_____

_____ 1410

5. Circle which reasons you think apply as to why he would be afraid.

    A. He didn't feel like anyone is Israel really worshipped God, therefore He was alone.

    B. She would send military men to get him, and they were far more skilled and powerful than the prophets.

    C. He was a threat to her ways.

    D. She wanted revenge for her husband's death. [1411]

6. After a day's journey with emotions which must have been running extremely high, he was assuredly exhausted. What did he ask for?

_____

_____ 1412

7. Instead of dying in his sleep, what happened?

_____ 1413

8. What three things did Elijah still have yet to do in his life?

_____

_____

_____ 1414

9. What does verse 18 tell us about why God didn't answer Elijah's prayer?

_____

_____ 1415

10. Circle which lessons we can learn from this passage:

    A. There may be information we are not aware of that will keep God from answering our prayers.

    B. God may have work for us to do in other areas that we are not aware of.

    C. After we have great spiritual victories, we can go deeply into a low.

    D. God loves the Ninevites. [1416]

LESSON 80

CHECK WHICH CIRCLE BEST REPRESENTS YOUR LIFE TODAY:

☐

☐

☐

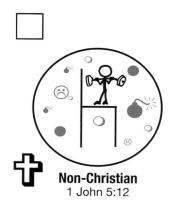

Non-Christian
1 John 5:12

Savior and Lord
Galations 5: 22-23

Savior
1 Corinthians 3:15

Since my last lesson,
I have practiced
Spiritual Breathing:

☐ 20⁺ Times

☐ 11 - 19 Times

☐ 6 - 10 Times

☐ 0 - 5 Times

READING ASSIGNMENT

CAT & DOG PRAYER

RETHINKING OUR CONVERSATIONS WITH OUR MASTER

Bob Sjogren & Gerald Robison

Start on page 99 where it says "A Revelation of Greater Glory" and finish out the chapter (page 104).

Questions to answer from the reading assignment:

1. One of the reasons God does not answer prayer is that the _____ that will be revealed with a "no" is _____ _____ the glory that will be revealed through a "yes." [1417]

2. Why did Jesus get a "no" answer from His Father?

   _____

   _____ [1418]

3. Hearing about God's glory shining more through a "no" answer to prayer is hard for Cats to hear because…

   _____

   _____ [1419]

4. List the five reasons the authors say, "If God answered 'yes' to every selfish prayer, we would be in danger because:

   _____

   _____

   _____

   _____

   _____ " [1420]

5. In a nutshell, if all of our prayers were answered positively, we would be focused on what we could _____ _____ _____ _____, with _____ concern for anyone else. [1421]

6. List the eight other reasons the authors say God says "no":

_____

_____

_____

_____

_____

_____

_____
1422
_____

BIBLE STUDY!

1. Read Mark 6:1-6.

2. Where did Jesus go and teach?

_____

_____

_____ 1423

3. What was special about this location?

_____ 1424

4. What does verse two tell you about how the people thought of Him?

_____ 1425

5. What does verse three tell you about their reaction to Him?

_____ 1426

6. What was the principle Jesus told them about in verse four?

_____ 1427

7. If you were Jesus' sister or brother, would you have a hard time believing He was God and why?

_____ 1428

8. Because they lacked the understanding of Jesus being God, what did they lack?

_____ 1429

9. Circle the lessons can we learn from this:

    A. Without faith, we won't see miracles.

    B. Those we know the closest are sometimes the hardest to trust.

    C. Prophets don't do well in their own hometowns.

    D. Some people are used in a greater way outside of where they grew up because no one knows their past. [1430]

LESSON 81

CHECK WHICH CIRCLE BEST REPRESENTS YOUR LIFE TODAY:

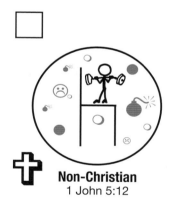

Non-Christian
1 John 5:12

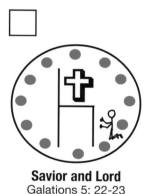

Savior and Lord
Galations 5: 22-23

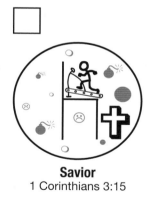

Savior
1 Corinthians 3:15

Since my last lesson,
I have practiced
Spiritual Breathing:

- ☐ 20⁺ Times
- ☐ 11 - 19 Times
- ☐ 6 - 10 Times
- ☐ 0 - 5 Times

CARTOON

Cats And Dogs Take Risks Differently

1. Why do Cats not want to take risks and what do your Cat peers cling to?

   _____

   _____

   _____ 1431

2. Why are Dogs willing to get out of their comfort zone and take steps of faith?

   _____

   _____

   _____ 1432

CHRIS and SARAH

It was the last youth group meeting before the summer break, and Sarah was inwardly wrestling with herself. The few minutes before and after youth group officially started were always awkward. People stood and sat in various circles around the church gym, each more or less segregated into the same groups they naturally split into every week. Freshmen mostly talked with freshmen. Cute lip-glossed junior girls laughed in one corner. The kids with studded belts and spiked hair lounged around the armchairs outside the gym doors. A few athletic seniors played basketball.

Every week was the same. People walked in, found their friends, and formed impenetrable huddles of laughter and mindless conversation. New kids were forced to form circles with other newbies or stand to the side, trying not to look desperate and looking extremely interested in texting until the music started and everyone gathered around the stage.

For most of the school year, Sarah had enjoyed hanging out with her fellow freshman girls, but the cliquey circles were now beginning to bother her. Weren't kids at youth group supposed to be better than this? New kids shouldn't be left hanging around the fringes of the gym. Cheerleaders should be able to hang out with the kids with purple hair. Wasn't that what the Body of Christ was all about?

Pastor Jake regularly encouraged the students to reach out of their little circles, and it always worked for a little while. There would be a few weeks of diversity as some students bravely ventured out of their groups. But eventually it died out. Kids always rubber-banded back to their familiar circles, socializing with students similar to them.

Prior to this week, Sarah had thought about it briefly, but she had also felt powerless to change it so she did nothing. She had just started making real friends here, and if she started branching out she knew she was going to lose the friends she had. Besides, she was only a freshman. There was no way she could change the entire youth group. Still, it had bothered her.

But this week Sarah felt something new: a prompting, an urge, a strong presence and strength to step out of her circle. Maybe she had really given her life to Christ for the first time. What Chris said made so much sense. With this fresh sense of God's presence, she stepped out. There were several new kids at youth group that night. She was too nervous to approach the older girl or the guy with a skull and crossbones t-shirt, but the other girl looked like she was about Sarah's age. Maybe she could invite her into the circle of freshmen girls Sarah always hung out with.

Taking a deep breath, Sarah left her friends and walked up to the new girl who was standing alone, pretending to be texting. Sarah tapped her on the shoulder. She turned around. Sarah's mouth dropped. It was Isabel with shorter hair! "Isabel, it's me, Sarah, from your Algebra class! Wow. You cut your hair. And your braces are off. You look great. How are you? I'm so glad you're here. Is this your first time here? Will you sit with me?"

As Sarah brought Isabel to her seat, something happened inside of her. It was joy.

For one of the very first times in her life she felt joy deep down inside. Why didn't anyone tell her that joy was awaiting her right outside of her comfort zone? She knew God was honoring her for taking a step of faith. God was real. He does show up. He does give joy—when we are focused on His kingdom and not our own!

As the night wore one, Sarah noticed that some of her friends were giving her weird looks. She also got a text saying "what are you doing with that ???" Sarah was shocked. *Aren't these suppose to be Christians?* she thought to herself. *Why are they being mean to me when all I'm trying to do is to be a friend to Isabel?*

And then it hit her. They weren't here for God. They weren't here to worship. They weren't here to make Him famous. They could have cared less about His kingdom. They were only here to be with their friends. To make their parents think they were interested in God.

Then the shocking thought came to her. Could it be that many of her friends who come to youth group really don't have a relationship with God at all? All they're doing is playing a game? They're Christian on Thursday nights and Sunday mornings, but all the rest of the time they're just focused on themselves? No wonder they seem to be so different in school.

And then it really hit her! This is what she had been doing for her entire freshman year. She acted out living for God. She wanted to impress her parents and brother, for them to believe she had really been spiritual. Thank God she had talked with Chris and

seen the real her—how she was being so selfish with God. All she had been interested in the whole time was using God to get good grades and friends—especially boys. Why couldn't she have seen this earlier?

She made a firm decision in her heart. With her new relationship with the Lord, this was going to change. She quietly prayed, *"Lord, here's my life again. I know I gave it to you with Chris the other night. I'm sure about that. And I know I know you beyond a shadow of doubt. But now I want to give it to you even more. Everything, Lord. I don't want to be a Christian hypocrite. Make me more excited about making You famous than making me famous."*

She looked at the text and pushed the delete button, then hooked her arm through Isabel's and pulled close to her. Isabel was going to have a friend this summer. Sarah was just sure of it!

Lesson 81 Questions: (The suggested answers are on page 55 in the *Answer Key.*)

1. Name the "familiar circles" at your youth group.

_____

_____

2. What "clicked" for Sarah regarding her friends that went to youth group?

_____

_____

3. How were Sarah's actions like that of a Dog?

_____

_____

4. Why should you not worry that if you ever tried to branch out and meet new people, you would lose the friends you had at youth group?

_____

_____

Oh Lord, I need to pass this quiz.

QUIZ!

1. God always has the right to answer your prayers with a "No."
   - A. True
   - B. False [1433]

2. One of the reasons God might answer our prayers "No" is because
   - A. we are asking for something outside of God's will.
   - B. our prayers are selfish.
   - C. a "no" will reveal God's glory in a greater way.
   - D. All of the above. [1434]

3. Since sin can keep our prayers from being answered, it is our job to keep analyzing our life to see if there is sin in it.
   - A. True
   - B. False [1435]

4. There are times when great men of God can ask God for something outside of His will.
   - A. True
   - B. False [1436]

5. Cat Christians rarely relate to
   - A. the big picture of what God is doing.
   - B. their needs.
   - C. their wants.
   - D. None of the above. [1437]

6. Sometimes a "no" to our prayers reveals
   - A. God's lack of trust in us.
   - B. greater glory than a "yes" answer.
   - C. how holy we are.
   - D. None of the above. [1438]

7. Even Jesus had prayers that were answered, "No."

    A. True

    B. False [1439]

8. If all of our prayers were answered "yes," we would

    A. become extremely self-centered.

    B. focus far more on God's presents than His presence.

    C. keep dreaming about what new things we could get from God.

    D. lose focus on His kingdom. [1440]

9. Clinging to a secret sin that no one knows about can keep God from answering our prayers.

    A. True

    B. False [1441]

10. The eight reasons listed for God giving a "no" to prayers

    A. does not apply to you.

    B. applies to you.

    C. applies only on Sundays.

    D. None of the above. [1442]

What are you going to do differently as a result of what you've learned? **Go to the end of your workbook and write it in for Lesson 81.** [1443]

PERSONAL APPLICATION

Free Day. No optional work!

OPTIONAL
LESSON

LESSON 82

CHECK WHICH CIRCLE BEST REPRESENTS YOUR LIFE TODAY:

☐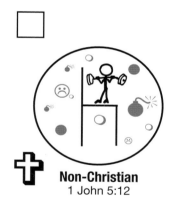

Non-Christian
1 John 5:12

☐

Savior and Lord
Galations 5: 22-23

☐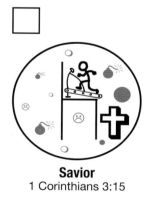

Savior
1 Corinthians 3:15

Since my last lesson,
I have practiced
Spiritual Breathing:

☐ 20⁺ Times

☐ 11 - 19 Times

☐ 6 - 10 Times

☐ 0 - 5 Times

READING ASSIGNMENT

CAT & DOG PRAYER

RETHINKING OUR CONVERSATIONS
WITH OUR MASTER

Bob Sjogren & Gerald Robison

Read "Prayers God Can't Answer" (pages 105-107).

Questions to answer from the reading assignment:

1. Write what you like and didn't like about Gerald's final thoughts.

   _____

   _____

   _____

   _____

   _____

   _____ 1444

2. Gerald suggests that we should take time to pray more _____,
   more _____, more _____. 1445

3. Gerald says that the more _____ our prayer is, the more we
   could see God display His _____. 1446

1. Read Matthew 14:13-21.

2. What did Jesus do when He got the food?

_____

_____

_____

_____ 1447

3. Which of the following does the text not seem to imply:

    A. He asked God to bless it.

    B. He asked them to be nourished by it.

    C. He asked God to make them thankful. 1448

4. Would you say some prayers around the table in American homes might be "less than biblical?"

    A. Yes

    B. No 1449

LESSON 83

CHECK WHICH CIRCLE BEST REPRESENTS YOUR LIFE TODAY:

☐   ☐   ☐

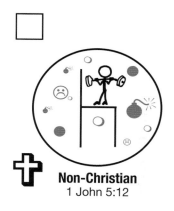

Non-Christian
1 John 5:12

Savior and Lord
Galations 5: 22-23

Savior
1 Corinthians 3:15

Since my last lesson,
I have practiced
Spiritual Breathing:

☐ 20+ Times
☐ 11 - 19 Times
☐ 6 - 10 Times
☐ 0 - 5 Times

READING ASSIGNMENT

CAT & DOG PRAYER

RETHINKING OUR CONVERSATIONS WITH OUR MASTER

Bob Sjogren & Gerald Robison

Read "Putting the 'Super' in Supernatural" (pages 109-113).

Questions to answer from the reading assignment:

1. Explain how our prayers can contradict themselves.

_____

_____

_____

_____

_____

_____

1450

2. Write down an example of how the author's prayers contradicted themselves.

_____

_____

_____

_____

_____

_____

1451

1. Read 2 Chronicles 26.

2. In verses 4 and 5, what did Uzziah do that was right and what was the result?

_____

_____

_____ 1452

3. What does verse 15 tell you about Uzziah's reputation?

_____ 1453

4. What does verse 16 tell you about Uzziah's greatest problem?

_____ 1454

5. Only the priests were allowed into the temple and allowed to burn incense. Circle which thoughts might have been going through Uzziah's mind which allowed him to go into the temple.

    A. God is so pleased with me, he'll allow me to be like a priest.

    B. God is on my side and nothing can stop me.

    C. God is so happy with me, He'd never do anything to hurt me.

    D. God thinks I'm the best! 1455

6. Why did the priests confront Uzziah?

_____ 1456

7. Why do you think Uzziah became angry?

_____

_____ 1457

8. What did the Lord do to Uzziah for his disobedience?

_____ 1458

9. There can be times when we are serving the Lord and we think He is pleased, but it can be very offensive in the eyes of the Lord.

Circle One: True   False   [1459]

10. Circle the lessons we can learn from this lesson.

A. We should never do anything a pastor does today.

B. Being used greatly by God can possibly be our greatest downfall due to the possibility of pride.

C. Thinking that we are "invisible" is OK when God is on our side.

D. God has the power and the right to stop us when we go too far.

E. Obedience is more important than blessings. [1460]

LESSON 84

CHECK WHICH CIRCLE BEST REPRESENTS YOUR LIFE TODAY:

☐

Non-Christian
1 John 5:12

☐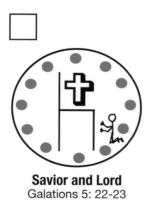

Savior and Lord
Galations 5: 22-23

☐

Savior
1 Corinthians 3:15

Since my last lesson,
I have practiced
Spiritual Breathing:

☐ 20⁺ Times
☐ 11 - 19 Times
☐ 6 - 10 Times
☐ 0 - 5 Times

1. Spend 45 minutes reviewing Lesson #2 of "Cat and Dog Theology" titled, "Self-Centered In The Church." You are going to begin teaching this in two weeks. You will find the slides, mp3 and memory picture all on the CD that came with this kit.

There are a couple of things to note:

• The mp3 is NOT to be played in conjunction with the slides. The mp3 is ONLY for you to learn from. Don't use it for teaching.

• Each time you teach, you might want to teach the first half and have someone else (your mom? a friend?) teach the second half.

2. Spend two minutes in prayer praying that:

• God will draw those to your group that He wants.

• God will prepare the hearts of those who are going to come.

• You will be totally dependent upon Him to speak through you.

• God will speak through you mightily during this teaching time.

3. If you haven't already, call and confirm and see what friends/family can be at your teaching session.

PERSONAL APPLICATION

What are you going to do differently as a result of what you've learned? **Go to the end of your workbook and write it in for Lesson 84.** [1461]

Lesson 84

Free Day. No optional work!

LESSON 85

CHECK WHICH CIRCLE BEST REPRESENTS YOUR LIFE TODAY:

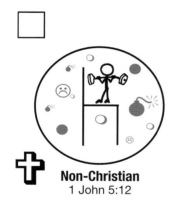

Non-Christian
1 John 5:12

Savior and Lord
Galations 5: 22-23

Savior
1 Corinthians 3:15

Since my last lesson,
I have practiced
Spiritual Breathing:

- ☐ 20+ Times
- ☐ 11 - 19 Times
- ☐ 6 - 10 Times
- ☐ 0 - 5 Times

No Reading Assignment:

Spend 45 minutes reviewing the notes for "YouTeach: Cat and Dog Theology" lesson two, "Self-Centered In The Church."   You will be teaching this in two weeks to your friends.

LESSON 86

CHECK WHICH CIRCLE BEST REPRESENTS YOUR LIFE TODAY:

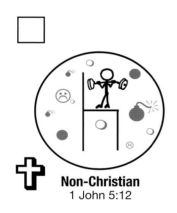

Non-Christian
1 John 5:12

Savior and Lord
Galations 5: 22-23

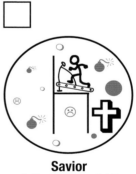

Savior
1 Corinthians 3:15

Since my last lesson,
I have practiced
Spiritual Breathing:

- ☐ 20+ Times
- ☐ 11 - 19 Times
- ☐ 6 - 10 Times
- ☐ 0 - 5 Times

No Reading Assignment:

Again, spend another 45 minutes reviewing the notes for "YouTeach: Cat and Dog Theology" Lesson #2: "Self-Centered In The Church." Try to go over the slides without looking at the notes. Remember, the mp3 is only there to help you. Don't play it and let the slides run. That won't work that way.

You can teach this with someone else. You don't have to do it alone.

Make sure you copy the slides to your hard drive. Don't try to run it from your CD-ROM drive. That will make it very slow.

LESSON 87

CHECK WHICH CIRCLE BEST REPRESENTS YOUR LIFE TODAY:

☐

☐

☐

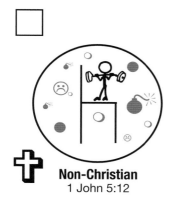

Non-Christian
1 John 5:12

Savior and Lord
Galations 5: 22-23

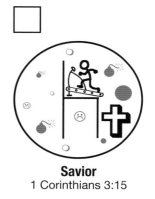

Savior
1 Corinthians 3:15

Since my last lesson,
I have practiced
Spiritual Breathing:

☐ 20⁺ Times
☐ 11 - 19 Times
☐ 6 - 10 Times
☐ 0 - 5 Times

TAKE 45 MINUTES TO STUDY FOR YOUR FINAL EXAM NEXT WEEK BY REVIEWING YOUR QUIZ QUESTIONS. DO NOT LOOK AT THE EXAM UNTIL YOU TAKE IT. IT WILL BE COMPRISED OF 100 OF THE QUIZ QUESTIONS YOU'VE HAD THUS FAR.

Free Day. No optional work!

OPTIONAL LESSON

CAUTION! The more your life is changed, the easier it is to spot Cat behavior in those around you. **Please don't ever use this material to judge others.** ("Oh, they are just a bunch of Cats.") Once we start judging others, we too are acting like Cats. **Use this material to encourage yourself and others to live for God's glory.**

LESSON 88

CHECK WHICH CIRCLE BEST REPRESENTS YOUR LIFE TODAY:

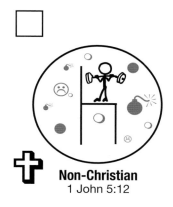

Non-Christian
1 John 5:12

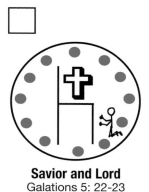

Savior and Lord
Galations 5: 22-23

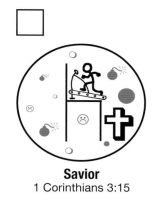

Savior
1 Corinthians 3:15

Since my last lesson,
I have practiced
Spiritual Breathing:

- ☐ 20⁺ Times
- ☐ 11 - 19 Times
- ☐ 6 - 10 Times
- ☐ 0 - 5 Times

1. If you are privately schooled, follow your teacher's instructions.

1. If you are homeschooled, meet together with your group of at least two people, hopefully younger than you. If you are nervous, tell them. They'll understand and it will make them feel better as well!

2. Start off in prayer asking God to speak through you.

3. Begin teaching Lesson #2 of "YouTeach: Cat and Dog Theology" titled, "Self-Centered in The Church." You can do this in a couple of ways.

   • First, you can simply go slide by slide, reading from the notes that specify what you are to say.

   • Or, you can simply show the slides and say what comes to your heart on each slide. (You will need to be extremely familiar with each slide in order to do this.)

   • You can teach together with your mom or dad, alternating slides. (You parent can do all of the even slides, you do all of the odd slides.)

   • Copy the slides from the CD to your hard drive. Do not try to play it from your CD-Rom drive. That will make it very slow.

4. Teach your small group "Self-Centered in The Church."

LESSON 89

CHECK WHICH CIRCLE BEST REPRESENTS YOUR LIFE TODAY:

☐   ☐   ☐

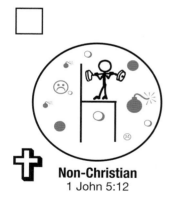

Non-Christian
1 John 5:12

Savior and Lord
Galations 5: 22-23

Savior
1 Corinthians 3:15

Since my last lesson,
I have practiced
Spiritual Breathing:

☐ 20⁺ Times

☐ 11 - 19 Times

☐ 6 - 10 Times

☐ 0 - 5 Times

No Reading Assignment:

TURN TO PAGE 457 AND TAKE YOUR YEAR END FINAL

LESSON 90

CHECK WHICH CIRCLE BEST REPRESENTS YOUR LIFE TODAY:

☐   ☐   ☐

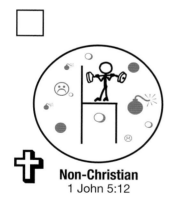

Non-Christian
1 John 5:12

Savior and Lord
Galations 5: 22-23

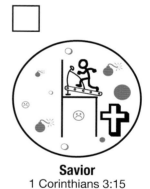

Savior
1 Corinthians 3:15

Since my last lesson,
I have practiced
Spiritual Breathing:

☐ 20⁺ Times

☐ 11 - 19 Times

☐ 6 - 10 Times

☐ 0 - 5 Times

1. **Throw a Cat and Dog Party for you and your family and friends. Celebrate what you're learned.**

   A. You might want to have a cake in the shape of a Cat or Dog!

   B. Get snacks and label them "Dog Food".

   C. Cut finger food in the shape of bones.

   D. Make a "kitty litter box" with popcorn and Tootsie Rolls!

   E. ??? Be creative!

   (If you come up with other creative "Cat and Dog Party" ideas, please e-mail your suggestions to: debby@mmpublishers.com, so we can include your party ideas in the next printing of this curriculum.)

FINAL EXAM!

Year End Final Exam:
No Time Limit
You may only use your Bible!

1. Romans 11:36 says:

    A. All things are from us, through us and to us.

    B. Most things are from Him, through Him and to Him.

    C. Everything is about saving the lost.

    D. All things are from Him, through Him and to Him. [1463]

2. You can feel quite guilty about something yet be walking in the power of the Holy Spirit (Life #2) directly after "spiritual breathing."

    A. True

    B. False [1464]

3. From Revelation 3, what does God do with lukewarm Christians?

    A. He wants to nurture them until they walk with Him.

    B. He will spit them out.

    C. He's putting them on "hold" until they get hot toward Him. [1465]

4. Deep down inside, Cat Christians really think that:

    A. They are guilty.

    B. They should live for God.

    C. God lives for them. [1466]

5. People following Cat Theology are more interested in

    A. People serving God.

    B. God serving people. [1467]

6. Romans 15:8,9 says that you were saved for a purpose. That purpose is so that

    A. You can get to heaven.

    B. You can glorify God.

    C. You can be blessed here on this earth. [1468]

7. Most Cats are into Christianity for

    A. Glorifying God

    B. What God gets out of it.

    C. What they get out of it.

    D. They're not really into Christianity. [1469]

8. Cats and Dogs can pray the exact same prayer word for word and have two totally different meanings.

    A. True

    B. False [1470]

9. If someone "prayed the prayer" as a young child growing up, they are definitely saved and guaranteed to go to heaven.

    A. True

    B. False [1471]

10. Dogs know they are guaranteed eternal salvation because:

    A. They prayed a prayer asking Jesus into their lives.

    B. They see a hunger for God in them they didn't have before.

    C. They see their life changing in a more godly way. [1472]

11. Cats worship God primarily for who He is, secondarily for what He's done for them.

    A. True

    B. False [1473]

12. All Cat songs are

    A. Wrong.

    B. Incomplete.

    C. Stupid.

    D. Unworthy. [1474]

13. Lordship to a Cat means

    A. Christ is Lord as long as it is comfortable.

    B. When God says, "Jump" a Cat only asks, "How high?"

    C. Christ is Lord as long as they don't have to move.

    D. Going anywhere, anytime for any reason. [1475]

14. Everyone is part Dog and part Cat. No one is a perfect Dog. At best, we can be "more Dog" and "less Cat."

    A. True

    B. False [1476]

15. Because you now understand the differences between Dog and Cat Theology, you should always point out the Catness in others, so they can become more like you, a Dog.

    A. True

    B. False [1477]

16. To a Dog, salvation is

    A. An end in itself.

    B. A means to an end.

    C. Just a stepping stone to something greater.

    D. A necessary first step to try and find Jesus. [1478]

17. Dog Theology is not the absence of Cat Theology, rather it is the completion of it.

    A. True

    B. False [1479]

18. Christ's death for our sins

    A. Was secondary to glorifying the Father.

    B. Was a part of God's plan to reveal His glory.

    C. Was solely for us.

    D. None of the above. [1480]

19. Jesus says that He will do whatever we ask in His name so that

    A. We might have a safe, soft, comfortable life.

    B. That our kingdom might expand.

    C. He may bring glory to the Father. [1481]

20. A simple way to define "living for the glory of God" is:

    A. Living in such a way as to make God famous.

    B. Living to point to how you look.

    C. Living to point to how you act.

    D. All of the above. [1482]

21. God is a jealous God.

    A. True

    B. False [1483]

22. God "lives for the sake of His name" means

    A. God lives to glorify God

    B. God's glory is so awesome it is the only thing worth living for, even for God.

    C. God lives to protect His glory at all times.

    D. All of the above. [1484]

23. If God lived primarily for the sake of lifting up, exalting and saving people, that would be a very bad move.

    A. True

    B. False [1485]

24. Though we can't live for ourselves, God can live for Himself because

    A. He won't sin.

    B. He can handle it.

    C. The above statement isn't true, God can't live for Himself.

    D. None of the above. [1486]

25. For God to exalt anything that is good, He must exalt Himself.

    A. True

    B. False [1487]

26. Since God tells us to die to ourselves, He too must be dying to himself and doing that by putting us as a higher priority than His glory.

    A. This is why Christ left the Father's glory to die for us.

    B. This is why Christ died for us.

    C. This is true.

    D. This is a bunch of garbage.

    E. A through C only. [1488]

27. If God were to live for any one or any thing other than Himself He would be

    A. Righteous

    B. Holy

    C. Committing idolatry

    D. All of the above. [1489]

28. If God did not live for Himself and point to Himself He would not be very loving.

    A. True

    B. False [1490]

29. The most loving thing God has ever done was to live for us over everything and everyone.

    A. True

    B. False [1491]

30. It's OK for God to be self-centered.

    A. True

    B. False [1492]

31. Satan's goals are to

    A. Rob God of His glory.

    B. Take God's place.

    C. Keep us from focusing on God's glory.

    D. All of the above. [1493]

32. It's very easy to be stuck in Cat Theology because what a Cat focuses on is

    A. safe and close to God's heart.

    B. what our old nature naturally focuses on.

    C. Both

    D. None of the Above. [1494]

33. Cats have a tendency to focus on

    A. verses that make them feel good.

    B. tough verses that are challenging.

    C. verse to make their lives safe, soft and comfortable.

    D. None of the above. [1495]

34. The Bible tells us only a few believers are called to suffer.

    A. True

    B. False [1496]

35. According to Ephesians 2:6,7, heaven is more about

    A. us getting there!

    B. what God gets to do.

    C. God revealing His grace forever.

    D. "B" and "C" [1497]

36. When reading their Bible, Cats
- A. usually only focus on the parts that make them feel good.
- B. have selective reading and listening.
- C. learn only lessons that are not that difficult to implement.
- D. All of the above. [1498]

37. God's plan for the nine generations that lived as slaves in Egypt was
- A. to live and die in slavery.
- B. to get free.
- C. none of the above. [1499]

38. We are not doing Christian families any favors if we are only talking to them about having a safe, soft, comfortable life and not preparing them to possibly suffer.
- A. True
- B. False [1500]

39. Cats don't want to relate to Job's kids because
- A. they weren't blessed.
- B. they died.
- C. "A" and "B"
- D. None of the above. [1501]

40. Most Cat prayers are focused on
- A. advancing God's kingdom.
- B. advancing their kingdom.
- C. themselves.
- D. God's glory. [1502]

41. Dogs say, "If suffering is going to bring you more glory, then Lord, bring it on for your name's sake."
- A. True
- B. False [1503]

42. The lamb's broken leg story tells us that
- A. God wants to bless us.
- B. God may hurt us for our good.
- C. God only wants to do us good.
- D. None of the above. [1504]

43. God allows tragic things to happen to His children to expand His kingdom.

    A. True

    B. False [1505]

44. Which of the following does God use for His glory?

    A. Good

    B. Evil [1506]

45. Revealing God's glory can, at times, be

    A. difficult.

    B. messy.

    C. hard.

    D. All of the above. [1507]

46. When Satan throws something at us that looks tragic,

    A. God is caught by surprise.

    B. God will use it for His glory.

    C. God has allowed it.

    D. All of the above. [1508]

47. When Dogs see difficulty coming at them, they run toward it.

    A. True

    B. False [1509]

48. Most Cats never grow to their full potential because they are trying to live most of the Christian life in their own power and strength.

    A. True

    B. False [1510]

49. "Cause Me" prayers are

    A. very biblical.

    B. crazy.

    C. giving God 100% of the glory.

    D. unbiblical. [1511]

50. If we are praying "Cause Me" prayers, we can sit on the couch all day because everything is up to God.

    A. True

    B. False [1512]

51. Coming to God with all of our problems (time and time again)

    A. burdens God.

    B. is a pain to God.

    C. honors God.

    D. glorifies God. [1513]

52. The author wants you to know that

    A. life begins at birth.

    B. life begins after you die.

    C. life begins when you finish high school.

    D. life begins when you get married. [1514]

53. The first thing Cats ask themselves about going overseas to be a missionary is,

    A. "Is it safe?"

    B. "Will I make a lot of money?"

    C. "Is it God's will?"

    D. "Is it adventurous?" [1515]

54. The phrase "God wants us happy" is

    A. not correct.

    B. correct, but incomplete.

    C. unbiblical.

    D. None of the above. [1516]

55. God designed life to be fair.

    A. True

    B. False [1517]

56. Life was designed to be

    A. safe, soft, easy and comfortable.

    B. a series of opportunities to reflect, radiate and point to God's glory.

    C. fun.

    D. All of the above. [1518]

57. It is very easy to sin by not making God our greatest joy and delighting more in

    A. sports.

    B. our accomplishments.

    C. our friends.

    D. our families [1519]

58. It is a good idea to fast whatever pleases us more than God.

    A. True

    B. False [1520]

59. God wants life to be

    A. one big worship service.

    B. all about us.

    C. all about saving others from hell.

    D. None of the above. [1521]

60. Reaching the nations with God's glory is

    A. only found in a few verses in the Bible.

    B. only for those who are called.

    C. the central theme of God's Word.

    D. None of the above. [1522]

61. A strict "diet" of "Me-ology" can affect

    A. your attitudes.

    B. your way of life.

    C. your prayers.

    D. your theology. [1523]

62. Many times the problem with prayer is in

    A. the words we use.

    B. the "pray-er" themselves.

    C. the glory of God.

    D. the fact that God is too busy to be bothered. [1524]

63. Some of the reasons Christians don't pray much is because

    A. they are so busy.

    B. they don't believe prayer really works.

    C. they haven't seen answers to prayers.

    D. All of the above. [1525]

64. Prayer

    A. works.

    B. is for the weak.

    C. works for people who have been Christians a long time.

    D. None of the above. [1526]

65. James 4:3 tells us that

    A. God wants to answer all of our prayers.

    B. God only answers selfish prayers.

    C. God doesn't answer selfish prayers. [1527]

66. Many Christians are taught that to ask God to lavishly provide for our wants is their right as a believer.

    A. True

    B. False [1528]

67. The Lord's Prayer is a pattern that we should follow. Praying it word for word is OK, but not mandatory.

    A. True

    B. False [1529]

68. Christians really need to ask themselves a tough question before they pray, and that is,

    A. "Are they really committed to living for themselves?"

    B. "Are they really committed to living for God's kingdom?"

    C. "Are they really praying in the right position?" [1530]

69. The opening words of the Lord's prayer ("Hallowed be Thy name) refers to

    A. making God famous.

    B. making God look good.

    C. God wanting to focus on us.

    D. lifting up and exalting God and His ways. [1531]

70. When we pray "Your will be done," Jesus is really asking,

    A. "Am I Lord of your life?"

    B. "Are you willing to submit to Me?"

    C. "How can I make you happy?"

    D. All of the above. [1532]

71. Sometimes a husband's prayer will not be heard because

    A. they don't live with their wives in an understanding way.

    B. they don't honor their wives.

    C. there is sin in their lives.

    D. All of the above. [1533]

72. Having a poor relationship with someone else can hinder your prayers, whether you are a husband or not.

    A. True

    B. False [1534]

73. Satan isn't really interested in targeting individuals like you and me, he just wants to target pastors.

    A. True

    B. False [1535]

74. A great way to start off a quiet time is to

    A. jump right in interceding for others.

    B. take a quick nap.

    C. praise God for who He is.

    D. exalt His name. [1536]

75. God puts a limit on what we can ask Him.

    A. True

    B. False [1537]

76. When we end our prayer with the words "in Jesus' name, Amen" we are guaranteed to get what we prayed for.

    A. True

    B. False [1538]

77. Our motivation in petitionary prayer should be primarily about

    A. advancing our kingdom.

    B. advancing God's kingdom. [1539]

78. If we think that Jesus wouldn't be praying the prayer we want to pray, then

    A. we have an opportunity to teach something new to Christ.

    B. we probably shouldn't be praying that prayer either.

    C. it probably isn't God's will.

    D. All of the above. [1540]

79. John 14:13 tells us that Christ wants to answer our prayers so that

    A. we can have a safe, soft comfortable life.

    B. He can bring glory to the Father. [1541]

80. Getting joy out of someone else (God) being glorified is

    A. crazy.

    B. biblical.

    C. what God wants for us. [1542]

81. When many Cat Christians pray, they are really hoping that they are praying to

    A. a celestial Santa Claus who will give them all their wishes.

    B. a powerless Being.

    C. Satan. [1543]

82. All of the works we do in the Christian life in our own strength are

    A. going to burn.

    B. going to be rewarded. [1544]

83. Ezekiel 36:26,27 tells us that God wants to

    A. help us become more like Him.

    B. cause us to be obedient to His commands.

    C. Neither A or B.

    D. Both A and B. [1545]

84. If we did the work of changing us spiritually,

    A. we would get the glory.

    B. it wouldn't last.

    C. God wouldn't get the glory.

    D. All of the above. [1546]

85. As soon as you pray the words, "Lord, help me," God notices the word "help" and is let down a little bit.

    A. True

    B. False [1547]

86. Instead of being a "couch potato Christian," we should

    A. act as if everything depended upon us and pray like everything depended upon God.

    B. act as if everything depended upon us and pray like everything depended upon God.

    C. act as if everything depended upon us and pray like everything depended upon God. [1548]

87. For many people, God is answering their prayers and they are not even aware of it.

    A. True

    B. False ¹⁵⁴⁹

88. Christians need to be aware that if they ask God to bless them

    A. God will always do it.

    B. their days may be unpleasant.

    C. seemingly bad things may happen to them.

    D. they will always get a positive answer. ¹⁵⁵⁰

89. The New Testament Greek word "makarios" for blessing is used in a context that is communicating

    A. great peace and joy only when things go your way.

    B. being so satisfied in God that no matter what the circumstances might be, you can still have peace and joy.

    C. God will bless you with lots of money. ¹⁵⁵¹

90. Paul was beaten multiple times and went through great trials, yet Scripturally he was greatly blessed by God.

    A. True

    B. False ¹⁵⁵²

91. One of the lessons we can learn from the Israelites wandering around in the desert is

    A. never be satisfied with just surviving.

    B. be thankful for what you've got, even if it isn't "everything you'd like." ¹⁵⁵³

92. Many Cat Christians are not happy with what God has given them because they are listening to the greed of the others around them.

    A. True

    B. False ¹⁵⁵⁴

93. We need to be very careful about what we are asking God for because without realizing it, by asking for certain things, we may be actually rejecting God.

    A. True

    B. False ¹⁵⁵⁵

94. It is actually possible for God to
    A. die.
    B. curse our blessings.
    C. Both A and B
    D. None of the above. [1556]

95. The phrase "God is looking for people who can survive the blessings" means
    A. He wants people to trust Him for big pay raises.
    B. He wants people to be willing to give up the big job and money for the sake of His great name.
    C. He wants people to trust Him for greater blessings.
    D. He wants people to be willing to give up what the world says should be rightfully theirs. [1557]

96. Some prayers get answered
    A. instantaneously.
    B. after a long period of time.
    C. Both A and B.
    D. None of the above. [1558]

97. Dogs pray,
    A. "Lord, don't answer my prayer if there are things I need to learn first."
    B. "Lord, please make my life safe, soft and comfortable."
    C. "Use this to advance Your kingdom, not my kingdom." [1559]

98. Dogs persist in praise
    A. even before their prayers are answered.
    B. after their prayers are answered.
    C. even if they get a "no" to their prayer request.
    D. All of the above. [1560]

99. God always has the right to answer your prayers with a "No."
    A. True
    B. False [1561]

100. If all of our prayers were answered "yes," we would

    A. become extremely self-centered.

    B. focus far more on God's presents than His presence.

    C. keep dreaming about what new things we could get from God.

    D. lose focus on His kingdom. [1562]

BONUS QUESTION #1: Now that you have learned all of this material, you have the right to judge others and call them out on their "Catness."

    Circle One: True   False   [1563]

BONUS QUESTION #2: Whenever you call someone a "Cat," you yourself are acting like a Cat.

    Circle One: True   False   [1564]

BONUS QUESTION #3: It is possible to challenge someone on their "Catness" by doing it humbly and in love.

    Circle One: True   False   [1565]

PERSONAL APPLICATION
SECTION

Lesson 3:

_____
_____
_____
_____
_____

Lesson 6:

_____
_____
_____
_____
_____

Lesson 9:

_____
_____
_____
_____
_____

Lesson 12:

_____

_____

_____

_____

Lesson 15:

_____

_____

_____

_____

Lesson 18:

_____

_____

_____

_____

Lesson 21:

_____

_____

_____

_____

_____

Lesson 24:

_____

_____

_____

_____

Lesson 27:

_____

_____

_____

_____

_____

_____

Lesson 30:

_____

_____

_____

_____

_____

Lesson 33:

_____

_____

_____

_____

_____

Lesson 36:

_____
_____
_____
_____
_____

Lesson 48:

_____
_____
_____
_____
_____

Lesson 51:

_____
_____
_____
_____
_____

Lesson 54:

_____
_____
_____
_____
_____
_____

Lesson 57:

_____

_____

_____

_____

_____

Lesson 60:

_____

_____

_____

_____

_____

Lesson 63:

_____

_____

_____

_____

_____

Lesson 66:

_____

_____

_____

_____

_____

Lesson 69:

_____

_____

_____

_____

_____

Lesson 72:

_____

_____

_____

_____

_____

Lesson 75:

_____

_____

_____

_____

_____

Lesson 78:

_____

_____

_____

_____

_____

Lesson 81:

_____

_____

_____

_____

_____

Lesson 84:

_____

_____

_____

_____

_____

_____

Appendix A
Additional Questions
You May Want To Ask!

1. Lesson 6

    a. Would you say you and your friends gossip about others after youth group is over?

    b. What do you like the most about youth group?

2. Lesson 9

    a. Would you say you go to youth group to meet more with your friends or with God?

    b. What do you think is the greatest way God wants to bless you?

3. Lesson 12

    a. Do you think it is possible to be in the center of God's will and have it be very difficult? Why or why not?

    b. Is there any area of your life you where you are avoiding doing God's will because you think it might be difficult?

4. Lesson 15

    a. What was wrong with Sarah's little "white lie" to get out of her uncomfortable situation?

    b. Right before Chris talked to his grandfather, he said a "quick prayer." Do you think God hears those and do you really believe He answers those?

5. Lesson 18

    a. Are there any successful people at church of whom you might be jealous?

    b. Do you keep your cell phone on during youth worship and if you do, do you get distracted by it?

6. Lesson 21

    a. When Sarah called her brother "Saint Christopher," do you think her sarcasm built him up or tore him down?

    b. Do you think we judge each other in our family, or class, and if yes, how?

7. Lesson 24

    a. Do you think you are at a point in your life where you would be willing to die for the Lord?

    b. Do you think we should ever consider leaving the church just if the teaching is hard to live out?

8. Lesson 27

    a. Jim was afraid of getting hurt, that's why he reasoned he shouldn't do homeless ministry or go overseas. Is there any evidence in the Bible of people getting hurt for the gospel? If so, where?

    b. What do you think is the main motivation people have for going to the youth group?

9. Lesson 30

    a. Would you say most of the prayers you hear in youth group are Cat or Dog?

    b. Would you say most of your prayers up to this point have been Cat or Dog and why?

10. Lesson 33

    a. Sarah saw God blessing her by getting to know Bryan better. If God were to really bless you in a tremendous way, what would that look like in your life right now?

    b. Romans 11:36 tells us that everything is to revolve around God. Do you think that includes texting and tweeting and even what you text and tweet? How did Sarah violate this purpose?

11. Lesson 36

    a. Do you think being a really good person for a long time earns "points" with God enabling him to bless you more? Why or why not?

    b. Why do you think God didn't answer Sarah's prayer for a good grade?

12. Lesson 48

    a. Whenever you don't feel like God is paying attention to you or caring for you, is that reason to stop trusting in God or stop walking with him? Why or why not?

    b. How do you think life isn't fair to you?

13. Lesson 51

    a. Do you think you do your chores with a good attitude toward God or with a bad attitude? Explain your answer.

    b. Have you ever gotten mad at God? What happened then that angered you?

14. Lesson 54

    a. Do you think you'd ever want to go overseas for God? Why or why not?

    b. Should a child's sports commitments take a higher priority than doing God's will? Why or why not?

15. Lesson 57

    a. What if God asked you to do something very tough, would you be willing to do it?

    b. Would you say your love for God is conditional or unconditional and why?

16. Lesson 60

    a. Have you ever tried to "trick" God into something by promising to do something if He'd do something for you? What was it?

    b. How do some Christians avoid having to deal with sin by saying, "I was just joking!"?

17. Lesson 63

    a. Do you think what Chris did in giving away the money he had saved up for the laptop was wise or not? Explain your answer.

    b. Do you find yourself being selfish with clothes or other things that God has given you? If yes, how?

18. Lesson 66

    a. Do you think it was wrong for Sarah to ask God to win in the race? Why or why not?

    b. What if some of your major goals and dreams never got accomplished. Do you think you would still trust in God? Why or why not?

19. Lesson 69

    a. Are there people at youth group you try to avoid like Sarah avoided Isabella? Why do you avoid them?

    b. Do you feel like you encourage others who are trying to hold Bible studies or who are trying to grow closer to God? Give an example.

20. Lesson 72

    a. If Bryan was cheating on his girlfriend with Sarah, why shouldn't Sarah think that if she started dating him, he would do the same thing to her?

    b. Although Jessica was Sarah's best friend, how was she really not a good friend?

21. Lesson 75

   a. Talk about how someone's "joking" (like the unnamed person who started the rumor that Sarah was sleeping with Bryan) could really hurt someone deeply and damage their heart and reputation.

   b. Would you ever want to lose the trust of your parents?

22. Lesson 78

   a. Name one good area of your life that God is pleased with that could become a "god" to you?

   b. Talk about how pursuing one person (a boyfriend or a girlfriend) can really hurt or damage the other areas of your life.

23. Lesson 81

   a. Would you say your friends would accept you—even join you—if you reached out to a "Isabella-type person"? Why or why not?

   b. Have you ever experienced a deep joy in serving God the way Sarah did? When was that?

Quiz and Final Scores

Lesson 3 Quiz: Possible 10: _____
Lesson 6 Quiz: Possible 10: _____ (subtotal:_____)
Lesson 9 Quiz: Possible 10: _____ (subtotal:_____)
Lesson 12 Quiz: Possible 10: _____ (subtotal:_____)
Lesson 15 Quiz: Possible 10: _____ (subtotal:_____)
Lesson 18 Quiz: Possible 10: _____ (subtotal:_____)
Lesson 21 Quiz: Possible 10: _____ (subtotal:_____)
Lesson 24 Quiz: Possible 10: _____ (subtotal:_____)
Lesson 27 Quiz: Possible 10: _____ (subtotal:_____)
Lesson 30 Quiz: Possible 10: _____ (subtotal:_____)
Lesson 33 Quiz: Possible 10: _____ (subtotal:_____)
Lesson 36 Quiz: Possible 10: _____ (subtotal:_____)

Lesson 48 Quiz: Possible 10: _____ (subtotal:_____)
Lesson 51 Quiz: Possible 10: _____ (subtotal:_____)
Lesson 54 Quiz: Possible 10: _____ (subtotal:_____)
Lesson 57 Quiz: Possible 10: _____ (subtotal:_____)
Lesson 60 Quiz: Possible 10: _____ (subtotal:_____)
Lesson 63 Quiz: Possible 10: _____ (subtotal:_____)
Lesson 66 Quiz: Possible 10: _____ (subtotal:_____)
Lesson 69 Quiz: Possible 10: _____ (subtotal:_____)
Lesson 72 Quiz: Possible 10: _____ (subtotal:_____)
Lesson 75 Quiz: Possible 10: _____ (subtotal:_____)
Lesson 78 Quiz: Possible 10: _____ (subtotal:_____)
Lesson 81 Quiz: Possible 10: _____ (subtotal:_____)

Your Total Quiz Points: _____ (total:_____)
Your Final Exam: Potential 100: _____

Your Total Points Out Of 340: _____
+ Points for YouTeach Presentations:
_____

Final Grade _____

Potential Quiz Points:
240

Potential Final Points
100

Total Potential Points:
340

Potential Bonus Points
3

306-340 = A
272-305 = B
238-271 = C
204-237 = D

Lesson